Spectroscopic Tricks

From:

APPLIED SPECTROSCOPY

Tricks and Notes

Especially Reorganized and Rearranged for this Edition

SPECTROSCOPIC TRICKS

Edited by
LEOPOLD MAY
Department of Chemistry
The Catholic University of America
Washington, D. C.

PLENUM PRESS · NEW YORK · 1967

[redacted]

The material contained in this volume originally appeared in sections of Tricks and Notes in *Applied Spectroscopy* from 1959 through 1965, and is reprinted here by permission of the Society for Applied Spectroscopy.

First Printing – June 1967

Second Printing – November 1968

Library of Congress Catalog Card Number 67-17377

Printed in the United States of America

[redacted]

FOREWORD

Spectroscopic Tricks was introduced in 1959 as a special section in the journal *Applied Spectroscopy.* Its purpose was to provide a means for communicating information on new devices, modifications of existing apparatuses, and other items of this nature to the working spectroscopist. That it has proved valuable is indicated by the continuing publication of this section. However, the usefulness of Spectroscopic Tricks scattered through many issues of the journal diminishes as time passes since the reader must consult the annual indices of many volumes of *Applied Spectroscopy* to find the contribution that may hold the solution to his problem. The collection of these contributions into a single volume, supplemented by several that were published not as Spectroscopic Tricks but as Notes, will certainly make it easier for the user to find the solution for which he is looking.

In this volume, the contributions are arranged according to the area of spectroscopy. Those concerned with the same device are placed together so that the reader can compare them readily. Three indices are provided — a subject index, an author index, as well as an index to the volume, page, and year in which the contribution was originally published in *Applied Spectroscopy.*

The use of the contributions has been approved by the Society for Applied Spectroscopy, whose cooperation in this matter is gratefully acknowledged.

Leopold May

CONTENTS

SECTION 1. EMISSION SPECTROSCOPY

SECTION 2. INFRARED SPECTROSCOPY

SECTION 3. MASS SPECTROSCOPY

SECTION 4. NUCLEAR MAGNETIC RESONANCE

SECTION 5. RAMAN SPECTROSCOPY

SECTION 6. ULTRAVIOLET AND VISIBLE SPECTROSCOPY

SECTION 7. X-RAY SPECTROSCOPY

SECTION 8. MISCELLANEOUS

SECTION 1
EMISSION SPECTROSCOPY

Use of Pyroceram Crucible Vials in Ashing Biological Materials for Spectrochemical Analysis* 1.1

S. T. Bass and Jane Connor

Deparment of Agricultural Chemistry, Michigan State University
East Lansing, Michigan

A number of spectrochemical techniques are described in the literature wherein a sample is heated in a crucible in a muffle furnace to decompose organic matter. Then the resulting ash is mixed in a mortar, or by mechanical means, with a buffer before excitation; for example, Farmer (*1*), Sayre (*2*), and Connor and Bass (*3*). Direct excitation of the ash, rather than a solution of its soluble constituents eliminates the difficulties with solutions but introduces some additional problems. It is difficult to transfer the ash quantitatively from the crucible to the mixing container which is time-consuming and requires an additional container. This note describes a technique that largely eliminates these difficulties and uses a container with sufficient physical strength to withstand the shock of mechanical mixing and the ashing temperature of 550°C.

---

*Published with the approval of the Director of the Michigan Agricultural Experiment Station as Journal Article No. *2459*.

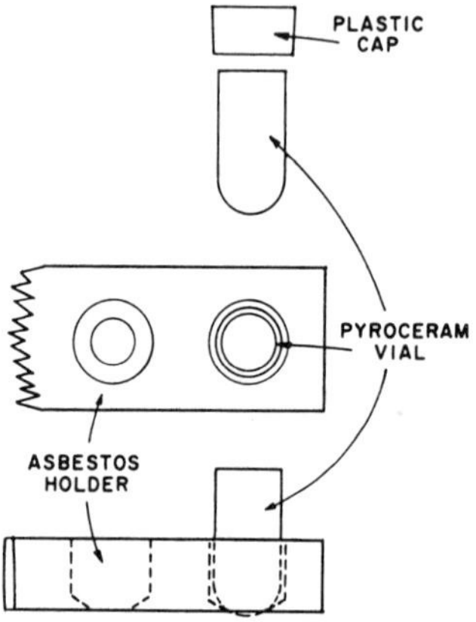

FIG. I. PYRECERAM CRUCIBLE VIALS AND HOLDER

A new glass material, *Pyroceram,* has been developed by the Corning Glass Works of Corning, New York.* Among its properties are a very low thermal coefficient of expansion, high shock strength, good thermal conductivity, highly-polished surface, ease of fabrication, and resistance to corrosion by alkali substances. Containers made of this material appeared promising as a combination ashing and maxing vessel, hence, were tested for this purpose.

Samples of peach leaves (0.250 g) were ashed in ceramic crucibles and *Pyroceram* crucible vials. The ash in the ceramic crucible was transfered to a plastic vial, and buffer in powder form was then added to the ash in both kinds of containers. The containers were closed with plastic caps and their contents mixed with a *Wig-L-Bug* mixer. Portions of each mixture were arced and the resulting spectrograms examined for contamination. Those spectrograms from samples ashed in ceramic crucibles sometimes showed silicon as a contaminant, but no contaminant of

*The authors are indebted to this company for the *Pyroceram* containers used in this investigation. Containers of various designs made of *Pyroceram* can be obtained from its special apparatus section at about two to four times the cost of Pyrex glassware.

biological significance appeared in those from samples ashed in *Pyroceram* crucible vials.

The plant material ashed well in the *Pyroceram* crucible vials, and the ash did not adhere to their walls. These containers also have adequate physical strength to withstand the shock of mechanical mixing with a *Wig-L-Bug* mixer.

The *Pyroceram* crucible vials used in this experiment were 0.5 inch outside diameter and 1.0 inch long (Figure 1). This size was adequate for the spectrochemical methods used in this labortory, but larger sizes could be supplied where they are required. Because of their round bottom, they were difficult to hold upright in the furnace. To overcome this difficulty a holder (Figure 1) for the vials was prepared by drilling holes (0.625 inch diameter) almost through a transite board (0.5 inch thick), and to keep the vials from falling through, a shoulder was left on the board.

After cleaning with detergents and HCl, the crucible vials can be reused. The advantages of the *Pyroceram* crucible vials were found to be the elimination of loss and possible contamination during transfer of ash. They also save time in the overall preparation of samples.

Literature Cited

1. V. C. Farmer, *Spectrochim. Acta 4,* 224 (1950)
2. J. D. Sayre, "*Trace Elements*", C. A. Lamb, O. G. Bentley, and J. M. Beattie, Ed., Academic Press, Inc., New York, Chap. 16 (1958)
3. Jane Connor and S. T. Bass, unpublished observations

Mounting Sheet and Tube Samples for Emission Spectrographic Analysis **1.2**

B. R. DePiazza

Lockheed Missiles and Space Company, Van Nuys, California

The primary function of this laboratory is to perform spectrographic analysis of all incoming metallic materials for conference to military specification. Consequently, in addition to other problems, a wide variety of forms and shapes must be analyzed. Thin-walled tubing and thin sheets pose problems for the spectrographer as far as mounting and surface preparation to eliminate skin effects. This laboratory has developed a simple method for mounting specimens which permits ease of surface preparation either by sanding or milling on a lathe. In addition, a heat sink is provided which has advantages over a water dam or a simple metal block clamped to the surface.

The method is as follows for thin sheets: A sample large enough to contact the Petrey stand is cut from the sheet while maintaining its overall flatness. A block or rod of similar material approximately 1½ in. diam. and 1 in. long is then machined or sanded flat on one end. A drop of Eastman 910 adhesive* is placed on the center of the plate and the rod placed on the plate. The rod is thus rotated on the plate to obtain a thin, even layer of adhesive. The plate and rod are then bonded together by applying hand pressure for a few seconds. A vise may also be used. This can then be mounted in a lathe for milling or surfaced by belt sander.

For tubing, a sample about three in, in length is cut lengthwise and spread open. A sheet or plate is formed by hammering the sample flat. The mounting procedure is the same as described above. During sparking of the sample the mounted sheet should make electrical contact with the electrode holder or Petrey stand, since the Eastman 910 adhesive* is an electrical insulator. Also, the adhesive is somewhat shock sensitive so some care should be exercised in handling the mounted samples.

No bias correction is required when massive standards are used to analyze sheet or tubing samples. This laboratory has successfully used this procedure for low alloy steels, stainless steels and aluminum and magnesium alloys.

---

*Eastman Chemical Company, Rochester, New York

Rivet Sample Holder for Spectrochemical Analysis **1.3**

Frank S. Marlow, Jr.

ACF Industries, Incorporated, Albuquerque, New Mexico

Recently, this laboratory was faced with the problem of analyzing steel and aluminum rivets using a Jarrell-Ash Direct Reading Spectrometer. The small size of these rivets prevented the direct use of the electrode holders in the arc stand. It would be necessary to melt the rivets into a briquette large enough to fit in the stand. Melting these

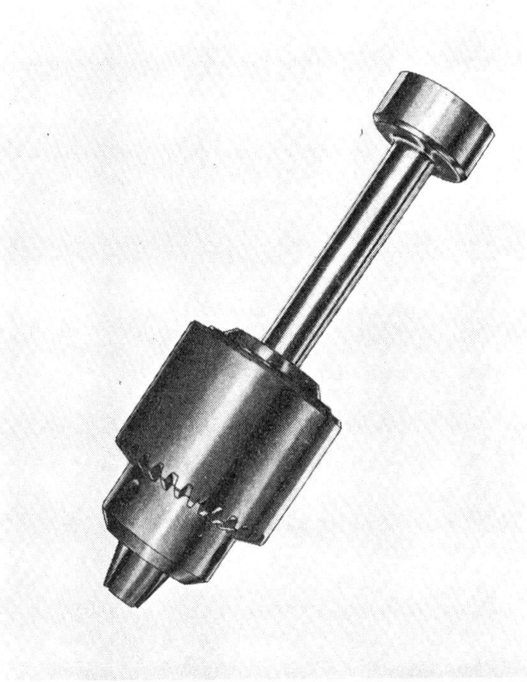

FIG. 1. RIVET SAMPLE HOLDER

rivets was time consuming, and the number of rivets necessary to make a sufficiently large briquette made it expensive.

This problem was solved by designing and fabricating a simple rivet holder as shown in Figure 1.

The holder is a $\frac{1}{4}$ in. Jacob's Chuck with aluminum shaft threaded on one end to fit chuck and other end is $\frac{3}{4}$ in. diam. shoulder. The dimensions are: Overall Height, 3-5/16 in.; Aluminum Shaft Height, 2 in.; and Aluminum Shaft Width, $\frac{3}{8}$ in. The jaws on chuck open up, and rivet is inserted. The chuck is locked into upper electrode holder and lowered to desired height. With this rivet holder, the electrode holder can be lowered sufficiently to allow rivets to be analyzed using only three or four instead of up to 100 rivets, which was previously used when briquettes were prepared.

1.4 A Possible Method of Pulverizing Mica and Other Flaking Materials for Spectrographic Analysis

A. Strasheim, K. Buijs, and J. van Wamelen
National Physical Research Laboratory,
Pretoria, Union of South Africa

Recently a method using the Wig-L-Bug* was described for grinding wool samples to a fine powder for use in the KBr disk technique for infrared spectral study *(1)*. The possibility of using this grinding technique for mica was investigated, as homogeneous pulverisation of mica samples for spectrographic analysis has long been a problem *(2)*. This technique was found to be very satisfactory.

To estimate the efficiency of the new technique, which consists of grinding in a special steel vial (Figure 1)

*Crescent Dental Manufacturing Co., Chicago, Ill.

completely filled with carbon tetrachloride, samples ground this way were compared with samples ground dry in the same vial and with samples ground by hand in an ordinary mortar. In the vial 200 mg samples were ground with two steel balls for 30 min. The efficiencies of the three grinding methods are illustrated in Figures 2-4. The photographs were taken with a Zeiss stereomicroscope and were enlarged 300 times with the samples being illuminated by reflection. The procedure which gave good contrast and little conglomeration of the particles in the pictures, was as follows:

A polaroid plate was put on a piece of black felt paper.

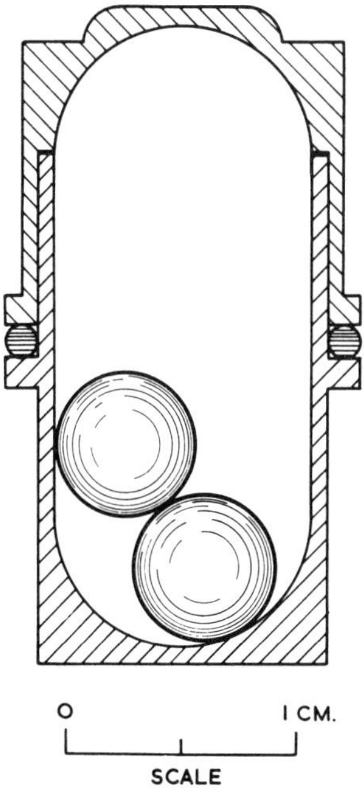

FIG. 1. STEEL VIAL USED FOR LIQUID GRINDING

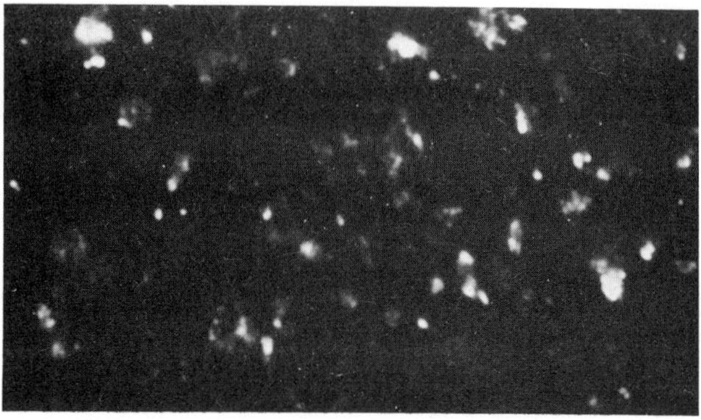

FIG. 2. MICA GROUND WET IN VIAL COMPLETELY FILLED WITH LIQUID

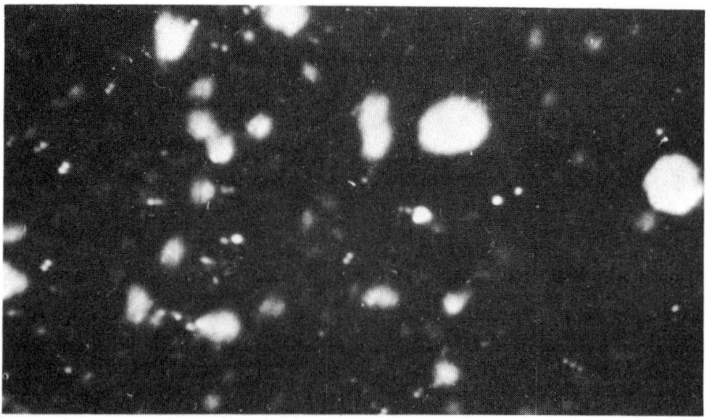

FIG. 3. MICA GROUND DRY

The sample, immersed in a 50,50 glycerol-water mixture, was placed on the polaroid plate and covered with a microscope glass slide. This sample holder was then illuminated with polarized light at an angle of about 60°. Before taking a photograph, the polarizer in front of the illuminating lamp was adjusted to minimize the amount of unwanted light reflected from the sample holder. Vibra-

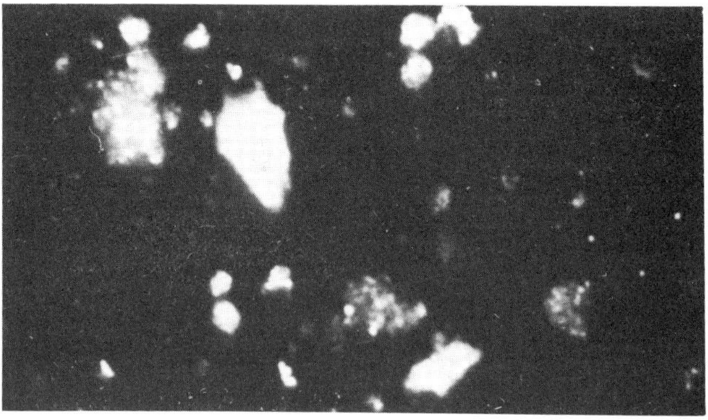

FIG. 4. MICA GROUND BY HAND

tions were avoided by opening the shutter in complete darkness and then switching on the illuminating lamp. The time of exposure was 8 min. This procedure gives a photomicrograph of whole particles, while a polarizing microscope would show only the crystallites.

It can be seen from the Figures that two conclusions can be drawn. Firstly, wet-ground samples are more homogeneous than the others, which contain quite a number of large particles. The sieving operation used by Plastinin *(2)* to obtain uniform samples is thus unnecessary. Secondly, iron cannot be determined in samples prepared by this wet-grinding technique. Bright round spots in Figures 3 and 4 probably originate from iron particles. It was also found that the dry-grinding technique produces more contamination from the steel vial than does the wet-grinding technique—samples ground dry were much darker in colour than those ground wet.

Using agate and polystyrene vials with two agate balls, no effective grinding was observed after 30 min. This is probably due to the low specific gravities of these materials. The specific gravities of agate and steel are 2.58 and 7.82 respectively. In this respect considering its high specific gravity (15.63) and hardness, tungten carbide might be very well suited for this type of milling.

Literature Cited

(1) A. Strasheim and K. Buijs, Spectrochim. Acta **16,** 1010 (1960)
(2) V. V. Plastinin, Zavodskaya Lab. **25,** 602 (1959)

1.5 Rapid Sample Fusion with Lithium Tetraborate for Emission Spectroscopy

M. S. Wang*

Agronomy Department, University of Illinois, Urbana, Illinois

Recently, lithium tetraborate fusion of mineral and plant ashes has become popular in preparing samples for both x-ray and optical emission spectroscopy. Lithium tetraborate fusion of soils, geological material, refractories, slags, and other silicates largely solves the problem of crystal and particle size differences and transforms such samples to homogeneous materials. Lithium tetraborate is especially suitable for x-ray emission spectroscopy, because lithium and boron have low atomic numbers and their absorption edges do not interfere with the emission lines of elements to be determined.

Some difficulties are encountered in handling fused materials, because they usually adhere to the platinum crucibles and are very difficult to remove. Wang *(1)* fused soil mixed with lithium tetraborate, quenched the bottom of the hot platinum crucible to shatter the glass-like material, then removed the fused material for crushing and grinding. This report presents a simple and rapid method for preparing specimen samples by lithium tetraborate fusion.

Samples that contain a large amount of organic matter (such as humus in soils) should first be heated overnight

---

*Present Address: Monsanto Chemical Co., St. Louis, Missouri

in a muffle furnace at 450°C. When an internal standard is used, it should be mixed with the lithium tetraborate before the tetraborate is mixed with the sample. For example, if GeO_2 is selected as the internal standard, a weighed amount of the GeO_2 should be mixed thoroughly with the lithium tetraborate so that multiple weighing errors will be diminished. It is desirable to use ethyl alcohol with this mixture to promote uniform blending. After being thoroughly mixed and ground, the mixture should first be dried under moderate heat (such as an infra-red lamp), then dried further in an oven at 105°C for four hrs.

Lithium tetraborate is capable of fusing silicates at ratios as low as 1:1. In selecting the proper ratio to use, consideration should be given to the spectral line sensitivity of the elements to be analyzed. Another factor that should be considered is the matrix effect. The higher the ratio of lithium tetraborate to sample the less the matrix effect. For analysis of major elements in soils, a 20:1 ratio gave excellent results.

The general procedure consists of mixing thoroughly a weighed amount of sample with the proper amount of the $Li_2B_4O_7 + GeO_2$ mixture. This mixture is placed in a covered platinum crucible, and the crucible is heated gently over a Meker burner for about 2 min and then maximum heat (about 1200°C.) is applied for about 8 min. After this the crucible is placed at an angle of 40°. If some of the mixture is still floating on the fused material, the crucible is swirled until it disappears. The crucible is kept covered and heated continuously until the fused material moves to the wall of the crucible, after which the lower part of crucible is quickly quenched in distilled water. During the quenching the crucible is kept at a 40° angle for easier removal of cooled material from the wall of the crucible. Care should be taken so that no water enters the crucible. After 3 sec of quenching, the glass-like material will start to crack; however, the crucible should be kept in water until cool enough to handle. The cracked glass-like material is removed with a stainless steel spatula. Any small particles are loosened from the wall by tapping on the sides of the crucible. Safety goggles should be worn (or ordinary glasses) during this process to avoid getting any of the sharp glass-like material in the eyes. The glass-like material is transferred to a tungsten carbide vial and ground for 3 min in a Wig-L-Bug No. 6*. The sample material is now ready to be mixed with graphite to form a briquet for optical emission work. For x-ray emission, the addition of graphite is not necessary before briquetting.

Dryer *(2)* found that regrinding the fused material gave results that improved the working curves. The entire sample should be ground for briquetting, because the fused material is not always homogeneous and subsamples give poorer analytical results. This may be attributed to the fact that segregation of the material occurs during fusion. Appreciable differences may be observed in the volumes obtained from fused products that differ in their carbonate or silica contents. Volume differences may be a source of error in x-ray emission analysis, because the concentration of elements in the final fused material may be altered by matrix differences. Consideration should be given to this phenomenon in preparing synthetic standards.

Platinum crucibles used for lithium tetraborate fusion can be cleaned by fusing the residue with sodium carbonate. A layer of sodium carbonate about 1 to 2 mm thick is packed around the bottom and wall of the crucible where residues from the fused material are present. Heat is applied until the material melts, and then the crucible is soaked in a dilute nitric acid solution. After the melt is dissolved, the crucible should be washed and dried before it is reused.

Literature Cited

(1) M. S. Wang, Ph.D. Thesis, University of Illinois, 1959
(2) H. Dryer, Applied Research Labs., Dearborn, Mich., Personal communication

*Crescent Dental Manufacturing Company, Chicago, Ill.

A Device for Introducing Powders into Flames 1.6

J. L. Nicholson

Electro-Optical Systems, Inc., Pasadena, California

In spectroscopic studies, it is sometimes desirable to introduce chemical species into a bunsen flame, either for analyses or to provide comparison spectra. A survey of the available literature failed to reveal a device capable of adding suitable materials uniformly over extended time intervals.

The device described here provides a means of introducing any finely divided material as a dry powder into the flame. The material may be introduced at a given rate over time intervals limited only by the capacity of the container, a rotating drum. By introducing the material as a powder, interference with normal flame combustion is minimized. Details of construction of the device are shown in Figure 1. Drum capacity of the model tested was approximately one half pound. This was sufficient for 30 min of intense flame coloration.

In operation, the partially-filled drum is rotated slowly. Vanes on the inside rim lift the powder above center, then spill it as rotation continues. The continuous agitation keeps the air space in the drum permeated with sus-

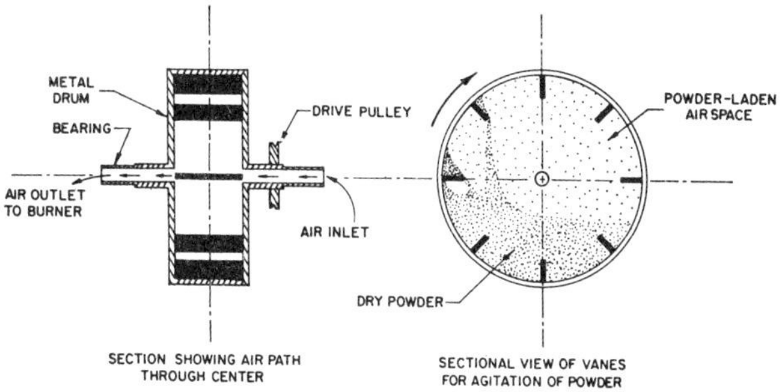

FIG. 1. DEVICE FOR INTRODUCING POWDERS INTO FLAMES

pended particles. An air supply for the flame is directed axially through the drum where it entrains the suspended particles and carries them into the flame. A needle valve for controlling the air flow rate should be placed on the inlet side of the drum to avoid constrictions in the particle-laden portion of the air stream. This air stream may be the one supplying air for combustion or an auxiliary one.

If explosive or easily-oxidized powders are to be introduced, it may be desirable to use the combustible gas supply as the particle carrier. The reader is cautioned to never use finely-divided metals with air or oxygen as a carrier.

1.7 Detergent Addition in Flame Photometry

John B. Mooney

Varian Associates, Palo Alto, Calif.

August Held *(1)* observed that the tip of the capillary of the total consumption burner was not uniformly wet by the solution, and that the "dry" spot wandered around the tip.

This dry spot could contribute to clogging in that it provides a site for solids to begin depositing. A surface active agent *(2, 3, 4)* was added to a concentrated salt solution, and the clogging rate was compared with a control that did not contain the detergent. Figure 1 shows the record of emission *vs* time for the two solutions.

The detergent solution contained 2.5 mg Li as sulfate, 10 g NaCl, and 3 mg N-lauryl beta-aminopropionic acid (General Mills' Deriphat 170C) per 100 ml. The control solution was the same except for the N-lauryl beta-aminopropionic acid. The flame photometer was a Beckman model DU spectrophotometer equipped with a model 4020 hydrogen burner, photomultiplier, and a Beckman Spectral

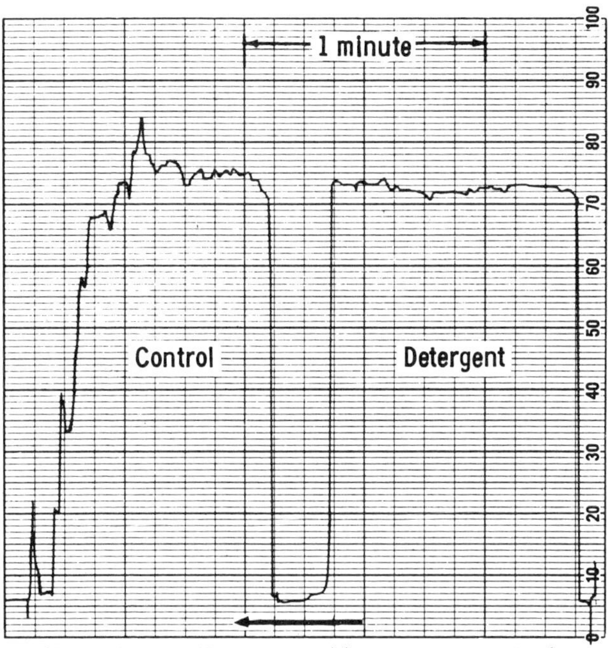

FIG. 1. FLAME EMISSION VS TIME FOR 10% NaCl SOLUTION

Energy Recording attachment. The instrument settings were: slit width 0.12 mm, 100% adjust on midrange, oxygen 14 psi, and hydrogen pressure optimized. The 671 mμ lithium line was used with the photomultiplier sensitivity on 3. A Varian G-10 10 mv recorder with a two in./min chart speed was used.

The solutions were aspirated five times each, and the control solution repeatedly clogged the burner within a minute, while the detergent solution did not clog the burner during aspiration times up to three minutes. The control solution clogged the burner in less than thirty seconds when the oxygen pressure was reduced from 14 to 12 psi and the hydrogen pressure from 3.75 to 2.5 psi.

The detergent content was determined experimentally as the minimum effective level for the conditions. The particular detergent was chosen because it was amphoteric and contained no metallic elements. No others were tried.

It was expected that better capillary wetting would reduce flame wander and improve emission stability; however, Figure 1 does not show a significant difference in this respect. The instability of the control after the first 15 sec was due to the extreme flame wander at the onset of clogging. A similar comparison of NaCl-free 0.25 ppm lithium solutions with and without the detergent did not show any significant difference in emission stability.

Literature Cited

(1) R. Barras, Discussion Period: "Unsolved Problems in Spectrochemical Analysis," Paper No. 92a, Second National Meeting, Society for Applied Spectroscopy; APPLIED SPECTROSCOPY **17**, 146 (1963); comment by P. T. Gilbert

(2) F. Burriel-Martí and J. Ramírez-Muñoz, *Flame Photometry,* Elsevier Publishing Company, Amsterdam, 1962, p. 234

(3) W. H. Foster and D. N. Hume, *Anal. Chem.* **31**, 2028 (1959)

(4) R. Herrmann and C. T. J. Alkemade, *Chemical Analysis by Flame Photometry,* John Wiley and Sons, Inc., New York (1963) pp. 352-3

On the Preparation of Samples for Laser Microprobe Analysis 1.8

Robert C. Rosan

Division of Histochemistry, Department of Pathology
Stanford Medical School
300 Pasteur Drive, Palo Alto, California 94304

The Q-switched laser microprobe *(1, 2, 3, 4, 5)* apparently facilitates more sensitive procedures for some elements than are usual in ordinary emission spectroscopy. Several circumstances may be responsible. The strongly self-absorbing lines which characterize plasmas caused by the laser impact invariably disappear when the plasmas are electrically cross-excited. This suggests that most of the elemental plasma reaches full electrical excitation. The nearly adiabatic conversion of solid samples to plasma suggests that little sample is lost in boiling, sputtering or condensation before the spark is applied. We believe the conversion is in fact nearly adiabatic because a well-tuned laser will vaporize a fairly constant mass of matrix from a wide variety of materials *(4)*. Another factor making for efficiency is the fixed position of the electrodes and spark relative to the slit. This is partly due to the high precision with which successive spurts of plasma appear at the same spot. Still another factor is the low black-body and cyanogen band noise, which permits the use of sensitive films such as 103-0 or Royal X Pan. Finally, it may be that the peculiar spectral redistribution of microprobe cross-excited spectra compared to ordinary spark or arc spectra in some way favors greater sensitivity. Whatever the reasons, the *increased sensitivity* of the laser microprobe (quite apart from its ability to selectively localize an inclusion in a matrix) makes it desirable to have a simple method for preparing divers samples for trace analysis with a microprobe. The following notes outline suitable procedures.

Supported by USPHS Grants # GM-09227 and HE-06716

The basis of the technic is to dissolve the sample and to disperse the solution in a gel. The gel we recommend is unfixed spectrographic emulsion. Such a matrix has several advantages. It is easily available. The manufacturers exercise good quality control over production of spectrographic emulsion; thus, there is little variation in the matrix in one laboratory or among several laboratories. The microprobe gives good impacting with the gelatin, and the probed samples may be simply stored in the laboratory notebook, in vials, or in boxes. The emulsion may be minutely examined after probing either with a metallographic microscope, or after clearing and fixing, with an ordinary microscope. The emulsion may be thus examined not only to assess the laser impact, but to ascertain that the gel is in fact homogeneous and that the solution is evenly distributed. The gelatin takes up solutions rapidly and dries quickly. Slurries and powders may be distributed with fair homogeneity and excellent retention on the surface of the emulsion.

In the typical experiment the following manipulations were performed. A series of circles was lightly punched into a clean strip of unfixed Kodak 649-0 35 mm film. The circles, about 2 cm in diameter, were distributed to individual fresh plastic Petri dishes. The sample, magnesium chloride plus filler, was dissolved in acid and diluted after neutralization. To each emulsion disc 100 μl of solution was added. The technic was to add the aliquot slowly—about 2 μl/sec—while gently puddling the droplet across the entire disc with the tip of the pipette. For this method constriction micropipettes are particularly useful. The solution was dried on the discs in a 60°C oven, and the discs were cut into strips.

The microprobe equipment used was as follows. A Jarrell-Ash Laser Microprobe was used employing a Cooke, Troughton, & Simms (Vickers) 20X, N.A. 0.25 long working objective in which the interlens cement had been removed. The electrodes, National L-4236 SPK, were arced for five seconds at ten amps to remove residual magnesium and then mounted in the probe. A spherical forelens was focused on a 1.5 m f/22 Wadsworth spectrograph loaded with 103-0 film. A 40 μ entrance slit was used. The shutter was kept closed except for the actual probing period. The electrodes were loaded at 1600 v, 50 μh plus residual inductance, and 20 μfd. As previously noted *(3, 4)* our samples lose about 1.5 μg with each laser impact. The spectrographic film was developed in the standard manner in D-19. With this method we calculated that about 5×10^{-12} g magnesium gave readable photometric densities at 2802.70 A and 2790.79 A. Up to an order less magnesium was detectable. In order to be sure that the results did not arise from the addition of the magnesium emission of the sample to the magnesium emission from the gelatin matrix itself or from the electrodes, samples of each of the latter were also microprobed. The pre-burned electrodes were magnesium-free, but very faint traces of magnesium were present in the emulsion of some batches. Blank determinations (all materials used except the magnesium chloride) gave the same results as emulsion alone. The low background noise was due in part to our use of de-ionized, triple-distilled water which had been stored in polyethylene containers in all diluting procedures. Similar procedures carried out with zinc and calcium substrates also gave increased sensitivity over conventional spectroscopy.

The technic has several simple variants. Multiple applications of aliquots to one disc may be carried out using an infrared lamp to speed drying while pipetting. Another variant is applicable to situations in which the previously microprobed solid sample, e.g. a lead block contaminated with zinc, shows no presence of the suspected contaminant. In this event place a number of droplets of dilute hydrochloric acid on the block. Remove the droplets consecutively to the emulsion matrix, facilitating evaporation with an infrared lamp. This method "averages" trace contamination from several locations but avoids the complications that occur if the original (e.g. lead block) sample is repetitively probed without racking the film (F. Brech's "rattatat" analysis). Repetitive probing without racking the film increases background due to increased noise from scatter, glare, electrode emission, cyanogen bands, etc. Dr. Cyrus Feldman at Oak Ridge has suggested the utility of the gelatin matrix method for dealing with the desirably small traces of radioactive material useful for spectroscopic analysis.

The final variant involves the transfer of chromatographed spots to the gel. The wetted spot is placed on the gel disc after each has been cut out. The reason why the paper should not itself be probed in precision work is the heterogeneity of elemental composition of the paper as well as its fibrous heterogeneity. Paper manufacturers seem to control residual contamination less well than film manufacturers control silver content. It is thus easier to estimate the size (mass) of a laser crater from data on the silver densitometry of a single shot of gel.

Certain precautions in the densitometric evaluation are necessary. If a seven-step wedge is used to establish the emulsion spectrographic curve, the operator must first take a shot at the same fish-tail setting with no wedge. The reason for this is that the very small spark, which has a relatively fixed position on successive analyses, may not be centered vertically upon the slit after the most meticulous aligning procedures. Only by examining the slit image of the *line* may this be ascertained, since the background may be uniformly negligible. This is particularly true of the method advocated in this paper. Without knowledge that the wedged densities are "true" densities, the operator will commit serious errors in trace analysis. It is easier to maintain this vertical alignment with a cylindrical lens, of course, and an added benefit is the lateral compression of the image of the spark. (The electrodes of the microprobes so far manufactured are horizontal). The usual increase in sensitivity occurs when the cylindrical lens is crossed by a second weaker cylindrical lens. When due caution has been exercised in preparation, calibration, and alignment, and when the laser is correctly tuned, the increase in sensitivity is accompanied by desirable photometric reproducibility. The variation between probings of gel matrix for magnesium, for example, are usually less than 50 per cent and sometimes less than 10 per cent at the 10^{-11} g level. The method in some ways combines the advantages of burning a measured sample to completion in an arc with the sensitivity of timed analysis.

The author wishes to express his appreciation for advice and encouragement to Dr. David Glick, Director of the Division of Histochemistry, Pathology Department, Stanford University Medical School, and to Mr. Fred Brech, Vice President in Charge of Research, Jarrell-Ash, Inc.

Literature Cited

(1) F. Brech and L. Cross, APPLIED SPECTROSCOPY **16,** 59 (1962)
(2) R. C. Rosan, M. K. Healy, and W. F. McNary, Jr., SCIENCE **142,** 236 (1963)
(3) R. C. Rosan, F. Brech, and D. Glick, FED. PROC. **23,** 174 (1963)
(4) R. C. Rosan, F. Brech, and D. Glick, FED. PROC. **24,** Supp. 14, S-126 (1965)
(5) W. F. McNary, Jr., R. C. Rosan, and M. K. Healy, Abstract 1st Boston Laser Conference, Northeastern University (1964)

Spectrographic Electrodes for Refractory Samples* 1.9

Morris Slavin
Chemistry Department, Brookhaven National Laboratory, Upton, Long Island, New York

When attempts are made to volatilize completely samples which contain a significant amount of certain refractory oxides in the carbon arc, difficulty is encountered in containing these samples in the electrode. Of the common substances the oxides of calcium and aluminum are the

*Research performed under the auspices of the U. S. Atomic Energy Commission.

worst offenders. After the more volatile constituents have been driven off, these oxides form a tight bead of very high surface tension, having no tendency to wet the carbon surface, and when this stage is reached the turbulent gas of the arc stream ejects the bead.

The bead is easily observed by looking down into the crater through a welding-glass during the burning period. This, of course, is possible only with open type arc stands; the new, totally enclosed stands so much favored at present make observation of the arc very difficult, and with these the operator may not realize that any loss of sample occurs. Undoubtedly, this is one cause of the poor opinion of the arc's reproducibility.

The difficulty appears to be purely mechanical in nature and can be eliminated by finding a more effective way of holding the bead in place than is provided by the flat, or nearly flat, floor of the conventional electrodes. A solution consists of shaping the crater floor in the form of a deep cone with an apex angle of 30°. While the walls of the crater burn down, the bead is held firmly at the sides and drops lower and lower into the cone as its diam. diminishes by volatilization. The size of the cone is dictated by the diameter of the bead when it is first formed. If the cone is too small, it will not hold the bead firmly and if it is too large, it will require the consumption of an excessive amount of carbon.

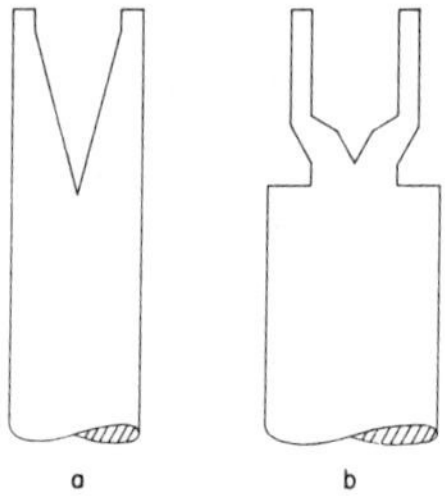

FIG. 1. TWO FORMS OF ELECTRODE DESIGNED TO RETAIN RESIDUAL OXIDE BEAD

Two forms of electrode with cone-shaped crater, used for years in the analysis of mineral and ceramic samples, are shown in Figure 1. These are 3/16-in. electrodes with a capacity of approximately 20 mg of silicate powder. In *a* the crater can be formed in one simple operation, and the cone will hold a relatively large bead, but the last of the oxide will not be driven off until the walls burn down to the apex. The form in *b* shows how a commercial type* may be modified while retaining the advantages of a necked tip and very little excess carbon, but is capable of holding only a small bead.

The common twist drill is unsuited to cutting deep cones. A much better tool for the purpose is a flat reamer, which can be ground from drill rod of appropriate diam., or which can be obtained on special order from one of the firms supplying drills†.

Spectrochemical Analysis of Oils Using "Vacuum Cup" Electrode 1.10

Raymond J. McGowan

U. S. Naval Civil Engineering Laboratory, Pt. Hueneme, California

Zink (*1*) described a new method for handling solution samples in spectrochemical analysis. This method was based upon a suggestion by Eichhoff (*2*) in which he proposed the use of a "capillary" electrode to bring the solution to the analytical gap. The method was modified by changing some of the design features of the capillary electrode and adding a Teflon cup. Attempts to obtain spectra of various oil samples by this method failed; this appeared to be due to the size of the axial canal, and the

*Either #*101L* of *United Carbon Products Co.* or #*3903* of *National Carbon Co.*

†These flat reamers were of 9/64-in. diam. and were made by the *Morse Twist Drill and Machine Co.*, 37 Park Row, New York, N. Y.

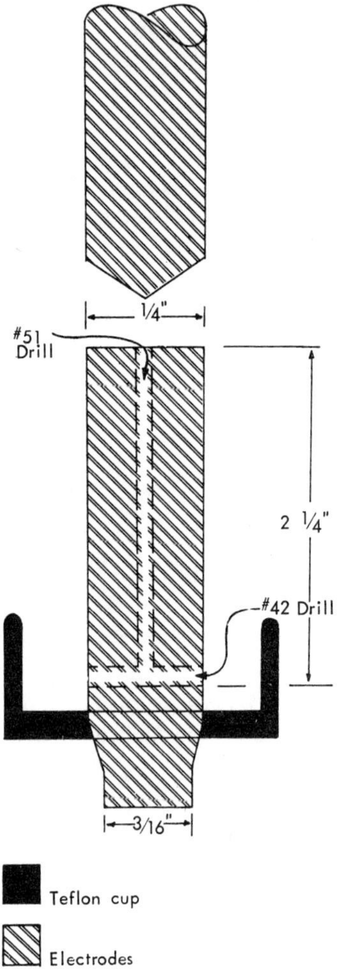

FIG. 1. MODIFIED "VACUUM CUP" ELECTRODE

eventual flaming of the oil sample which seriously disrupted the excitation process.

In order to meet the need for a method to analyze oils spectrographically the "Vacuum Cup" method was modified in the following manner so that it would produce satisfactory spectra. This was accomplished by first redesigning the electrode as shown in Figure 1; note that the axial canal is made with a No. 51 drill and the feed hole is made with a No. 42 drill. With these modifications it was possible to "lift" the oil sample 2¼ in. The second modification was to cut the electrode in such a manner that the Teflon cup would fit on the lower end of the electrode. With this arrangement it was possible to have the Teflon cup and oil sample below the excitation stand as shown in Figure 2. The fire hazard is thus removed.

In these preliminary studies it was possible to detect 0.05% cobalt, 0.23% lead, and 0.07% magnesium in a sample of lubricating oil. The spectrographic conditions and apparatus used are given in Table I.

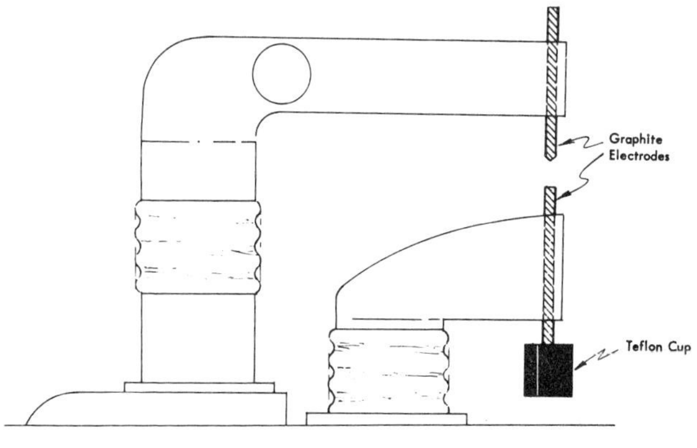

FIG. 2. ARRANGEMENT OF ELECTRODES IN THE SPARK STAND

TABLE I. APPARATUS AND SPECTROGRAPHIC CONDITIONS

Analytical gap, mm	5
Excitation unit	ARL Multisource ac Arc
Capacitance, μfd	60
Resistance, ohms	15
Source selector	Low voltage
Discharge point control	90
Power circuit voltage	250
Spectrograph	
Wavelength range, A	2400 to 4130
Slit width, μ	60
Filter	None
Intensity control	10%
Photographic emulsion	Eastman SA-2
Developer	Kodak D-19, 20°C, 3 min

This development will enable the determination of inorganic materials found in oil samples, without going through the ashing process, which is very time consuming and presents many analytical problems. This is a preliminary report of our findings; a more complete report will follow upon further investigations into the application of the "Vacuum Cup" method for the analysis of oil samples.

Literature Cited

(1) T. H. Zink, APPLIED SPECTROSCOPY **13,** 94 (1959)
(2) H. J. Eichhoff and K. Picard, SPECTROCHIM. ACTA **7,** 396 (1955-6)

1.11 A Versatile Hollow Cathode Lamp for Atomic Absorption Spectroscopy

A. Strasheim and L. R. P. Butler

National Physical Research Laboratory, Council of Scientific and Industrial Research, Pretoria, Union of South Africa

One of the most important items of equipment necessary for atomic absorption spectroscopy (*1-3*) is the hollow cathode lamp. Of all light-sources available, it has been found to give the narrowest spectral lines with reasonable intensity, and it has the added advantage that it also provides very constant light output. Several types of hollow-cathode lamps have been developed in the past. The gas circulating system described by Tolansky (*4*) is not necessary, since sealed off hollow cathode tubes have successfully been made (*2*, *5*). In these cases efficient outgassing of tubes has been achieved by the use of getters, but Walsh (*6*) has shown that, provided pure gas is used and careful outgassing of the tube is achieved, the use of a getter is not essential. Zeeman and Butler (*7*) described a lead lamp with a water cooled cathode, which could be dismantled. This lamp proved to be so successful that a similar type of lamp, using other cathodes which were not watercooled, was designed and built. In Fig. 1 a diagram of this new type of lamp is shown.

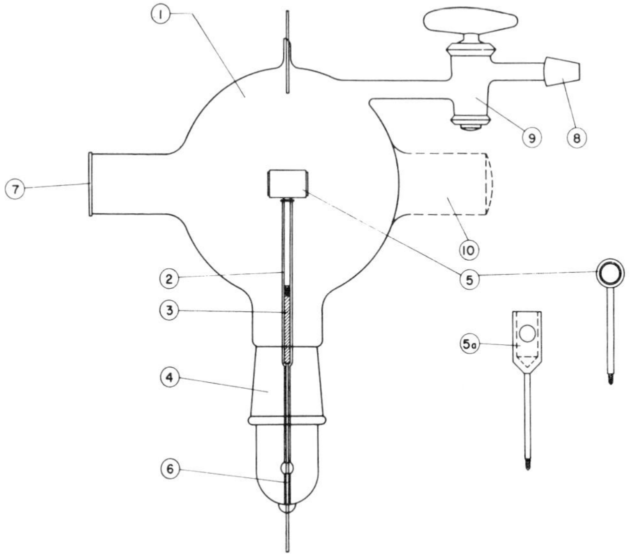

FIG. 1. DIAGRAM OF THE HOLLOW CATHODE LAMP

The body of the lamp, *1*, is a 750 ml pyrex flask. Walsh (6) found that the life of a lamp could be appreciably increased by using lamps with large volumes. The flask is provided with a high-vacuum tap, *9*, and joint, *8*, for connection to the vacuum system. A 34/45 joint, *4*, is connected to the neck of the flask. Another 3 cm-diam. neck is attached, onto which a quartz window, *7*, is cemented. A 1.5 mm-tungsten rod, 6, is sealed into a 34/45 stopper to provide electrical connection to the cathode. The cathode is a cylindrically shaped metal electrode, 20.0 mm long, with an inside diam. of 9.0 mm and a wall thickness of 1.3 mm. The cathode is attached to a short rod which can be screwed onto a brass rod, *3*, which in turn is encased in a glass tube, 2. Should the element to be investigated be suitable, the cathode can be machined directly from stock consisting of this element. In most cases however the cathode is machined from copper, and a cylindrical liner inserted into the copper cylinder, being held in position by swaging over the ends of

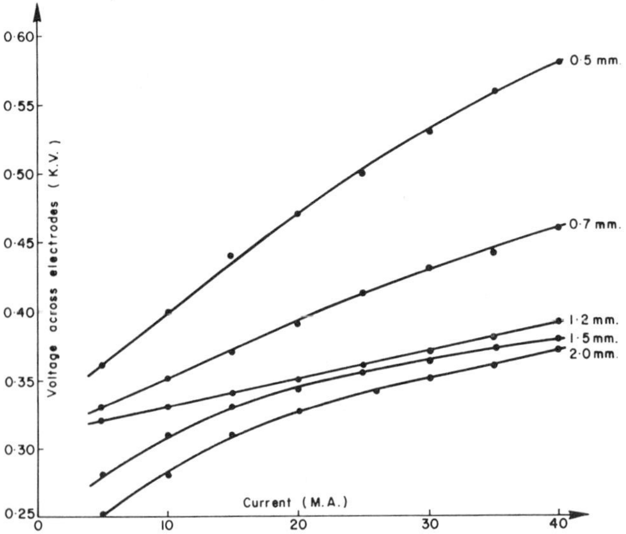

Fig. 2. Influence of Gas Pressure on Voltage-Current Characteristics

the liner. In the case of metals having low melting points (e.g., Pb) a cuplike cathode, *5a*, can be used.

The lamps are evacuated by means of a simple vacuum system with a rotary pump and a two-stage mercury diffusion pump. Liquid air traps prevent mercury vapor from entering the lamps. Silicone grease is used on all ground glass joints. The lamps are degassed in much the same way as described by Walsh (6). It was also found that a getter is not necessary. The best argon gas pressure proved to be 1.2 mm Hg. The rate of sputter at this pressure is fairly high, but due to the fact that the lamps can be easily and cheaply reconditioned, and because the discharge is very stable, this pressure is used. It was found that when the gas pressure is correct, there is a linear relationship between voltage drop across the lamp, and the anode current. Figure 2 shows the voltage-current characteristics of a lamp at different gas pressures. With all the cathodes tested this linear relationship was evident, and it proved to be very useful as a means for determining the correct pressure in the lamp.

The main advantages of this type of lamp are: (a) it can be dismantled, cleaned, and the cathode reconditioned or changed very easily, and (b) a watercooled cathode can be introduced by replacing the 34/45 stopper with a watercooled metal stopper onto which the connecting rod, *3*, has been attached. In this case, mica guards are necessary to prevent sporadic discharges to the metal.

It is suggested that if more than one element has to be determined simultaneously (e.g., with direct reading spectrograph), a second projection, *10*, be made at the rear of the lamp and provided with a quartz lens instead of the quartz window. The image of the cathode of a second lamp, mounted in tandem behind the first lamp, can then be projected into the cathode of the first lamp, and both characteristic spectra then passed through the absorbing flame.

The authors gratefully acknowledge the contribution made by Mr. G. J. Wessels in noticing the linear voltage-current relationships of the lamp during its development.

They also thank the workshop staff for their willing and able help.

Literature Cited

(1) A. Walsh, SPECTROCHIM. ACTA **7,** 108 (1955)
(2) B. Russell, J. P. Shelton, and A. Walsh, IBID. **8,** 317 (1957)
(3) A. C. Menzies, ANAL. CHEM. **32,** 898 (1960)
(4) S. Tolansky, *High Resolution Spectroscopy,* Methuen and Co., London, 1947
(5) G. Dieke and H. M. Crosswhite, J. OPT. SOC. AM. **42,** 933 (1952)
(6) W. G. Jones and A. Walsh, SPECTROCHIM. ACTA **16,** 249 (1960)
(7) P. B. Zeeman and L. R. P. Butler, TEGNIKON (SOUTH AFRICA) 96 (Oct. 1960)

1.12 Improved Burner Adjustment for Atomic Absorption Spectrophotometers

R. A. Murie and R. C. Bourke

Allison Division, GMC, Indianapolis, Indiana

The usual standard aspirator and sample burner assemblies of atomic absorption spectrophotometers are designed to be adjusted by simple manual rotation or elevation of the supporting shaft. The shaft is then held in place by tightening a set screw. To achieve maximum sensitivity it is necessary to align the burner slot parallel to, and in the center of, the sample beam. The edge of a white card is held manually exactly vertical and in the exact center of the burner slot, first at one end of the burner and then at the other while raising or lowering and rotating the assembly. This method requires an assistant to achieve good alignment and is time consuming. The authors have designed an adjustment rack that adapts

FIG. 1. FRONT VIEW, BURNER ASSEMBLY

to existing burner assemblies to permit very accurate and rapid alignment to be carried-out by only one person.

The complete assembly is shown in Figures 1 and 2. An "alignment plate" to take the place of the white card is shown in Figure 3. Three modes of adjustment, vertical, horizontal and rotational, are permitted by the gear arrangement shown. The center shaft of the burner assembly is rigidly mounted in the center of a circular plate that has gear teeth machined into the edge. As can be seen from Figure 1, when knobs B are loosened, knob A will turn the disc. This permits the burner slot to be positioned exactly parallel to the light beam path. The assembly is positioned in a horizontal plane by turning knob D. This permits the base plate to slide in the keyways. The burner slot may now be moved in or out of the light beam. Vertical adjustment is made by turning knob C which operates a continuous screw to raise or lower the assembly until the position of maximum sensitivity is found in the light beam. Calibration markings, Figure 2, are placed on the center shaft to permit repositioning the burner to its original position should different samples have greater sensitivities in different parts of the flame.

The "alignment plate", Figure 3, is shown mounted on the burner in Figures 1 and 2. The plate has a small guide ground to fit the width of the burner slot. Place-

FIG. 2. SIDE VIEW, BURNER ASSEMBLY

FIG. 3. ALIGNMENT PLATE

ment of the guide in the slot automatically aligns the machined, beveled edge accurately and vertically in the exact center of the burner. This permits exactly 50 per cent transmission of the light beam when the assembly is properly positioned. In aligning the burner the plate is placed first at one end and then the other while the proper knobs are quickly adjusted to effect a 50 per cent light reduction on the sample photocell. If moving the plate from one end to the other causes no change in light reading, the burner alignment is complete. The plate is removed and the burner may now be started. The vertical adjustment is made by knob C to determine the region of the flame in which the maximum sample sensitivity occurs.

The authors wish to express their appreciation to Mr. Clarence Savage and Mr. Joe Stout for helping in the machining and assembly of the unit.

1.13 Vertical Flame Adjustment on a Beckman DU Spectrophotometer*

Ray Woodriff† and J. J. McCown

Argonne National Laboratory, Idaho Division, Idaho Falls, Idaho

In flame photometry, it is often desirable to scan the flame vertically. A device for moving the burner up and down on a Beckman DU spectrophotometer has been reported by May, Kramer, and Curtis *(1)* and also by Beck *(2)*. These devices, have two disadvantages: a) they require some fairly complicated machine work to construct and b) when the burner alone is moved up and down, the adjustment of the solution feed is destroyed.

A simple, yet satisfactory, device for vertical scanning of the flame can be added to the Beckman flame attachment with ordinary hand tools (see Figure 1). Since the whole flame housing is attached to the spectrophotometer by a hinge and a locking screw, the locking screw can be replaced by a spring and a strike plate, and the whole housing can be raised and lowered along the hinge pins. The vertical position of the housing can be precisely controlled by an adjustment screw through a little block of metal bolted to the end of the burner housing. There is a flat area extending from the top hinge to the mounting support on the spectrophotometer for the adjustment screw to strike against.

To make a precise scan of the flame, the mirror in the flame housing is covered to prevent light from unknown parts of the flame entering the slit, and the adjustment screw is turned while the intensity of the spectral line in question is watched. After the flame position for maximum intensity is found, the mirror is uncovered and adjusted to further increase the intensity.

---

*This work was performed under the auspices of the U. S. Atomic Energy Commission Contract 31-109-eng-38.

†Permanent address: Department of Chemistry, Montana State College, Bozeman, Mont., summer employee of Argonne National Laboratory, Idaho Division.

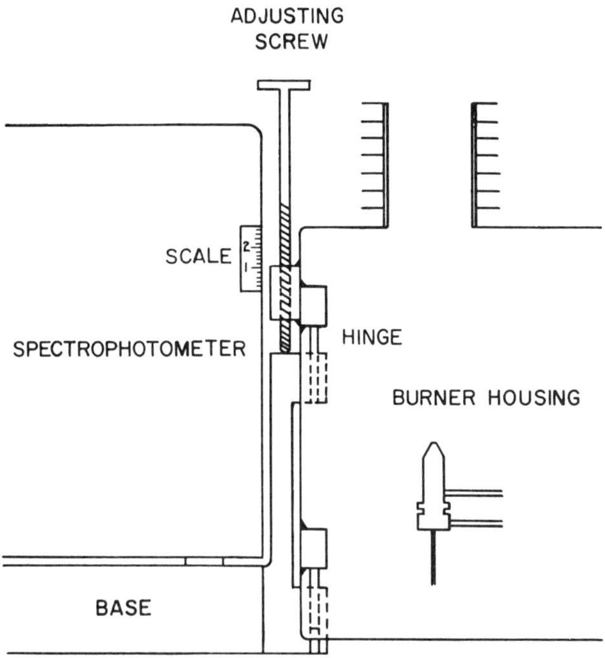

FIG. 1. VERTICAL SCAN DEVICE FOR BECKMAN FLAME HOUSING

The range to be covered by the scan can be adjusted by removing the phototube housing from the back of the spectrophotometer and rotating the entrance slit mirror about its horizontal axis. If still more vertical range is desired, the hinges can be cut down. A millimeter scale can be attached to the end of the spectrophotometer.

Literature Cited

(1) I. May, H. Kramer, and E. L. Curtis, ANAL. CHEM. **29,** 1388 (1957)
(2) B. L. Beck, REV. SCI. INSTR. **33,** 756 (1962)

1.14 Controlled Atmosphere Excitation Chamber for D.C. Arc Analysis

M. P. Brash and J. P. Phaneuf

Research and Advanced Development Division, Avco Corporation, Wilmington, Massachusetts

Spectra produced in the d.c. arc with graphite or carbon electrodes suffer from cyanogen interference between 3500 and 4150 *A* as well as poor line-to-background ratio in the ultraviolet region *(1)*. In order to take advantage of the sensitivity of the d.c. arc method, a chamber for exciting the sample in a nitrogen-free controlled atmosphere eliminates the cyanogen interference and increases the line-to-background ratio.

Several adaptors have been described for inert or controlled atmosphere excitation, but they are usually very complex and once installed are not too easily interchanged *(2,3,4)*. The inert gas excitation chamber described in this paper permits a rapid change from air to controlled atmosphere when using pin or cup electrodes. The chamber* was constructed of quartz, since this material possesses desirable thermal and optical properties. The design permits easy installation and removal. For simplicity and ease of cleaning, the chamber was made solely for ¼-in. pin type electrodes and constructed in two pieces. This chamber was designed for the *Jarrell Ash* arc stand *No. 1940*† and, with slight modification, it could be adapted to other arc stands.

A clear quartz tube 1⅛-in. i.d. x 4 in. long was used for the chamber. (See Figure 1.) A ¼-in. hole was drilled 2 in. from the end of this tube along a diam. perpendicular to the axis of the tube. A ¼-in. i.d. x ¼-in. long quartz tube was welded to each of the holes to provide guides for the electrodes, which then serve to align the unit. The ¼-in. i.d. guide hole leaves 0.008-in. clearance for gas vapor when 0.242-in. electrodes are used. Another hole was

---

*The chamber was made by Syncor Products, Inc., Malden, Mass.
†*Catalog No. G-2-53,* Jorrell Ash Co., Newtonville, Mass.

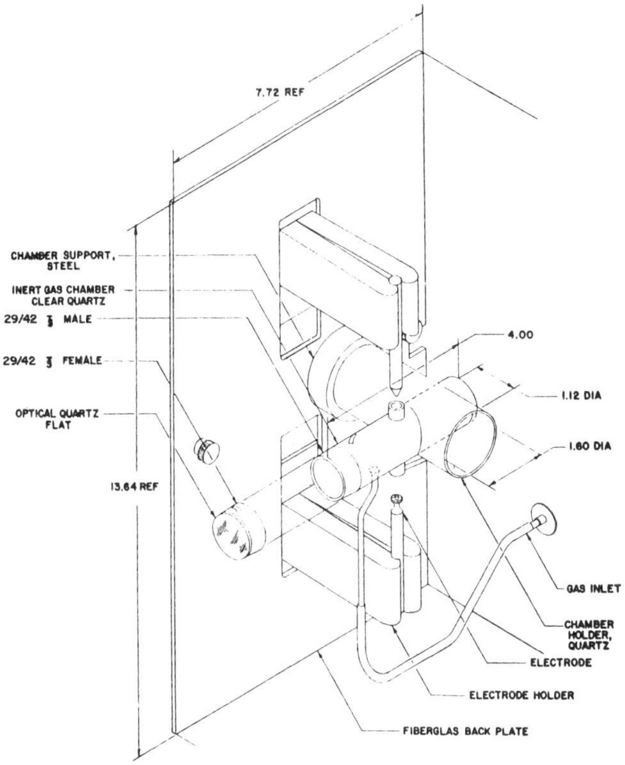

FIG. 1. CUTAWAY VIEW OF THE ARC STAND WITH EXCITATION CHAMBER

All dimensions are in inches.

drilled forward of the bottom electrode guide and fitted with a gas inlet tube which was bent to facilitate the opening of the electrode holder without disturbing the chamber. The front end of the chamber was provided with a 29/42 standard taper male joint. The 29/42 standard taper female joint which closed the tube, was fitted with an optical quartz flat for photographing the spectra. This arrangement was used so that the unit could be cleaned on the inside with a minimum of difficulty.

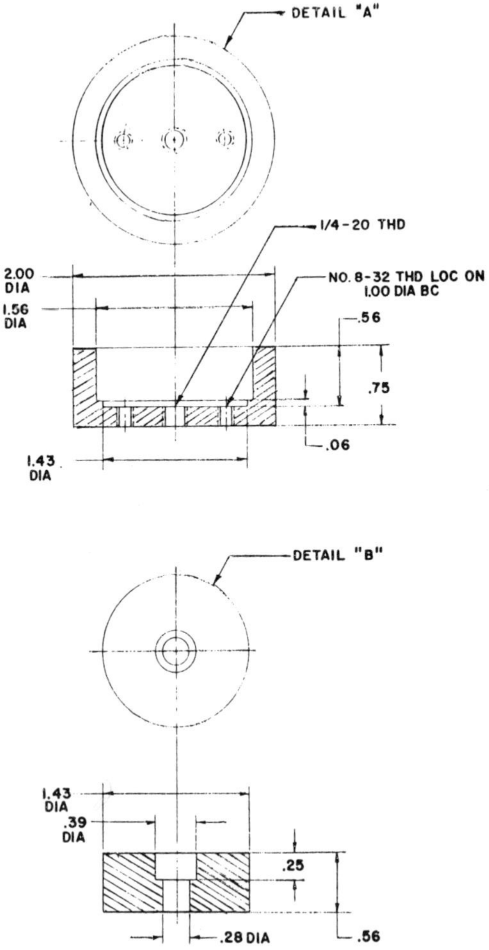

FIG. 2. STEEL HOLDING-RING ASSEMBLY
All dimensions are in inches.

FIG. 3. SPECTROGRAMS OBTAINED IN AIR AND IN THE CHAMBER USING ARGON-OXYGEN ATMOSPHERE
Cyanogen bands at approximately 3600, 3880, and 4150 A are shown

To hold the chamber at the required height on the optical train, a second back plate was fabricated, a duplicate of the one that was in the arc stand, and provided with a chamber support ring. (See Figure 2.) The ring was made from two pieces of mild steel, the outer one, A, $\frac{3}{4}$-in. long by 2 in. diam. and bored $1\frac{9}{16}$-in. in diam. by $\frac{1}{2}$-in. deep. This latter hole was further machined to provide a well $1\frac{7}{16}$-in. diam. and $\frac{1}{16}$-in. deep. The second piece, B, was $1\frac{7}{16}$-in, diam. by $\frac{9}{16}$-in. long and fitted the well provided in the first ring. The two pieces were joined by a $\frac{1}{4}$-in. No. 20 allen head screw, and the ring mounted by screwing to the back plate at the proper height.

The quartz chamber was mounted in a clear quartz tube of $1\frac{1}{2}$-in. diam. A hole was drilled through the walls of this tube to accept the chamber and the pair were welded together. This tube, which had been used to design the above holding ring, was then cut to the proper length to align the chamber with the electrodes and to permit the arc stand door to be closed.

Finally, two $\frac{1}{4}$-in. holes were drilled through the arc stand, one through the rear and the other through the side into the interior of the arc stand. These holes were fitted with polyethylene hose adaptors and tubing to provide for the gas inlet while the arc stand was closed and the safety circuit completed.

This controlled atmosphere excitation chamber is used routinely in this laboratory for the analysis of refractories in the d.c. arc. Figure 3 shows the difference between spectrograms obtained by excitation of identical samples and electrodes in air and in the chamber using an argon-oxygen atmosphere. The possibility of analyzing for carbon by using electrodes with a nitrogen atmosphere and measuring the density of a suitable cyanogen band head is a potential application *(5)*.

Literature Cited

1. R. E. Thiers and B. L. Vallee, "*Proceedings of the Colloquium Spectroscopicum Internationale VI*" Pergamon Press, London, 179 (1957)

2. V. A. Fassel and W. A. Gordon, ANAL. CHEM., **30,** 179 (1958)
3. A. Arrak and A. J. Mittledorf, APPLIED SPECTROSCOPY, **13,** 85 (1959)
4. B. L. Vallee and M. R. Baker, J. OPT. SOC. AM., **46,** 77-82 (1956)
5. W. H. Dennen, SPECTROCHIM. ACTA, **9,** 89 (1957)

An Economical Apparatus for Controlling the Atmosphere in Spectrochemical Analysis 1.15

Raymond J. McGowan

U. S. Naval Civil Engineering Laboratory, Pt. Hueneme, California

A problem encountered in spectrochemical analysis is the formation of cyanogen bands due to the nitrogen in the atmosphere. These bands will appear in the wavelength region from 3000 to 4500 A during the excitation of a carbon arc. The only way to eliminate these bands is to perform the excitation in an atmosphere free of nitrogen.

A simple, practical, and economical method of producing a spectrum free of cyanogen bands is to use a small quartz vessel, which can be purchased for less than twenty dollars*, to control the atmosphere surrounding the carbon arc and substitute an inert gas for air, which is 78% nitrogen. The use of inert atmospheres on highly inflammable materials such as gasoline would permit direct arcing. There are several types of gases that can be used for this purpose, such as He, CO_2, CO, and A. Hydrogen and discharge gases containing hydrogen have been employed and found to yield weak spectra. Also they form explosive mixtures when mixed with air and must be used with great caution. According to Morrison and Fassel *(1)* argon will serve as the better atmosphere, because with a higher current for the excitation of spectra it gives a much lower

*Ringsdorff Carbon Corporation, East McKeesport, Pa.

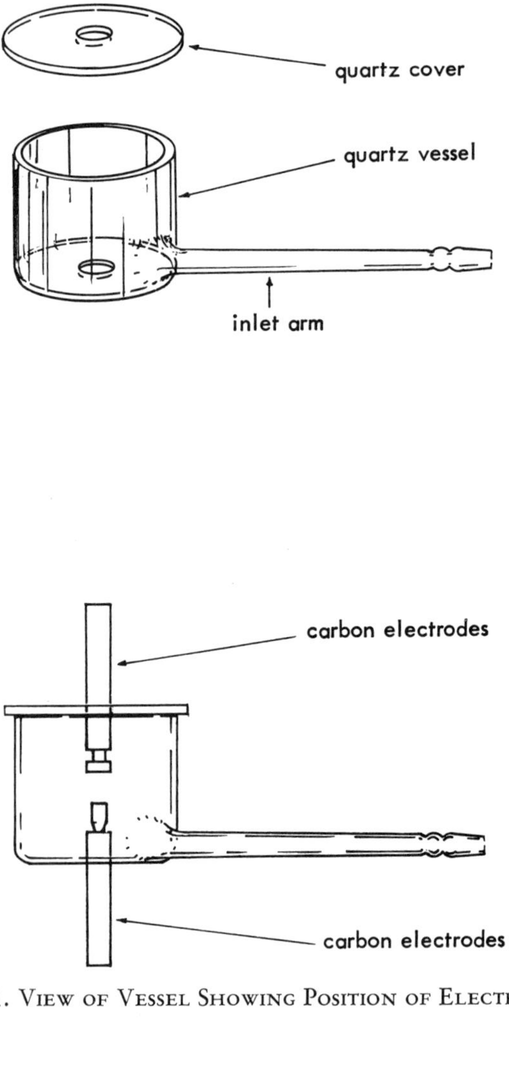

FIG. 1. VIEW OF VESSEL SHOWING POSITION OF ELECTRODE

temperature than in air. The carbon electrode reaches 2600°K with argon, compared to 2900°K in helium, 3700°K in nitrogen, and 4500 to 5000°K in air.

To control the environment of the excitation, a quartz vessel *(2)* shown in Figure 1, was used. This vessel has a hole in the base through which the lower electrode passes, and the protruding inlet arm is used to conduct the inert gas into the chamber. The cover which is also made of quartz has a hole in the center through which the upper electrode passes. This arrangement holds the cover in place. The flow of gas into the chamber is regulated in such a manner that the quartz cover will rotate slowly. This action disperses the gas in the chamber and maintains a constant pressure. One of the many advantages of this design is its small size as compared with other chambers used to control the atmosphere in emission work. It is simple to manipulate and only requires a very small volume of gas to maintain a controlled environment.

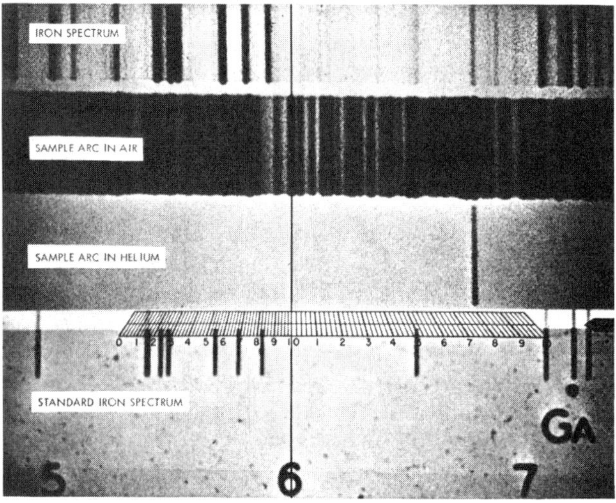

Fig. 2. Spectra of Sample and Standard Iron

The results of using this quartz vessel with helium as an atmosphere is shown in Figure 2. The range shown here is from 4144.0 to 4171.0 A with the lead line at 4168.0 A. This clearly shows the elimination of the cyanogen bands as compared with the spectrum excited in air. The asymmetry in the lead line is possibly due to the rate of flow of the helium.

Controlling the atmosphere with a quartz vessel has proven to be very valuable in carbon arc excitations. It reduces the background intensity and permits one to use longer exposures. It is extremely economical when compared with other units. With an atmosphere free of nitrogen, the cyanogen bands are eliminated and many of the analytical lines of elements in this region become available, such as Pb, Ce, and Tl between 3000 and 4500 A.

Literature Cited

(1) G. H. Morrison and V. A. Fassel, MICROCHEM. J. SYMP. SER. **1**, 3 (1961)
(2) A. Schontag, SPECTROCHEM. ACTA **11**, 243 (1957)

1.16 Arc Chamber for Spectral Excitation in Controlled Atmospheres

M. S. Wang and W. T. Cave

Central Research Department, Monsanto Company
St. Louis, Missouri

A chamber to permit the use of a controlled atmosphere has been developed. It is inexpensive and simple to fabricate and provides significant advantages in convenience, reproducibility and sensitivity.

Most of the controlled atmosphere devices described in the literature *(1-8)* appear to fall into two categories. One type is the Stallwood Jet type which has the annular gas inlet adjacent to the electrode to form a jet stream surrounding the arc column *(3, 5, 6, 7, 8)*. Stallwood *(9)* originally used an air stream to control vaporization of samples and several investigators have used the device to exclude air by supplying other specific gas streams *(6, 7, 8)*. Modified related devices are reported by Margoshes and Scribner *(5)* and Arrak *(3)*.

The second type features an enclosing chamber which fills with the inert gas but does not provide a jet stream

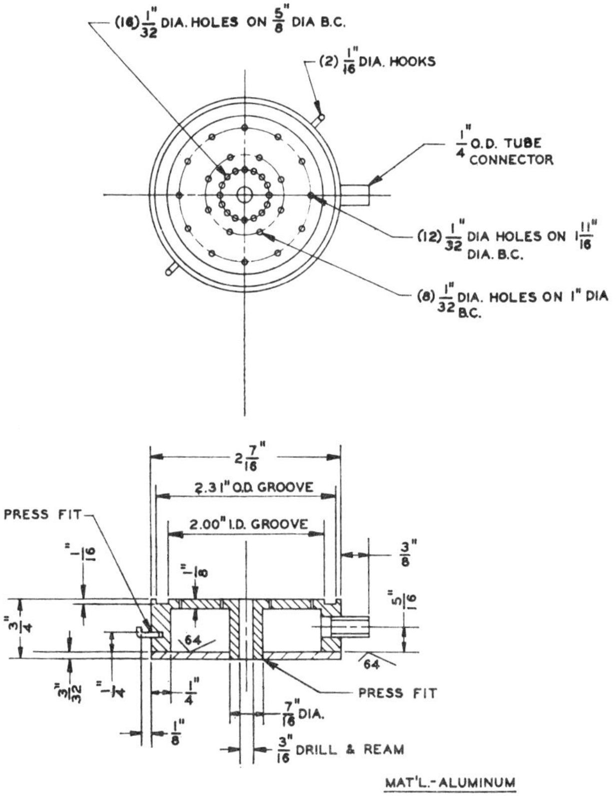

FIG. 1. GAS DIRECTOR

surrounding the arc column. Vallee *(1)*, Stone *(4)* and Fassel *(2)* used this type. Like the Stallwood Jet as modified by use of a quartz dome (Spex Industries, Inc., Metuchen, New Jersey), the equipment herein described is intermediate in type. It is used routinely in our laboratory for qualitative, semi-quantitative, and quantitative spectrographic analyses.

Although controlled atmospheres have been widely applied in spectrographic analyses, many practical difficulties have been encountered as pointed out by Margoshes and Scribner *(5)*. Delays encountered in changing electrodes, the time required for flushing the chambers, and the clouding of chamber windows by deposits of samples and electrode material have often made this technique impractical for routine analysis. The Stallwood Jet with a quartz dome, so far the most popular commercially available controlled atmosphere device, has not solved all of the problems and improved performance was the object of developing this design.

A drawing of the gas director (base-plate) is shown in Figure 1. A photograph of the complete assembly with a quartz enclosure covering the gas director is shown in Figure 2. Two coil springs fasten the device to the lower clamp of the arc stand. The sample electrode is held directly by the lower clamp through the center hole of the gas director. The optimum position of the upper electrode is 12 mm above the base plate. A quartz cylinder 57 mm OD and 41.5 mm high fits into the groove of the director. There is a cutout of 11 x 20 mm on the lower portion of the quartz cylinder which faces the slit of the spectrograph and this opening serves as the optical aperture. The quartz cover is 63.5 mm in diameter and has a center hole of 6.5 mm. The dimensions given are for the use of 3/16 in. electrodes.

The sample electrode is placed higher than in the usual Stallwood Jet permitting easier manipulation. This also reduces the hazard of contamination from the base plate, especially when high current is used. The small holes direct the gas stream smoothly upward and no spiral motion has been observed. The gas input to the chamber is spread over the base plate and thus the symmetry of a narrow aperture annulus around the electrode is not a critical parameter. Errors caused by imperfections in the shape of the sample electrode or its position respecting the jet aperture which often result in asymmetrical burning in the jet types are thus avoided.

Experiments were made to determine the optimum flow rate of the surrounding gas. Table I shows a blank electrode consumption rate using argon gas. The electrodes were Ultra Carbon 105S and 105U.

More graphite was consumed at lower flow rates due to the admixture of air through the optical aperture of the chamber. A flow rate of 6 l/min is enough to exclude

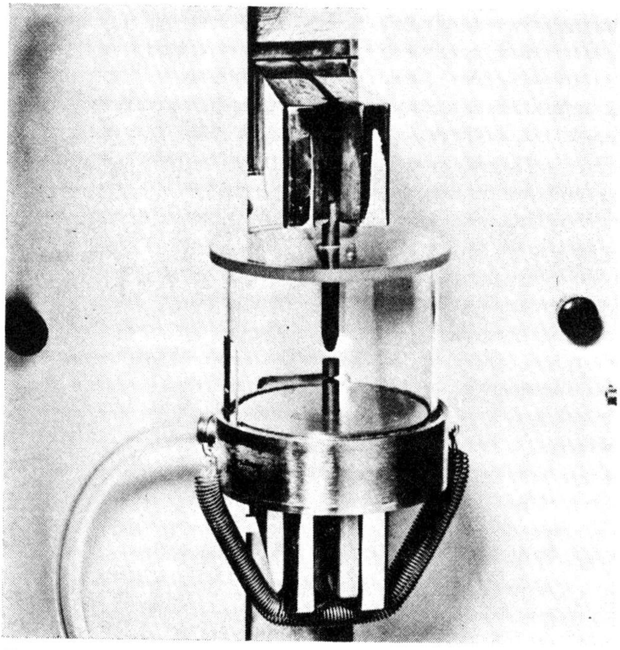

FIG. 2. GAS DIRECTOR AND QUARTZ ENCLOSURE FOR CONTROLLED ATMOSPHERE SYSTEM

TABLE I. RELATIONSHIP BETWEEN ELECTRODE CONSUMPTION RATE AND FLOW OF ARGON GAS TO THE CHAMBER (13 AMP DC ARC)

Argon Flow (1/min)	*Burning Time (min)*	*Decrease of Weight in 105S Electrode (mg)*
10	5	0.2
8	5	0.3
6	5	0.9
4	5	1.8
3.6	5	2.1
3.4	5	6.1
3.0	5	12.5
2.5	5	23.8
2.0	5	48.1

air for a 5 min burn. At the more usual arcing time of 2 min the decrease in weight of an electrode was found to be 0.7 mg at an argon flow of 3.5 l/min.

Table II shows the relative intensity of the cyanogen band head at 4216.0 A for various gas compositions, rates of flow, and arcing times at 13 amperes. The efficient suppression of the cyanogen emission confirms the rates of flow necessary to exclude air.

An experiment was made to compare the performance of a Stallwood Jet with quartz dome cover with that of

TABLE II. RATES OF FLOW AND ARC TIMES FOR THE SUPPRESSION OF THE CYANOGEN BAND AT 4216.0 A

Composition	*Rate (1/min)*	*Arc Time (min)*	*Relative Intensity**
Ar	6	5	0.20
Ar	3.5	2	0.31
Ar } O_2	2.6 } 1.1	1	0.31
Air	open arc	1	∞

* Obtained from a suitable step of seven-step filter for accurate measurement of per cent transmission.

this new device. A Spex Mix powder was diluted with graphite to contain ten ppm each of 49 elements. One part of this was mixed with nine parts of a 1:1 lithium carbonate:graphite mixture. A 10 mg portion of this final mixture was weighed into 105S Ultra Carbon electrodes. Table III shows the comparison of relative intensities obtained from both devices using a 13 amp dc arc, a gas mixture of 2.6 l/min argon and 1.1 l/min oxygen, a Jarrell-Ash 3.4 m Ebert Spectrograph, and Kodak SA-1 plates. The data shown are from a single plate.

The increased sensitivity obtained with the new device suggests that the rapidly moving sheath of gas in the Stallwood Jet cools the arc column. In our device the sample burned to completion in 50-55 sec whereas with the Stallwood Jet the sample lasted 30-35 sec. A lower concentration of oxygen in the immediate vicinity of the arc column, as provided by the new device, no doubt accounts for the longer burn time.

Using the conditions and sample preparation method specified above, nickel in W-1 *(10)* was determined for a comparison of precision of the two devices. Relative intensity of the Spex Mix standard was used to plot the analytical curves. These curves were then used to determine the nickel in the sample. A mean of 77 ppm and a

TABLE III. COMPARISON OF RELATIVE INTENSITIES* FROM GAS DIRECTOR AND STALLWOOD JET. DILUTION OF SPEX MIX WITH GRAPHITE. BUFFERED BY NINE PARTS OF 1:1 Li_2CO_3 AND GRAPHITE.

		New Device			*Stallwood Jet*		
Si	2516.12	0.33	0.33	0.31	0.22	0.28	0.32
Mn	2576.10	0.30	0.31	0.29	0.22	0.24	0.31
Al	3082.15	0.14	0.16	0.14	0.06	0.07	0.07
Be	3131.07	0.39	0.42	0.40	0.38	0.39	0.51
In	3256.09	0.11	0.11	0.16	0.04	0.07	0.09
Ag	3280.68	0.67	0.63	0.64	0.25	0.36	0.44

* Obtained from suitable steps of seven-step filter for accurate measurement of per cent transmission.

standard deviation of 14 ppm were obtained by the Stallwood Jet for nine determinations in two plates on separate days. By the new device, a mean of 74 ppm and a standard deviation of 9 ppm were obtained in the same way for eight determinations.

The following advantages have been achieved:

1. Electrode alignment is simple because both sample and counter electrodes are held directly by the clamps of the original arc stand. The two springs hold the chamber firmly to lower clamp and can be used on almost any make of stand. Special adapters are avoided.

2. Similarly, electrode contamination is completely avoided because insertion or removal require no force and forceps are adequate for manipulation. This is particularly pertinent when using boiler cap or metal electrodes.

3. For samples whose burning gives copious "smoke," such as gallium or indium metal, the larger chamber provides better visibility and requires less frequent cleaning.

4. No flushing of the chamber is required and the amount of controlled atmosphere gas used is small.

5. Smoother, longer burns are obtained. Particularly when separate exposures of a single burn are required, this is advantageous.

6. As indicated in Table III and by the precision experiment, sensitivity and reproducibility are improved.

The authors acknowledge with thanks, helpful discussions with D. R. Beasecker, whose earlier work encouraged our further attempts at novel design.

Literature Cited

(1) B. L. Vallee, C. B. Reimer, and J. R. Loofbourow, J. Opt. Soc. Am. **40,** 751 (1950)

(2) V. A. Fassel, paper given in 11th Annual Southeastern Symposium on Spectroscopy, January 1963, University of Florida

(3) A. Arrak, The Spex Speaker **8,** No. 3, 1 (1963)

(4) H. Stone, J. Opt. Soc. Am. **44,** 411 (1954)
(5) M. Margoshes and B. F. Scribner, APPLIED SPECTROSCOPY, in press
(6) C. S. Annell, and A. W. Helz, U. S, Geol. Survey, Profess. Papers No. **400-B,** 227 (1960)
(7) R. F. O'Connell and A. J. Mitteldorf, The Spex Speaker **5,** No. 2, 1 (1960)
(8) C. D. Curtis, Nature **196,** 1087 (1962)
(9) B. J. Stallwood, J. Opt. Soc. Am. **44,** 171 (1954)
(10) H. W. Fairbairn, W. G. Schlecht, R. E. Stevens, L. H. Ahrens, and F. Chayes, U. S. Geol. Survey Bulletin No. **980** (1951)

Simple Arc Devices for Spectral Excitation in Controlled Atmospheres* *1.17*

Marvin Margoshes and Bourdon F. Scribner

National Bureau of Standards
Washington, D.C. 20234

The replacement of air around a carbon arc by other gases has been shown to have several effects in the excitation of spectra, the most obvious being the elimination of cyanogen bands when the atmosphere surrounding the arc contains no nitrogen. Although the effects of controlled atmospheres have been applied in spectrographic analysis, work along these lines has been limited by the practical difficulties involved. These difficulties include delays in changing electrodes between samples, the need for flushing the chamber before excitation can be started, and clouding of chamber windows by deposits of sample and electrode vapors.

*Presented in part at the Second National Meeting, Society for Applied Spectroscopy, San Diego, Calif., 1963 (APPLIED SPECTROSCOPY **17,** 142 (1963)) and the XI Colloquium Spectroscopicum Internationale, Belgrade, 1963.

Several simplified arrangements have been described for the operation of arcs in controlled atmospheres. Though originally intended only to control vaporization of samples, the Stallwood jet *(1)* can be used to partially exclude air, but it is not entirely satisfactory unless a chamber is added *(2)*. In addition to providing a controlled atmosphere, the Stallwood jet with a chamber directs the gas stream so as to stabilize the arc.

Samples can be vaporized and excited in arcs in controlled atmospheres by enclosing the electrodes and the excitation zone in a flow of gas, thus eliminating the need for a chamber. Devices to accomplish this have been described by Annell and Helz *(3)*, O'Connell *(4)*, and Curtis *(5)*. In all of these devices, two of the disadvantages of arc chambers have been eliminated, namely clouding of windows and the need for extensive flushing. However, when a device like that of O'Connell was tried, it did not provide complete exclusion of air, and the devices of Annell and Helz and of Curtis had the disadvantages of necessitating some modification of the arc stand and of requiring more manipulation of the electrodes when changing samples than is needed when the samples are excited in air.

The device illustrated in Figure 1 makes it possible to excite samples as rapidly and as conveniently in atmospheres of argon or helium as in air. It will fit into any arc stand having lower electrode jaws which can hold ½-in. tubing and which provides a space of at least two in. from the top of the lower electrode jaws to the optical axis of the spectrograph. The gas is brought in at the bottom and passes through a water-cooled jacket into the chamber. The gas then passes through a pierced plate into the tapered portion of the chamber, forming a tubular stream around the lower electrode. The outer diameter of the chamber is one in. at the bottom and ½ in. at the top, and the height of the tapered portion is ¾ in. The graphite collar at the top of the chamber is ½ in. high and ½ in. diam., and it has a wall thickness of 0.03 in. This collar is held in the tapered portion of

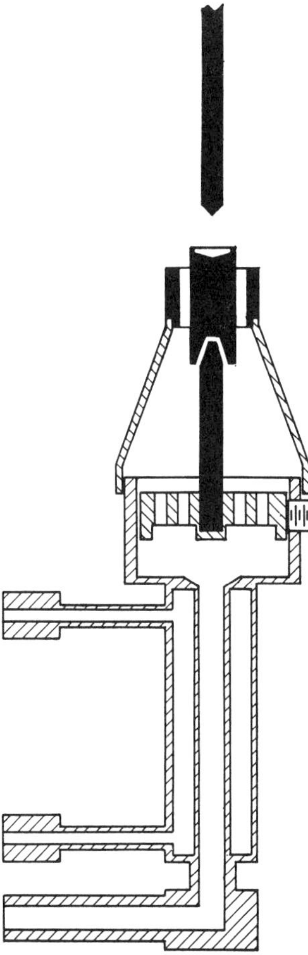

FIG. 1. GAS-SHEATHED ARC FOR USE WITH GASES THAT DO NOT CONTAIN OXYGEN

the chamber by a friction fit, and the tapered portion is similarly fitted onto the base of the unit. The sample is held in an anode cap electrode, of the type described by

Scribner and Mullin *(6)*, which is placed on a ⅛-in. diam. graphite pedestal mounted in a hole in the pierced plate. The position of the plate can be adjusted so that the anode cap projects about 1/8 or 3/16 in. above the graphite collar. Aside from the portions shown in black in Figure 1, which are graphite, the entire unit is made of brass with all joints silver-soldered.

In experimenting with several different designs for this device, it was found that some taper of the chamber is necessary to properly direct the gas stream. A straight tube, as used by O'Connell *(4)*, did not exclude air from the arc as effectively as the tapered tube shown in Figure 1. The graphite collar was also found to be necessary, particularly when the arc is operated at a current above 15 or 20 amp. When the upper part of the chamber was made of brass, it became hot enough to vaporize slightly, as shown by the appearance of lines of copper and zinc in the spectra. Annell and Helz *(3)* used a ceramic tube for this part of their device. The use of other heat-resistant materials for these parts is possible but could lead to problems with contamination. The water-cooling jacket on the bottom is also important, since otherwise enough heat is conducted to the gas inlet to soften plastic tubing connected there.

The use of an anode cap electrode *(6)* supported on a pedestal makes it easy to change electrodes rapidly. These electrodes and pedestals are listed in the catalogs of the manufacturers of graphite electrodes. The design and materials of the anode cap electrode can be modified according to the requirements of the analysis. The electrodes can be made of either graphite or carbon, the crater diameter and depth can be changed, and other modifications are possible, such as undercutting.

When the device shown in Figure 1 is operated with carbon dioxide or with mixtures of argon or helium with oxygen, particularly at currents above about 15 amp., the graphite collar and the pedestal must be changed frequently. The form shown in Figure 2 is more convenient for use with such gases. It is constructed of cop-

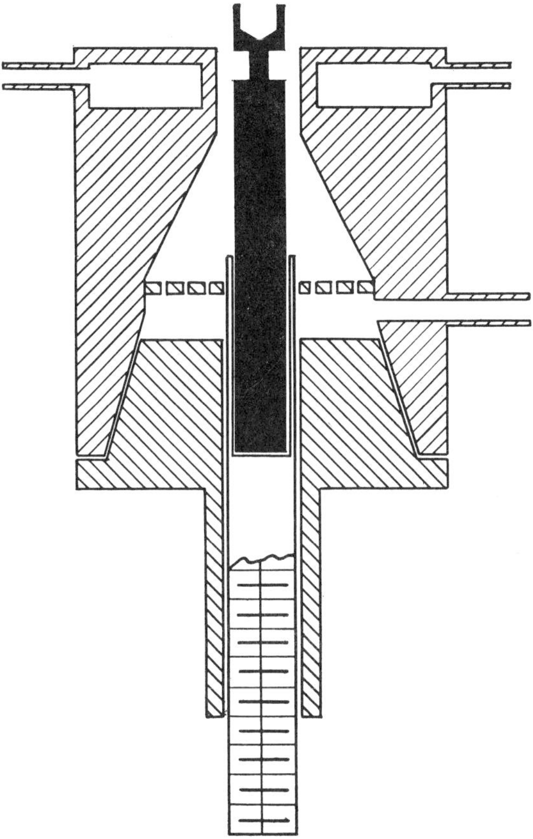

FIG. 2. GAS-SHEATHED ARC FOR GENERAL USE WITH GASES INCLUDING THOSE CONTAINING OXYGEN

per except for the electrode holder, which is made of stainless steel. The inner dimensions of the chamber are similar to those of the device shown in Figure 1, and the outer diameter is 1⅝ in. The top of the chamber is water cooled, and there have been no problems from vaporization of the copper even at arc currents as high as 30 amp.

The height of the electrode can be adjusted by turning the threaded electrode holder. The unit accommodates a variety of electrode shapes. If it is desired to adjust the electrode position during operation of the arc, the electrode holder can be replaced by the somewhat more complex holder of the Spex Industries Stallwood Jet.*

The device has been used with gas flows of 5 or 10 l/min, the slower flow providing less complete exclusion of air as shown by the appearance of weak CN bands in the spectrum. No flushing is needed after the system has once been purged of air, so that the arc may be ignited within a few seconds after the gas flow has been started. At the more rapid gas flow, a 200 ft^3 cylinder of gas will last for ten hr of continuous operation, and the gas may be conserved by turning it off while changing the electrodes. For this purpose, it is convenient to install a lever-operated (toggle) valve in the gas flow system so that the gas can be turned on and off rapidly without disturbing the setting of the control valve.

Because the electrodes can be changed easily and because it is not necessary to flush the unit for a long period before starting the arc, a device of the type described makes it possible to vaporize and excite samples rapidly and conveniently in an atmosphere of almost any desired composition. In addition, the sheath-like flow of gas stabilizes the arc to a marked degree, presumably by overcoming the convection currents which ordinarily cause the arc to wander. The device, which may be called a gas-sheathed arc, has been used successfully with atmospheres of helium and argon and mixtures of these gases with oxygen in a study of the effect of the composition of the atmosphere on vaporization and excitation in arc discharges.

Literature Cited

(1) B. J. Stallwood, J. Opt. Soc. Am. **44**, 171 (1954)
(2) D. M. Shaw, O. Wickremasinghe, and C. Yip, Spectrochim. Acta **13**, 197 (1958)

*Spex Industries, Metuchen, N. J., Catalog No. 9025 or 9027

(3) C. S. Annell and A. W. Helz, U. S. Geol. Survey, Profess. Papers No. **400-B,** 227 (1960)
(4) R. F. O'Connell and A. J. Mitteldorf, Spex Speaker **5** (2), 1 (1960)
(5) C. D. Curtis, Nature **196,** 1087 (1962)
(6) B. F. Scribner and H. R. Mullin, J. Res. Natl. Bur. Std. **37,** 379 (1946)

Stable Plasma Jet for Excitation of Solutions* *1.18*

Louis E. Owen
Goodyear Atomic Corporation, Portsmouth, Ohio

The plasma jet, as adapted for the spectrochemical excitation of solutions and used with a photoelectric spectrometer to measure light intensities, provided coefficients of variation of one to two percent *(1)*. A significant portion of the error was attributed to discharge instability. The swirling flow of gas surrounding the jet "flame" at the cathode forces the arc to make electrical contact to the cathode by an arc streamer. It is this streamer moving randomly over the cathode surface which makes the discharge unstable. It appeared that stabilization of the electrical path to give excitation position stability would be necessary to improve the precision of the plasma jet as an excitation source *(2)*.

Various cathode configurations were investigated at Goodyear Atomic Corporation before the use of an external electrode was suggested *(3)*. A consumable graphite electrode (Figure 1) was mounted in a motor-driven device and fed into the jet about 5 mm above the cathode surface. Discharge stability resulted from the elimination of the arc streamer. A decrease in the sound intensity and the arc voltage drop was also achieved. The use of an external electrode for complete or partial electrical return has since been noted for high power plasma jets

*This work was performed under Contract AT-(33-2)-1 with the U. S. Atomic Energy Commission.

(4). This mode of operation is generally referred to as "transferred arc". An improved version of the external electrode uses a tungsten rod which is only slowly consumed.

The plasma jet for solution excitation (Figures 2 and 3) has a tungsten rod as an external, yet integral, cath-

FIG. 1. SOLUTION PLASMA JET WITH GRAPHITE EXTERNAL ELECTRODE

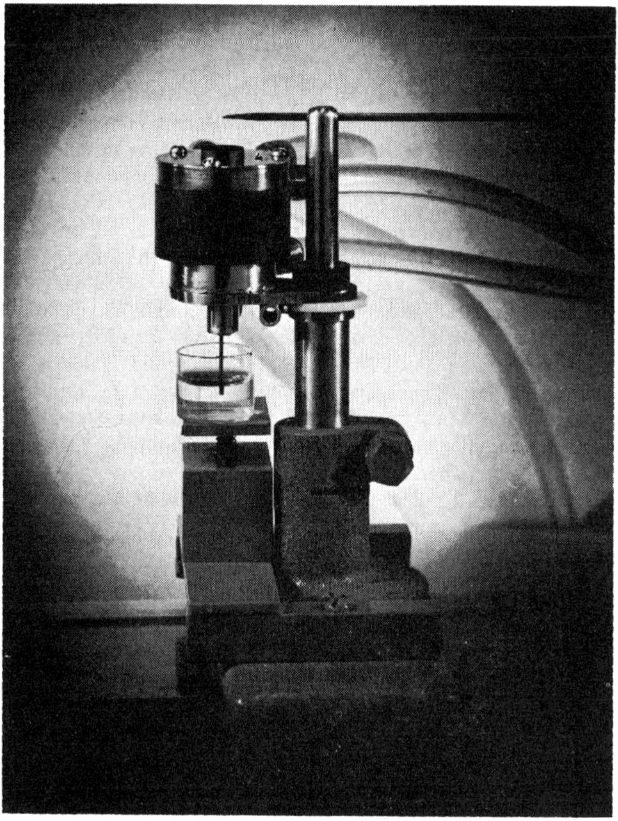

FIG. 2. SOLUTION PLASMA JET WITH TUNGSTEN EXTERNAL ELECTRODE

odic electrode. The tungsten rod is electrically connected to the exit orifice electrode and is at ground potential for use with a negatively grounded dc arc power supply. The discharge is initially between the anodic electrode, through which the sample is sprayed into the discharge zone, and the "flame" exit cathodic electrode. As the "flame" contacts the tungsten rod the electrical path transfers to it. After this transfer, the exit orifice electrode is not involved in the arc discharge and consequently does not erode. The tungsten electrode is so slowly consumed that manual adjustment between samples, or every several min,

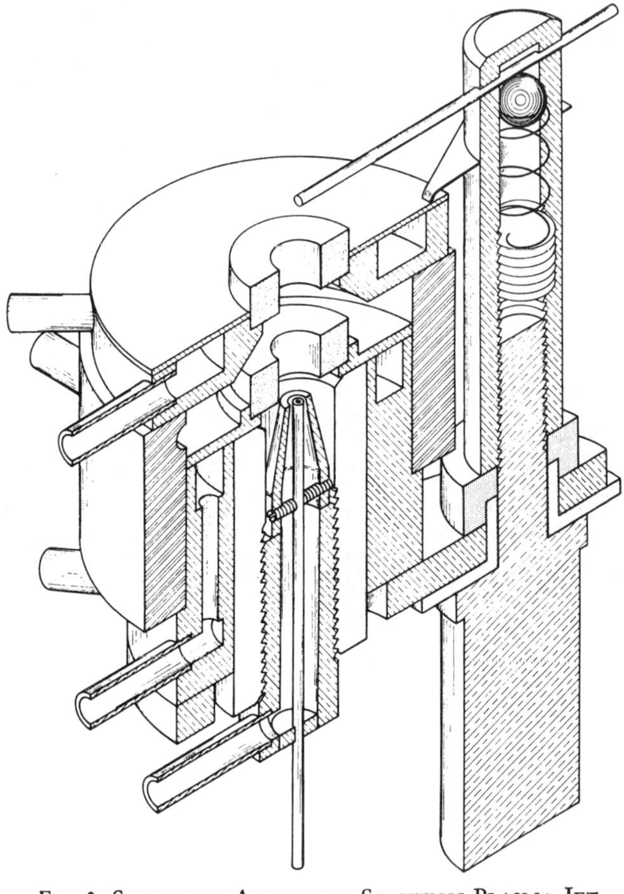

FIG. 3. SECTIONED ASSEMBLED SOLUTION PLASMA JET

is sufficient. The position of this electrode is not critical as long as the "flame" impinges upon it. If the tungsten does burn away from the "flame", an arc streamer forms back to the exit electrode, and the voltage drop across the device increases.

The jet parts (Figure 4 and Table I) are fabricated of concentric brass and plastic pieces requiring only lathe and brazing operations. While atomizing assemblies can be made from brass stock and stainless steel capillaries, it is simpler to salvage parts from a commercial atomizer-burner*, or the essential parts can be purchased. For use with ungrounded power sources, the support rod of the jet can be plastic with electrical connection made to the post carrying the tungsten electrode.

The general operation of plasma jets has been explained by Margoshes and Scribner *(1)*. For the assembly detailed here, the gas flows are monitored by flowmeters. Twenty l/min of helium are introduced tangentally into the chamber while approximately 3 l/min of argon are used as an atomizer "lift" gas. The argon flow is varied for a particular solution type to provide the sample rate desired. The chamber pressure during operation is around 60 mm of water, but this pressure is not monitored for operational information. A voltage drop of about 95 v occurs with a current of 15 to 25 amps.

Programming controls are used to provide safe and reproducible operation. The argon is supplied in two stages. The initial low flow rate of argon while inadequate for atomization is sufficient to prevent "blow back" of hot gases through the capillary. The programmed operation is: *Step 1*—Tangental helium, low-flow argon, main power and ignition spark are all started. *Step 2*—After a timed delay, or as desired, full argon flow for atomization of the sample is begun. *Step 3*—When the desired excitation period is over, the argon flow is reduced and *Step 4*—After the atomization has ceased, gas and power are removed.

*Catalog No. 4030, Beckman Instruments, Inc., Fullerton, California

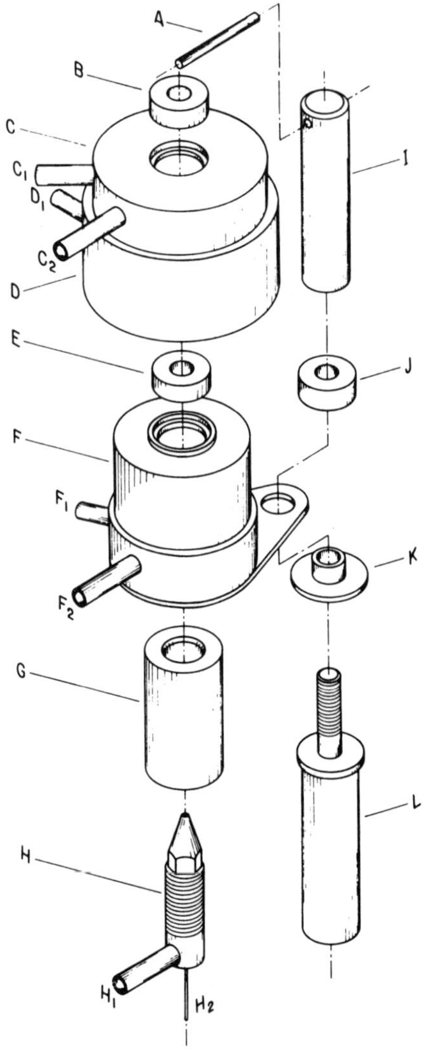

FIG. 4. EXPLODED VIEW OF SOLUTION PLASMA JET

TABLE I. COMPONENT PARTS OF SOLUTION PLASMA JET

Key[a]	*Description*	*Material*	*Dimensions*
A	External electrode	Tungsten	3/32 in. o.d. rod
B	Cathode electrode, "Flame" exit point	Graphite	12.5 mm o.d., 5 mm i.d., 5 mm thick
C	Cathode assembly	Brass	1 ¾ in. o.d., ¼ in. thick
C_1, C_2	Water cooling inlet and outlet	Copper	3/16 in. o.d.
D	Chamber body	Bakelite	1 ¾ in. o.d., 1-5/32 in. i.d., ¾ in. high
D_1	Tangental gas inlet	Copper	3/16 in. o.d.
E	Anode electrode	Graphite	12.5 mm o.d., 5 mm i.d., 5 mm thick
F	Anode assembly	Brass	Outside diam. to fit inside diam. of chamber body, step edge to give desired separation of graphite electrodes, ⅝ in. i.d.
F_1, F_2	Water cooling inlet and outlet	Copper	3/16 in. o.d.
G	Atomizer assembly insulator	Teflon	⅝ in. o.d., ⅜ in. -24 internal thread
H	Atomizer assembly	Brass	Inner part of Beckman 4030 Atomizer
H_1	Lift gas inlet	Copper	3/16 in. o.d.
H_2	Sample capillary	Platinum sheathed in steel	
I	External electrode holder	Brass	⅜ in. o.d. rod, inside threaded ¼ in. -20
J	Insulating washer	Bakelite	⅝ in. o.d., ¼ in. thick
K	Insulating washer	Teflon	1 in. o.d., ¼ in. thick
L	Support rod	Brass	⅝ in. o.d. (for Bausch & Lomb holders)

[a] Key for Figure 4

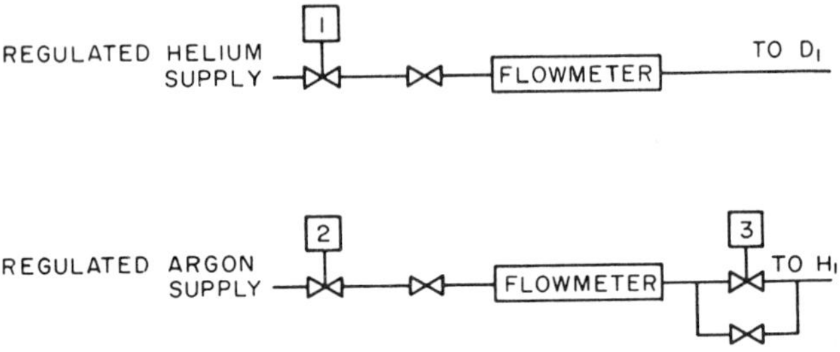

FIG. 5. GAS SYSTEM FOR SOLUTION PLASMA JET

The gas manifold is shown schematically (Figure 5). Solenoid valves *1* and *2* are energized at the beginning of an excitation. Helium flows through a needle valve and flowmeter to the tangental inlet D_1 of the jet. The argon flows through a needle valve and flowmeter to solenoid valve *3*, which initially vents to the atmosphere. Argon also flows through a needle valve to H_1 to protect the atomizer capillary from the arc. When the sample is to be sprayed into the jet, solenoid valve *3* operates to provide the necessary additional argon flow.

It is difficult to make general statements about electrode life, but the graphite electrodes exhibit little electrical erosion and do not contribute to the spectrum even when grossly contaminated. Their longevity is determined by the requirements of a specific analytical procedure. The life of the tungsten electrode is a function of current and time. Several in./hr. may be used at 25 amp. The tungsten electrode does not contribute spectra to the discharge region between it and the graphite electrode.

The stabilized plasma jet promises full utilization of the jet's special inherent feature of high temperature excitation of homogeneous samples which can be reproducibly introduced into its excitation zone. This assumption was borne out when the stabilized version was tested at the National Bureau of Standards with the same spectrometer and comparable solutions as in the original work. With the stabilized jet the limiting factor seems to be the constancy of atomization. With reliable atomization, coefficients of variation of 0.5% or less should be achieved with good reliability.

Literature Cited

(1) M. Margoshes and B. F. Scribner, Spectrochim. Acta **14,** 138 (1959)
(2) M. Margoshes, *Some Properties of New or Modified Excitation Sources,* in *Symposium on Spectrochemical Excitation.* Special Technical Publication No. **259,** Am. Soc. Testing Materials, Philadelphia, Pa.
(3) R. B. Stambaugh, Personal communication
(4) A. B. Osborn, J. Sci. Instr. **36,** 317 (1959)

A Rotating Platform Assembly 1.19

Edwin S. Hodge

Mellon Institute, Pittsburgh 13, Pa.

Following the introduction of the rotating platform for sample excitation a few years ago, at least two such devices are now commercially available for rotating a platform electrode. These mechanisms are supplied with a constant speed motor so that there is no opportunity to investigate the effect of speed of rotation upon the results if this is desired.

In a recent investigation on spectrochemical analysis of solutions the author *(1)* studied the rotating platform which was specially designed to give disk rotation from 3 to 30 rpm. The device was constructed by using the motor and gear train of a time switch at quite a cost savings over the available single speed models. This note outlines the construction of a rotating platform assembly. (Figure 1).

FIG. 1. ROTATING PLATFORM ASSEMBLY

A suitable motor was found in a recycling cam timer* which could be fitted with a selected gear assembly to give any one of a wide selection of speeds. The micro switch and cam were removed from the timer assembly. Screws at the back of the motor (A) hold it to a base plate (B) which fastens the device to the base of the excitation stand. A U-shaped bracket (C) holds the driven gear (D) in place with the gear assembly (E). A solid micarta rod (F) insulates the high potential from the motor and ground. A brass bushing (G) which fits closely the shaft of the platform holder (H), carries the electrical contact between the electrode clamp and the electrode. A variety of rotational speeds can be obtained by selecting the appropriate gear rack assembly (I), and ten rpm† was found satisfactory.

---

*Model CM-O-5W Industrial Timer Corporation, Newark, New Jersey
†Gear rack assembly No. B-12, Industrial Timer Corporation, Newark, New Jersey

Literature Cited

(1) W. K. Baer, and E. S. Hodge, APPLIED SPECTROSCOPY **14**, (1960)

Rotating-Disk-Sample Electrode Method 1.20

M. S. Wang*

Agronomy Department, University of Illinois, Urbana, Illinois

Sample rotation during excitation in metal emission spectroscopy is quite common. Rotating sample holders are available commercially. The advantages of sample rotation during excitation are: 1) More representative sampling is achieved as more of the sample surface is exposed to electrical discharge; 2) Improved spectral intensity, because a larger area of sample is exposed during emission; and 3) Minimum matrix effect, because the rotating sample can avoid local heating. Results with techniques using rotating samples have been reported by Wang *(1)* and Wang, *et al.*, *(2)* who used briquetted soil samples, which had been fused and mixed with graphite, by Mitchell and Scott *(3)*, who used plant-ash briquets, and also by Gillete *et al.*, *(4)* who analyzed cements and nickel ores.

The technique suggested here is a modification of one reported by Wang *(1)* and the method used by Mitchell and Scott *(3)*. An ½-in. briquet is formed by using a special press mold whose upper die is fitted with a conical tip. This tip makes a perfectly centered inset on one side of the briquet. The briquet is then mounted as shown in Figure 1. The briquet holder made by Jarrell-Ash Company is a rotating-disk electrode system, which has been modified to hold the briquet. The modified attachment is made so that the briquet, *b,* is held lightly in position between the rotor head, *f,* and the pointed spring rod press, *e.* The rod is pointed to fit the inset in the briquet.

* Present Address: Monsanto Chemical Co., St. Louis, Mo.

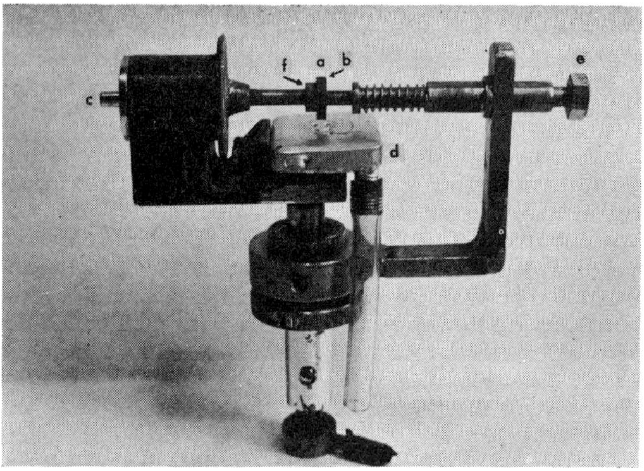

FIG. 1. ROTATING-DISK-SAMPLE ELECTRODE SYSTEM

a—Position of counter electrode (not shown), b—Rotating-sample-disk electrode, c—Connecting point to motor, d—Box for air-jet, e—Knob for removing briquet, f—Rotor head.

This serves to self-center the briquet in the holder. When the electrical discharge is completed, the knob, *e*, is pulled to release the excited sample, and a new one is then placed in position. The main advantages of this device are a self-centering system that can keep more consistent gap distance for better reproducibility and ease of changing samples that contributes greatly to the efficiency of operation.

Jets of air or gas can be used to cool the sample electrodes and stabilize the electrical discharges. Although cooling usually causes some loss in sensitivity of the elements, reproducibility is usually improved. The entire sample holder can be encased in a sealed box to permit gas injections to control the excitation atmosphere.

Literature Cited

(1) M. S. Wang, Ph.D. Thesis, University of Illinois, 1959

(2) M. S. Wang, L. T. Kurtz, and S. W. Melsted, SOIL SCI. SOC. AM. PROC. **26**, 19 (1962)
(3) R. L. Mitchell and R. W. Scott, The Macaulay Institute for Soil Research, Aberdeen, Scotland, Personal communication
(4) J. M. Gillette, B. R. Boyd, and H. A. Shurkers, APPLIED SPECTROSCOPY **8**, 162 (1954)

A Tape Feeding Attachment Adaptable to Standard Arc Stands 1.21

A. Strasheim and E. J. Tappere

National Physical Research Laboratory, Council for Scientific and Industrial Research, Pretoria, Union of South Africa

Spectrochemical spark results can appreciably be improved if each individual spark is permitted to strike fresh material. The tape machine developed by Danielsson (*1*) achieves this by drawing an adhesive tape with a powdered sample on it, through the spark at a speed of 21 cm/sec. The Danielsson machine first folds the tape coming from the unused roll in such a way that the central portion of the tape is left open. The tape then passes under a trough containing the sample to be analysed. All excess material not sticking to the central portion of the tape is blown clear before the tape passes through the spark.

The attachment to be described here is simple in design, easy and inexpensive to manufacture, and can be adapted to fit most standard arc stands. The tape is not folded, and the sample is put onto the tape by a feeding mechanism, which does not require the removal of excess material. After passing through the spark, the tape is rerolled and can be discarded, when a fresh roll is fitted to the attachment. This attachment can be used for all the analytical procedures which have been described by Danielsson.

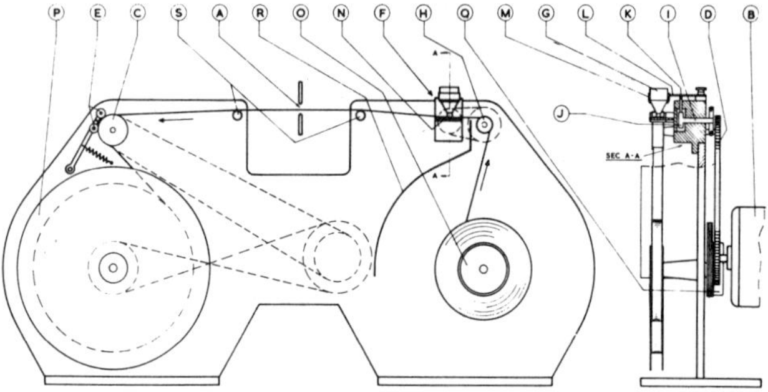

FIG. 1. TAPE FEEDING ATTACHMENT

Figure 1 shows a wheel arrangement which is mounted on a supporting plate, suitably positioned to drive an adhesive tape at a constant speed through an electrode gap, *A*. A geared motor, *B*, running at approximately 100 rpm drives wheel, *C*, by means of a light chain, *D*. The tape maintains contact with this wheel by pressure from two spring-loaded wheels, *E*. By changing the drive gears, the tape speed can be varied between 5 and 21 cm/sec. To prevent the adhesive side of the tape sticking to the wheels, *E*, their surfaces have been machined to produce small squares, reducing the contact area.

A powder sample feeding mechanism, *F*, consisting of a resilient plastic funnel, *G*, which can vibrate in a vertical direction, is mounted above the adhesive side of the tape enabling a controlled amount of powder to be fed onto it. Wheel *H* is driven by the tape itself, and its shaft is connected by a belt to the main spindle, *I*, in this feed mechanism. Attached to the shaft is a cam, *J*, comprising eighteen flats machined onto the periphery of a steel disc. This, by means of a follower pin, *K*, vibrates a beryllium-copper strip, *L*, which terminates in the funnel holder, *M*. This vibration changes between 2,500 and 9,000 reciprocations/min as the speed of the tape changes, feeding the powder evenly for all speeds. As the tape passes under the neck of the funnel it is supported by a stainless steel platform, *N*. The neck of this funnel is of thin wall section and its diam. determines the width of the sample deposited on the tape. The funnel is an adapted standard Elpac funnel (*2*), the inner shoulder of which has been drilled out.

Fresh rolls of tape fit onto wheel *O*, and wheel *P* is driven by slip clutch, *Q*, at a speed, which ensures constant tension when accepting the used tape. To protect the rolls of new tape from contamination, a guard, *R*, is suitably positioned to deflect any spilt powder from falling on wheel O. For accurate positioning of the tape between the electrodes, two rollers, S, can be adjusted in a vertical direction.

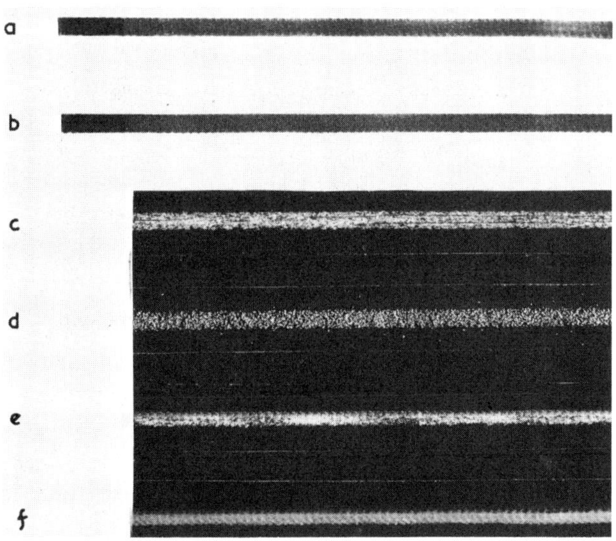

FIG. 2. STRIPS OF TAPE CONTAINING DIFFERENT MATERIALS

a—graphite powder, b—lithium carbonate - graphite powder buffer, c—calcium oxide, d—resin, e—calcium carbonate, f—lithium carbonate

For ease of operation the switch controlling motor *B* is placed near the slit control of the spectrograph, or near the expose switch of the spectrometer used with the attachment.

To estimate the efficiency of the attachment in distributing the material along the adhesive tape at the speeds required for each individual spark to strike fresh material, the following materials were used: graphite powder, lithium carbonate, resin, calcium oxide, a spectrographic buffer consisting of a 1:1 mixture of lithium carbonate and graphite powder, and calcium carbonate. Photographs of short portions of the tape fed with these materials are shown in Figure 2.

Using a 4 mm strip, this attachment consumes 21.7 mg of a 1:1 lithium carbonate/graphite buffer per 10 sec exposure. This amount can be halved using a 2 mm diam. funnel, but it was found that for this width of sample strip, about 2% of the spark holes fall outside the strip. With a 3 mm strip, all the individual sparks strike through the material. This attachment's sample consumption is very reasonable, if the fact is considered that a standard electrode with cavity depth 8 mm and internal diam. of 2 mm holds approximately 22 mg of the buffer, when the electrode is hand-packed.

If the speed of the tape was reduced to half that necessary for each spark to strike fresh material, it was found that the spark would penetrate twice through the same hole before striking a new one. For determination of low concentrations, this condition was found to give slightly superior sensitivity and line to background ratios than the single penetration condition. More than two penetrations through the same hole, were found to be less satisfactory.

To analyse the trace elements Zn, Ni, Co, and Mo in plant materials a concentration procedure is generally necessary prior to the spectrographic procedure. In Table I the sensitivities of these trace elements in a lithium carbonate-graphite base (1:1) using this tape method are listed. The spectra were photographed by means of a

TABLE I. SENSITIVITIES OF CERTAIN TRACE ELEMENTS IN A LITHIUM CARBONATE GRAPHITE BASE

Element	*Analysis Line, A*	*Detection Limit, ppm*
Zn	3345.0	1000
Ni	3101.6	40
Co	3453.5	16
Mo	3194.0	40

Hilger Medium spectrograph, on Ilford Ordinary plates using an exposure of 30 sec. The source was a low voltage spark of 1000 v, 360 μh inductance and 19 μf capacitance.

The coefficient of variation of the results was of the order 5-10%—normally found for trace element work using a photographic procedure.

For the past eighteen months the attachment described above has been in use and its operation has been found to be most satisfactory. Its chief assets are: 1) the ease of fitting fresh rolls of tape; 2) the small quantity of material used; 3) the uniformity of the layer of material spread along the tape; 4) the ease with which the material remaining in the sample feeder can be replaced in its original container without undue loss; 5) the fact that no sample is lost when the tape breaks, due to the sample feeding mechanism being directly driven from the tape; and 6) the ease of aligning the attachment, especially in a laboratory where the same instrument is used for a number of different procedures.

The authors thank Mr. H. R. van der Walt for experimental help, Mr. L. Martins for help with the drawings and design, and Mrs. D. B. de Villiers for assistance in the preparation of the manuscript.

Literature Cited

(1) A. Danielsson, F. Lundgren, and G. Sundkvist, SPECTROCHIM. ACTA **15,** 122 (1959)
(2) A. Strasheim and E. J. Tappere, APPLIED SPECTROSCOPY **13,** 12 (1959)

1.22 A Modified Electrode Loader for Spectrochemical Analysis

Ann Calhoun and Isabel H. Tipton

Department of Physics, The University of Tennessee
Knoxville, Tennessee

Electrode loaders for dry samples are such useful time-saving devices that it is surprising they have not come into wider use. So far as we know there are only two kinds of loaders commercially available in this country, the Jayco Instrument Company Elpac and the Spex Industries Loader (both distributed by Spex Industries).

Both loaders operate on essentially the same principle. In the Jayco Elpac the electrode is held erect and agitated while the sample is fed in from above, and in the Spex Loader the sample contained in a vial is agitated and enters from below into the inverted electrode suspended over it. In the Elpac the sample is directed into the crater through a funnel fitted to the electrode and tamped with a stainless steel rod tapered to fit the crater. In the Spex Loader no funnel is required, and the electrode acts as its own tamper. Although the Spex Loader is simpler and less expensive, it is not so versatile nor does it provide so reproducible a sample as the Elpac.

It is very easy to adapt the Spex Loader to operate in the same way as the Elpac, however. We have devised a brass adapter that holds the electrode erect in the agitator in place of the sample vial. A graphite or carbon tamping rod is placed in the collet that is suspended above the agitator. For some of our electrodes a $1/8$ in. rod is satisfactory as it is, for others the end of the rod must be turned down to fit smaller craters. Since we ordinarily run samples in quadruplicate, a tamper is discarded after filling four electrodes. This is not necessary, however, since we have used the same graphite rod to fill as many as ten electrodes and carbon rod to fill twice as many without showing appreciable wear or cross contamination.

TABLE I. COMPARATIVE STUDY OF UNADAPTED AND ADAPTED SPEX LOADER

	3/16 in. Graphite Electrodes		*1/8 in. Graphite Electrodes*		*3/16 in. Carbon Electrode Undercut 1/16 in. Below Rim*	
	No. of Trials	*Wt., mg in Crater*[a]	*No. of Trials*	*Wt., mg in Crater*[a]	*No. of Trials*	*Wt., mg in Crater*[a]
			Electrode Inverted[b]			
Time, 10 sec	8	22 ± 2				Impossible
15 sec	19	18 ± 2	8	11 ± 0.2		to fill inverted.
20 sec	8	25 ± 2				Electrodes broke.
			Electrode Erect[b]			
Graphite tamper	8	31 ± 0.7	8	12 ± 0.1	8	16 ± 0.6
Carbon tamper	6	32 ± 0.5				
Steel tamper[c]					8	14 ± 1.1

[a] Mean ± standard deviation
[b] All electrodes vibrated at 70 vps.
[c] From Jayco Instrument Company Elpac

Assuming that an excess of sample is placed in the funnel, the amount of sample packed into the crater depends on the maximum rise of the tamper. This can be easily controlled on the Spex Loader. A rubber gasket may be placed between the collet and frame to serve as a cushion and keep the electrode from excessive stress when the tamping rod is near the upper limit of its motion. In our adapted Spex Loader the tamper in its position of maximum rise touches a microswitch which shuts off the motor. Thus it is the amount of sample in the crater rather than a pre-set interval timer which determines the length of time the device is in operation.

Table I shows the results of a brief comparative study of the unadapted and adapted Spex Industries Loader. The sample was equal parts of human l-tissue ash and graphite. For certain types of electrodes the unadapted loader could not be used because the electrodes broke. In all other trials the adapted loader gave a more reproducible sample.

1.23 A Spark-In-Spray Attachment for Commercially Available Arc-Spark Stands

A. L. Schalge and J. Russell

Marathan Oil Company, Littleton, Colorado

A very simple technique which is apparently reproducible *(1)* as well as sensitive *(2)* has been called the spark-in-spray technique. Malmstadt and Scholz *(1)* as well as Schalge *(2)* used a Beckman atomizer to spray the solution between horizontally mounted electrodes across which a high voltage spark was impressed. There are many objections to using horizontally mounted electrodes. For instance, nearly all spectrographs and arc-spark stands are constructed for vertical electrodes. Also, it is more difficult to control the excess spray when using horizon-

FIG. 1. SPARK-IN-SPRAY ATTACHMENT MOUNTED IN ARC-SPARK STAND

tally mounted electrodes than when the usual vertically mounted electrodes are used. The purpose of this communication is to describe an attachment that allows the spark-in-spray technique to be used with commercially available excitation stands. Figure 1 shows such an attachment mounted in a Jarrell-Ash No. 19300 Arc-Spark stand (Jarrell-Ash Company, Newtonville, Mass.). The only alterations which had to be made to the arc-spark stand were the addition of a second gas inlet and the drilling of two ⅛-in. threaded holes in the movable platform of the stand. These holes are needed for mounting the attachment in the arc-spark stand.

The attachment as shown in Figure 1 features an automatic pneumatically operated sample lifting system and three dimensional adjustment of the atomizer tip relative to the analytical gap. The excess spray is collected at the back of the arc-spark stand and drained to a 50-ml beaker. The excess-spray collector is constructed of 0.125-in. thick, 1.625-in. i.d., 1.0-in. long stainless steel tubing mounted on a 0.250-in. thick pressed asbestos sheet. These materials are necessary for the spray collector because highly volatile solvents such as toluene become ignited and produce an extremely hot flame, which would otherwise burn the back of the arc-spark stand.

Both aqueous and non-aqueous solvent systems can be handled with equal ease and with no alteration to the present set-up. The attachment has been used in this laboratory for the direct analysis of trace metals in crude oils diluted in toluene. Acid solutions of rocks have also been analyzed for their trace elements for over a year using this attachment with no corrosion to the arc-spark stand or surrounding equipment. The electrode clamps of the arc-spark stand are wiped with a moistened tissue after each day's use.

A Beckman No. 4030 medium bore atomizer has been used in most of the experiments. A special glass atomizer has recently been obtained from Beckman Instruments, Inc., Fullerton, Calif. that allows the atomizer tip to be positioned as close as 1 mm from the analytical gap. The

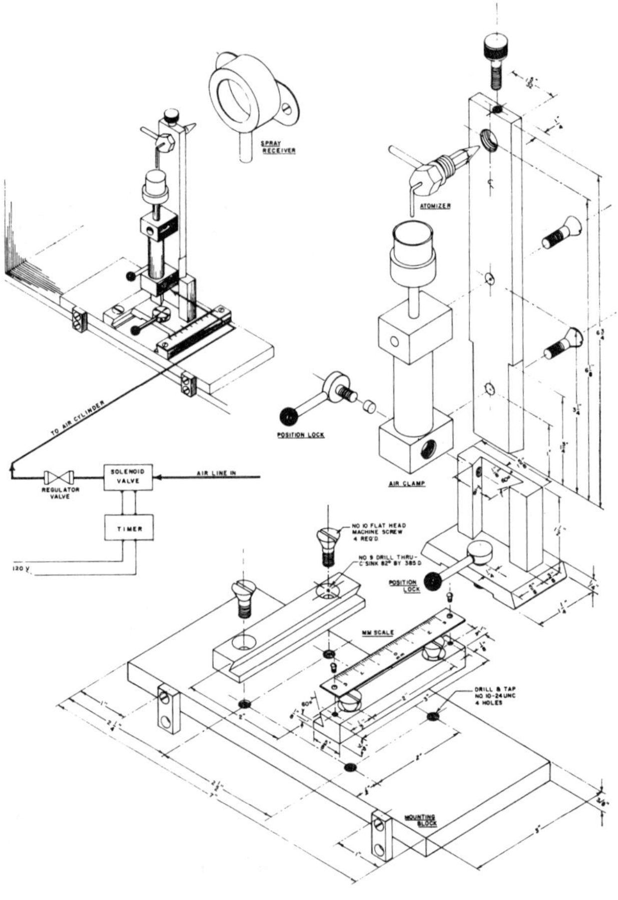

FIG. 2. CONSTRUCTION DETAILS OF SPARK-IN-SPRAY ATTACHMENT

closer one can get to the atomizer tip, the more constant is the geometry of the spray and the smaller the cone of the spray, thus allowing small analytical gaps to be used without a spattering problem. In the case of a brass atomizer, if one gets too close (within 5 mm with a 2 mm analytical gap) an occasional discharge to the atomizer tip occurs, thus altering the geometry of the spray and also altering the discharge characteristics.

Detailed drawings for the construction of the attachment are given in Figure 2.

Literature Cited

(1) H. V. Malmstadt and R. G. Scholz, ANAL. CHEM. **27**, 881 (1955)
(2) A. L. Schalge, Ph.D. Thesis, University of Illinois, 1959

Vapor Trap for Arc-Spark Stands 1.24

C. L. Chaney

General Atomic Division of General Dynamics Corporation, John Jay Hopkins Laboratory for Pure and Applied Science, San Diego, California

When solution samples are analyzed spectrographically, gas and liquid vapors are released. Generally, these combustion products are exhausted out of the arc-spark stand by a ventilating system consisting of exhaust blowers, dampers, and ducting. During the exhausting process, liquids and gas vapors condense on parts of the ventilating system. This condensation leads to corrosion of the ventilating system and, eventually, to its replacement. The condensation can also trap toxic and radioactive particles released when solid samples are analyzed.

To eliminate the condensation problem, a "cold finger-dry ice" trap was designed as shown in Figure 1. The corrosive vapors are removed by freezing them on a cold-finger surface provided by the large test tube shown in Figures 1 and 2 when filled with dry ice. By freezing out the vapors prior to their entry into the main exhaust

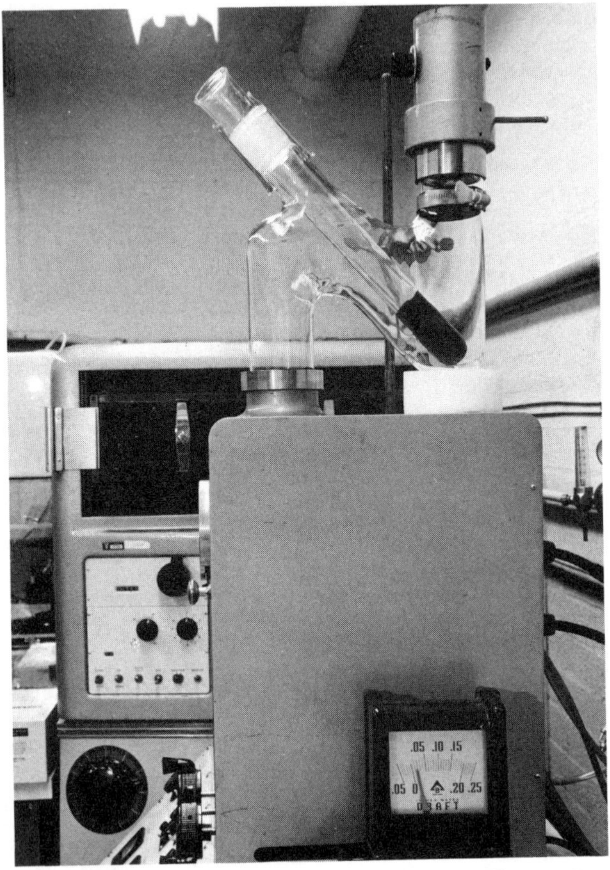

Fig. 1. Cold Trap Installed on the Excitation Stand

system, corrosion of the system is retarded and the release of toxic material to the atmosphere is reduced. When the test tube is filled with dry ice, it will provide a freezing surface for approximately 3 to 4 hr. As the condensate builds up on the cold finger, there may be some reduction of the exhausting velocity, in which case increasing the velocity by dampers solves the problem.

After the spectrographic analysis is done, the dry ice is left in the test tube to evaporate. The condensate which was frozen on the cold finger melts, and the resulting liquid is left to drain out of the trap through a 1¼-in.-long tubular outlet (base of the trap in Figure 2) and

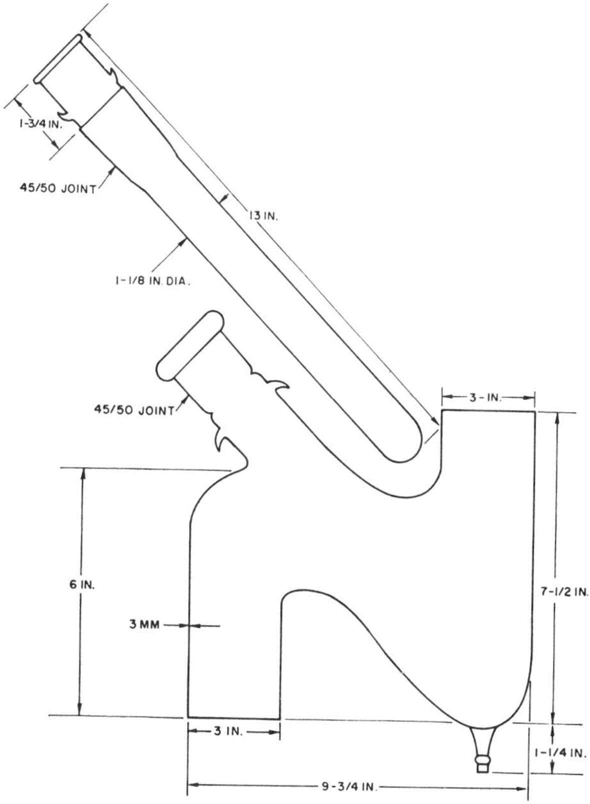

FIG. 2. COLD TRAP SCHEMATIC WITH SUGGESTED DIMENSIONS

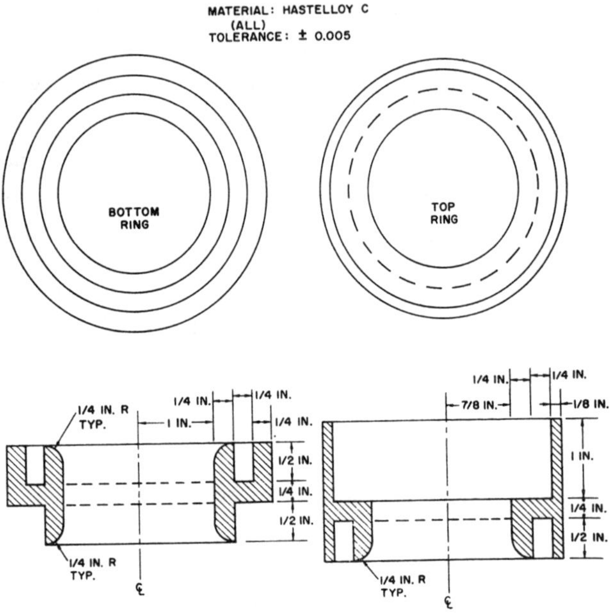

FIG. 3. COLD TRAP ADAPTER RINGS

through a piece of attached Tygon tubing to a waste drain. A ½-in. hole must be made through the top of the arc-spark stand for the outlet and Tygon tubing.

The supporting material on which the base of the trap rests, shown on the bottom right-hand side of Figure 1, is a 2″ x 4″ diam. polyurethane hollowed out to fit the base and with a hole through it for the small tubular outlet. The trap must also be supported by a side brace.

Figure 3 shows the adapter ring used on each end of the trap. The bottom ring is used to mount the trap to a Jarrell Ash arc-spark stand. The top ring is used to mount the trap to an exhaust system. The ¼″ x ½″ slots shown serve as wells for mounting the trap. After assembling the trap suitable material can be packed between the glass walls of the trap and the adapter ring, if needed. The adapter rings are made of Hastelloy-C because of its high resistance to corrosive vapors. The top ring has a 1″ x 2¾″ well for the insertion of a Spex Industries Air Filter Holder, and it is also made to fit loosely into a Jarrell Ash Draft Control No. 19-550.

Lens Shield 1.25

Drexel W. Baker*

University of Tennessee, Knoxville,* Tennessee

It is common practice to use some sort of lens system between the arc-spark stand and the spectrograph in spectrochemical analyses. In many instances the lens closest

*Present Address: Goodyear Atomic Corporation, Portsmouth, Ohio

FIG. 1. LENS SHIELD

to the arc gap receives considerable spatter from the arc and gradually deteriorates. A metal shield, shown in Figure 1, limits the unobstructed path between the arc gap and the lens to the cone required by the optical arrangement. This reduces the number of spatter particles hitting the lens, especially the destructive heavy particles which require trajectories that are cut off by the shield. The device also aids in keeping dust off the lens.

1.26 A Variable Three-Step Sector Rotating Filter

R. M. Kennedy and A. Paolini, Jr.

Campbell Soup Company, Camden, New Jersey

Many spectrographic procedures require the use of filters in the optical path, some calling for two transmittance steps and others for three. The filtering of the transmitted light has normally been accomplished with the use of calibrated metallized quartz or, in some instances, with fixed aperture sector wheels. Laboratories that handle a considerable variety of materials for analysis would, out of necessity, need an assortment of these filtering devices. With this in mind, a variable three-step rotating sector has been devised. It permits the recording of 100% and any two combinations of 50% of the transmitted light (*i.e.*, 100%/0 to 50%/0 to 50%), with step three less than step two. The filtering arrangement is inexpensive and relatively easy to construct. It consists of three discs mounted on a shaft, which is rotated through the transmitted light at the appropriate position on the optical bench. The shaft can be mounted on a motor used for step sector rotation or on a conventional laboratory stirrer.

The discs are constructed of 1 mm aluminum or 0.5 mm stainless steel. Two discs have o.d. of 90 mm; one disc has an o.d. of 88 mm. All other dimensions of the three discs are identical and are shown in Figure 1. Two

90° segments of each disc are cut away, leaving an i.d. of 65 mm. A center of 20 mm diam. is cut out for mounting on a shaft. The two larger discs are calibrated for percent transmittance as shown, with 1.8° equal to 1% of the transmitted light. The discs are painted with a non-reflecting black paint.

The shaft for mounting the discs is shown in Figure 2. It can be fabricated from a 40 mm diam. rod turned down to 20 mm to accommodate the three discs. A portion of

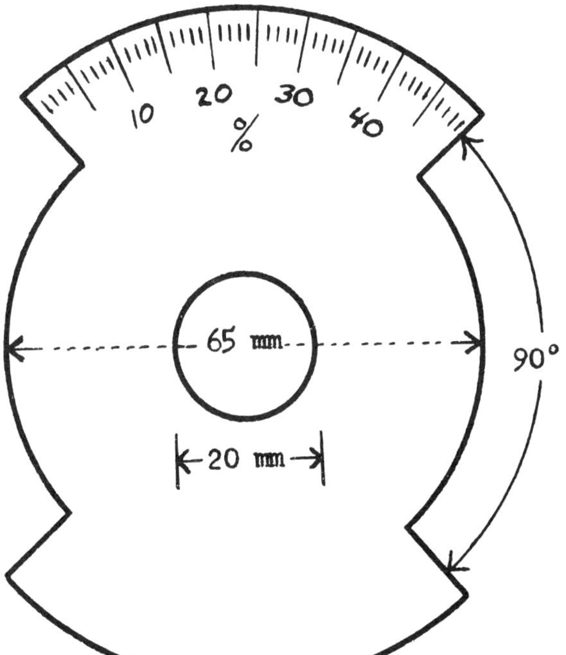

FIG. 1. LARGE DISC CALIBRATED FOR PERCENT TRANSMITTED LIGHT

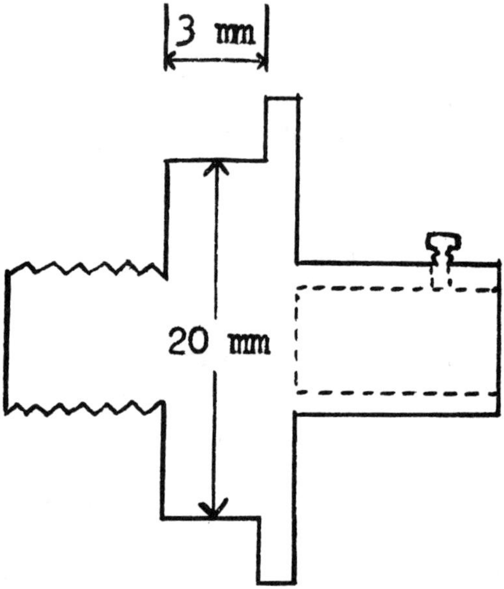

FIG. 2. MOUNTING SHAFT

the rod is turned down and threaded to allow the discs to be locked securely in place with a nut. The rear of the rod is equipped with a set screw to facilitate mounting on the drive mechanism.

The two larger discs are mounted on the shaft with the calibrated side facing out; the smaller disc is then mounted and the lock nut tightened. With this arrangement in place on the optical bench it is possible to record three transmittance steps of one mm each on three mm of plate or film and to change the transmittance values by merely loosening the lock nut and rotating the discs to the desired settings.

Spectrum Line Distortion Caused by Step Filters 1.27

T. P. Schreiber, R. F. Majkowski and B. W. Joseph
Research Laboratories, General Motors Corporation, Warren, Michigan

Spectrum line distortion, shown schematically in Figure 1, was recently encountered when a step filter was used directly in front of the slit of a stigmatic spectrograph. The character of the distortion was investigated by using a wide slit and observing the visible spectrum of mercury with an eyepiece. The striations were found to be due to interference fringes which occurred within the filter.

In addition to the plane filter used in obtaining Figure 1, two other plane filters and one step filter lens were investigated. All plane filters exhibited interference fringes while no fringes were observed with the step filter lens. Fringes were also observed by using the spectrograph as a monochromator. The filter was placed at the plate-holder position and illuminated by the Hg 5460.7A line. By using a magnifier of about 10 power the fringes were clearly seen. The fringes evidently result from the filters being slightly wedge shaped. The angle between the fringes and the step dividing line (θ in Figure 1) is constant for a particular filter and is determined by the orientation of

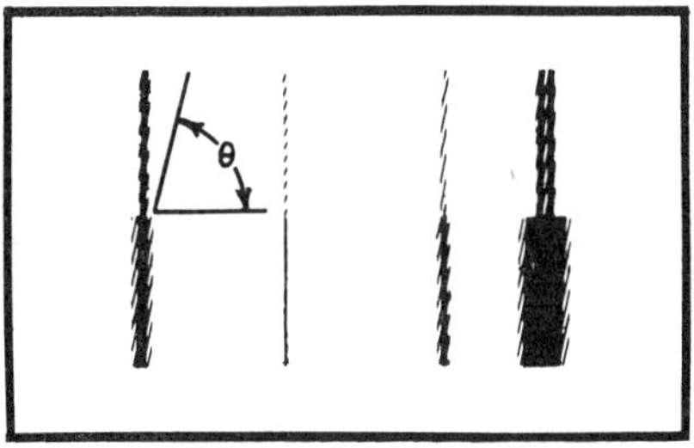

FIG. 1. STEP FILTER INTERFERENCE FRINGES
Schematic of the 2860 A region of the Cd spectrum showing distortion caused by interference fringes in a step filter. θ is the angle between the fringes and the step edge.

the wedge apex. Ironically, the most perfect filters, i.e., those with the smallest wedge angle, produce the most widely spaced and thus most troublesome fringes.

To avoid distorted spectrum lines from the interference fringes discussed above it is only necessary to slightly misalign the face of the filter and the optical axis of the spectrograph.

1.28 Selective Spectrum Masking Device for Attachment to Spectrographs

R. W. Lewis
Bureau of Mines, U. S. Department of the Interior, Boulder City, Nevada

The principal objective of this device is to provide a reliable way to record the emission of spectral energy from a sample in one exposure so that the spectral lines of the element for analysis are of the proper density for satisfactory quantitative determinations.

Before this device was installed it was necessary to make three exposures of one metal sample for different time intervals in order to obtain impurity-element spectral lines of suitable density. With the device described here, different exposure times may be accomplished by manipulating the masks by means of toggle switches located conveniently outside of the spectrograph.

The device will be made clear by reference to Figures 1 and 2. Figure 1 is a photograph showing the attachment. Figure 2 is a schematic of the electrical circuit for operating the solenoids which in turn control the masks. The components are lettered on the photograph and identified in the following description of operation. Four separate units operating in exactly the same manner are used

FIG. 1. SELECTIVE SPECTRUM MASKING DEVICE IN OPERATION

S—solenoid, C—iron core of solenoid, P—pivot arm, G—guide for shaft, M—spectrograph plate mask, 1, 2, 3, 4,—attachment masks.

to cover the entire film or plate. The unit on the right (Figure 1) will be described.

When a voltage controlled by a toggle switch on the front panel of the spectrograph is applied to the solenoid (*S*),* the iron core (*C*) is pulled upward by the magnetic field. Pivot arm (*P*) which is attached to the core and pivoted at the center, is pulled upward. This movement thrusts the selective mask *(4)* downward to cover a portion of the photographic plate behind the spectrograph plate mask (*M*). The plate mask is a part of the spectrograph and limits the height of the spectral lines. A brass guide (*G*) is used to insure exact positioning of the mask *(4)*. The guide is attached to a mounting, which in turn is bolted or otherwise affixed to the spectrograph. The shaft slides in the guide hole and is lubricated occasionally with a light oil to insure its free movement.

Masks 1 and 2 show how they may be cut in various ways so as to cover certain portions of the spectrum.

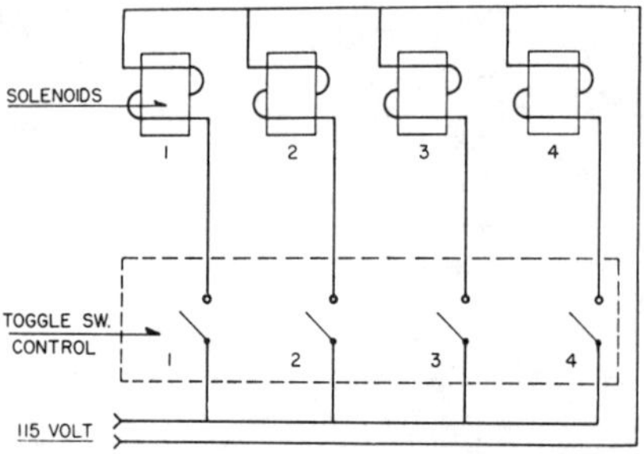

FIG. 2. SCHEMATIC, ELECTRIC CONTROL CIRCUIT
Solenoids 1, 2, 3, and 4 are operated by toggle switches 1, 2, 3, and 4 respectively . . .

Mask 2 and 4 are in masking position, while masks 1 and 3 are in their normal position, allowing the energy to be recorded. Filters may be substituted for the masks whenever desired.

The pivot arms are spring-loaded to insure return of the masks to the normal position.

Although this device has been used on one particular spectrograph*, it could be easily modified for installation on most other types.

1.29 A Polaroid Attachment For A Medium Quartz Spectrograph

J. B. Lombardo
Research Department, Organic Chemical Division, American Cyanamid Company, Bound Brook, New Jersey

Bryan *(1)* and Bryan and Runge *(2)* have applied the Polaroid emulsion to emission spectroscopy. Although no details of construction are given in these applications, it is apparent that no provision is made for the location of the film in the oblique angle, curved field of the medium

**Baird* 3-meter spectrograph.

quartz spectrograph. Therefore, a commercially available Polaroid Land camera back was modified so that it could be used interchangeably with conventional 4″x10″ spectroscopic plates without any alteration of the optics of such a spectrograph.

The smaller film area of a Polaroid emulsion compared with the 4″x10″ glass plate necessarily decreases the available spectral range to 4¼ in. This, however, is not a serious loss, since it is well recognized that very often approximately half of the 10-in. common spectroscopic plate is wasted when exposed on a medium quartz spectrograph. Experience over a number of years has shown that the spectral range above 3500 A has been of very little value due to the cyanogen band interference and to poor dispersion. The spectral range below 2288 A has very little to offer; first and foremost, because of the anemic character of most spectra in that region and second, because of the paucity of strong, useful, and indispensable lines.

The Polaroid negative as incorporated in this attachment is capable of covering the range 2250 to 3500 A. Within this region will be found the U_1 lines of Cd, Be, Au, B, Sn, Mg, Si, Pt, Bi, Cu, Ag, Ta, and Ni; the U_2 lines of Te, P, Ge, V, Li, and Zn; the U_3 lines of Ga, Al, In, and Na; and the useful Fe 3020-3021 A grouping.

The spectral range can be selected without future choice by permanently positioning the Polaroid back over any area on the original plate holder. This can be ascertained by placing a glass plate with a known spectrum in the normal position in the plate holder and marking off on the curved track 4¼ in. of desirable spectral range. Although the negative spectrum will be 4¼ in., the positive will be masked down so that only 3¾ in. will show. However, there is a choice as to whether to sacrifice one end or the other, i.e., the ½ in. of negative can be sacrificed at either the low (equivalent to 60 A) or high (equivalent to 200 A) wavelength region. This choice is made at the moment of development and can be changed with each frame.

The term "frame" is used as being synonymous with the term "exposure" in the photographic arts.

The curved plate track of the Hilger plate holder must be relocated so as to give proper (3⅝ in.) track width to accommodate the Polaroid negative. Based on the marking when the spectral range is chosen, metal rollers R_1 and R_2 are placed as shown in Figure 1. These rollers are spring-loaded so as to maintain the negative snugly on the track. Spring fingers are added to each track to aid in holding the negative taut on the curved field. (The slide has been removed for constructional convenience.) Figure 1 also shows aluminum angle cleats upon which the Polaroid back will be fastened.

The Polaroid Land camera back (front cover, bellows, and braces removed) is modified as follows: a slot S_1 is cut at the negative end so as to allow the negative to move

FIG. 1. PLATE HOLDER BEFORE ATTACHING CAMERA
R_1—Roller 1, R_2—Roller 2

FIG. 2. CAMERA WITH LEVER LATCH MODIFICATION

through freely from the original negative well to roller R_1 as shown in Figure 3. At the positive side, a slot S_2 is cut parallel to S_1 at the point indicated but not visible in Figure 3. A roller R_3 is located on the medial side of, adjacent and parallel and in the same large plane as S_2.

The lever latch is modified by cutting off the thumb end so as to leave a metal circle about ¾ in. diam. As shown in Figure 2, a 3/16-in. diam. shaft is fastened to the circle so that rotation can be effected by shaft torque instead of the finger lever. Finally, the shaft is bent and further braced as shown in Figure 3.

The Polaroid back is fastened to the plate holder so located that the negative slot S_1 is over roller R_1 while slot S_2 is located over roller R_2. Small aluminum plates are attached in the open spaces between plate holder and Polaroid back. Light leaks are patched with epoxy cement.

Before placing the roll on the camera, the end (leader) of the black protective paper of the negative roll is sharpened by cutting off triangles about 1½ in. from each corner. The negative roll is separated from the positive roll, the former is dropped into its receptacle (well) and the sharpened end threaded through the slot S_1 down between the track and roller R_1, along the track and over roller R_2, up over the medial side of roller R_3, through slot S_2, and finally over the conventional Polaroid roller. The negative is pulled further until the original point of positive attachment to the negative is reached. The negative is backed up one in. at which point the positive is fastened by means of pressure sensitive tape. The system is now treated as described in the original Polaroid directions accompanying the camera.

Following exposures made in the usual way, the cutting bar is lifted, exposing the ends of the positive and negative.

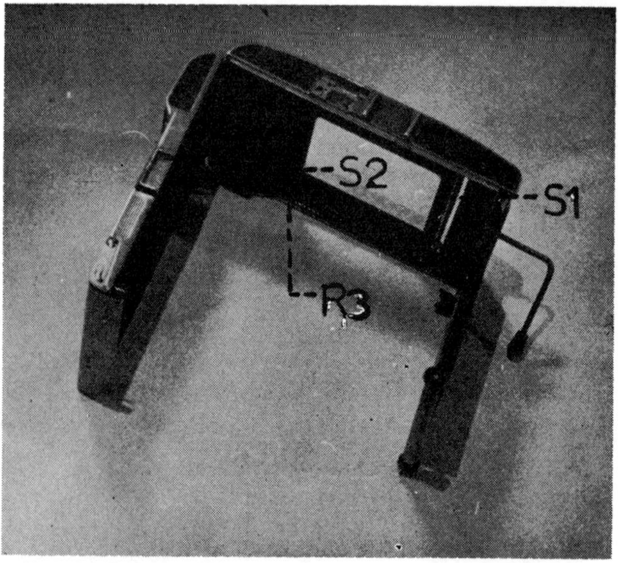

FIG. 3. CAMERA MODIFIED WITH SLOTS AND ROLLERS
S_1—Slot 1, S_2—Slot 2, R_3—Roller 3

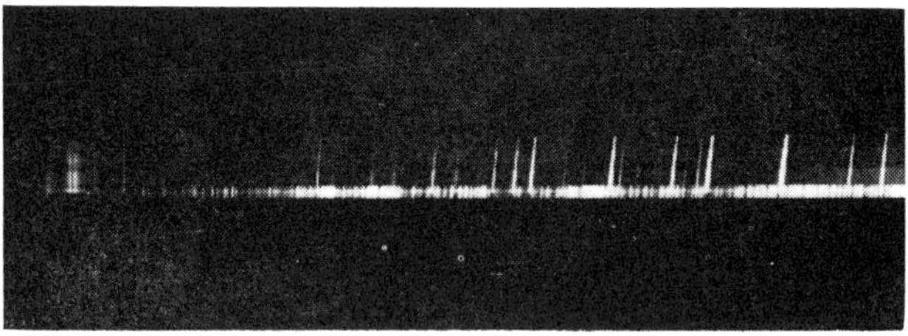

FIG. 4. CADMIUM SPECTRUM FAVORING LOW WAVELENGTH

The negative only is pulled out to extend from 1 to 1¾ in. beyond the positive. (The smaller will favor the low wavelength region: the larger will show more of the long wavelength.) The positive release button is pushed, and both positive and negative are pulled out together.

Occasionally the positive and negative rolls are practically cemented together by the development jelly of the previous frame; hence the negative cannot be pulled separately from the positive. This difficulty can often be overcome by inserting a thin stainless steel spatula between negative film and positive paper frame through the open picture door. A better solution is to discard one frame, if inspection through the picture door discloses a hardened, glue-like effect of the developing jelly that is a condition resulting from a long unused period.

Seven frames can be obtained from one 8 "exposure"

FIG. 5. COPPER SPECTRUM FAVORING HIGH WAVELENGTH

roll. One frame is sacrificed to compensate for the greater travel path of the negative.

Figure 4 shows the cadmium spectrum which includes highly self-absorbing Cd 2288 A. Also shown at extreme left are Cd 2267 A and Cd 2265 A. This extent into the lower wavelength region compares favorably with common spectroscopic plates. Figure 5 shows the copper spectrum from a frame slanted towards the higher region with the prominent CN band head at 3590 A. A Hartmann diaphragm iron spectrum is included in each exposure.

Literature Cited

(1) F. R. Bryan, J. Chem. Ed. **37**, 471 (1960)
(2) F. R. Bryan and E. F. Runge, Applied Spectroscopy **15**, 16 (1961)

1.30 Current-Sensor for DC Arc Power Units

Louis E. Owen

Goodyear Atomic Corporation, Portsmouth, Ohio

A simple dry-reed switch *(1)** incorporated in spectrochemical source units can be depended upon to start exposure controlling timers the moment the arc is established. Such a current-sensing circuit should be a part of all dc arc power source units. In spark-ignited arc units a device is needed to limit spark spectra by terminating the spark as soon as possible.

Commercial source units use current-sensing circuits based on second-order effects of arc current flow such as the voltage drop across a series resistor or the specific voltage across the power tranformer's primary coil under load. A non-overloading current relay in series with the arc is

*Revere Glaswich E-5600, The Revere Corporation of America, Wallingford, Connecticut

simpler and is used, in effect, by a circuit utilizing magnetic dry-reed switches. In a magnetic field of sufficient intensity, the reed switch closes a normally open contact. Taped to the winding of a core-and-coil smoothing choke in a rectified dc arc power supply, the reed contact is operated by choke leakage-flux when current flows to the arc. The switch contact starts programming timers and operates a relay which terminates the ignition spark. A dry-reed switch is also functional inside the air-wound rf choke which is always incorporated in spark ignition circuits *(2)* for dc arc power supplies. When arc current flows, the choke's magnetic field is strong enough to actuate the switch. Since the contact points operate in an evacuated chamber, their longevity is excellent for this light duty.

As a component in current-sensing circuits, the magnetic dry-reed switch is a simple, reliable device for precise control in spectrochemical source units.

Literature Cited

(1) W. B. Ellwood, ELECT. ENG. **66,** 1104 (1947)
(2) L. E. Owen, APPLIED SPECTROSCOPY **13,** 158 (1959)

Ignitor Unit for D.C. Arcs **1.31**

Louis E. Owen

Goodyear Atomic Corporation, Portsmouth, Ohio

Many spectrochemical laboratories still use supplies designed without provision for automatic arc ignition, despite the commercial availability of modern d.c. power supplies for arc excitation. Brockman and Hochgesang (*1*) published two basic ignitor circuits which use a two winding r-f transformer to couple a triggering spark into the d.c. circuit. Sinclair (*2*) used a simpler circuit with a single winding autotransformer.

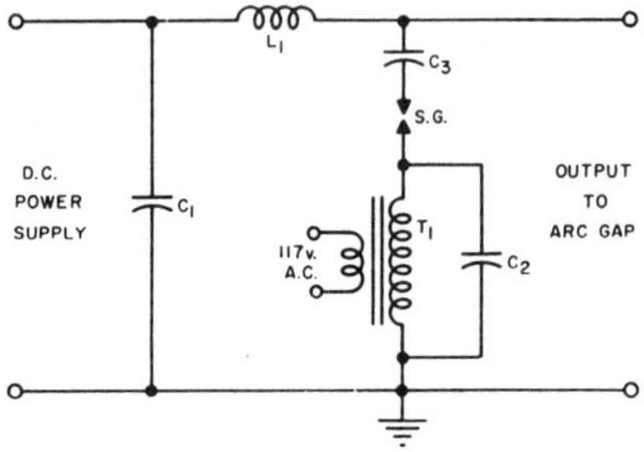

FIG. 1. CIRCUIT DIAGRAM OF ARC IGNITOR

C_1—0.01 μF, 600 V; C_2,C_3—0.001 μF, 12.5 KV; L_1—R.F. Choke (90 Turns of 14 Gauge Wire on Tube, 6 in., 1¼ in. diam.), T_1—Primary, 117 V, Secondary, 10 KV at 18 ma; S.G.—Spark Gap (8 mm between 1/16—in. tungsten rods)

A design which does not use an r-f transformer is shown in Figures 1 and 2. The high voltage secondary of the trigger transformer is coupled in shunt with the arc gap. While any of the six combinations of S.G., C_3, and the secondary of T_1 in a series arrangement will work, the one shown permits the spark gap to connect C_2 and C_3. Capacitor C_1 bypasses the feedback r-f and can be incorporated into an "arc sustainer" resistor-capacitor network if necessary. The voltage for T_1 can be supplied by a control circuit which receives a start and stop command from

FIG. 2. ARC IGNITOR

a current sensing circuit as published by Nobbs (3). Slightly more sophisticated control is necessary, however, if inadvertently extinguished arcs are not to be reignited.

The components listed are not necessarily optimum but were those readily available. These ignitor units are used in gas diode, controlled thyratron, and constant-current, solid-state rectifier power circuits. They work successfully with output cables which are ten feet long.

Literature Cited

1. F. G. Brockman and F. P. Hochgesang, *Anal Chem.* *14*, 796 (1942)
2. D. A. Sinclair, *J. Opt. Soc. Am.* *38*, 547 (1948)
3. J. M. Nobbs, *Brit. J. Appl. Phys.* *4*, 118 (1953)

Improving Temperature Control of ARL Model 2300 1.32

Louis E. Owen

Goodyear Atomic Corporation, Portsmouth, Ohio

The ARL *Model No. 2300* is a commonly used photographic processing machine in spectrochemical laboratories. Temperature control in this unit comes from a thermostat which by a relay energizes a solenoid valve on a cold water inlet when the bath temperature is too high. Bath temperature variations can be reduced if an additional relay contact is used to run the tray rocking motor of the machine whenever cold water is being admitted. The agitation which results decreases the over-shoot which otherwise can occur before the thermostat senses the lowered temperature. The only operational precaution is to switch on the rocking motor when a plate or film is to be developed even though the machine is rocking when the darkroom is entered. Otherwise the rocking may be turned off during a processing if the thermostat is satisfied.

1.33 Automatic Plate Washer-Rinser-Dryer*

Louis E. Owen

Technical Division, Goodyear Atomic Corporation, Portsmouth, Ohio

An automatic washer-rinser-dryer for spectrographic plates has been developed to supplement the film washer-rinser-dryer previously described *(1)*. While the principle of operation is similar to that of the film strip unit, the design was modified to accommodate plates (Figure 1). A versatile controller permits the choice of one of three processing cycles best suited to the emulsion. The holder for a 4- by 10-inch photographic plate fits snugly in the main chamber. The small side chambers which feed water to the spray holes leading into the main chamber are connected (Figure 1) and share inlets of both tap and distilled water used in washing and rinsing the film. The plates are dried by compressed air and strip heaters. The control circuit shown in Figure 2 is set for a two-minute wash, one-minute rinse, and six-minute dry cycle.

As the operator lowers the plate holder into the main chamber he depresses switch S_2. The closing of this switch operates relay R_0 which remains energized through its contact R_{0A}. Simultaneously, the cam driving motor M_1 starts and solenoid valve V_1 opens commencing the washing spray on the plate. At the same time, the stepping contact S_{RC} advances one step because coil R_S is energized through switch S_3. A driven by M_1 operates S_3 once each minute and the stepping contact consequently advances one step per min. When the stepping contact comes to step 3 the circuit to relay R_2 is completed and held by contact R_{2B}. Contact R_{2A} is actuated and closes valve V_1 stopping the flow of wash water and opens valve V_2 commencing the distilled water rinse. Flasher relay R_1 is also energized operating R_{1A} which periodically breaks the circuit causing the rinse water to alternate on and off every few sec. This alternating action permits complete rinsing with minimum water consumption. After one minute of intermittent

*This work was performed under Contract AT-(33-2)-1 with the United States Atomic Energy Commission.

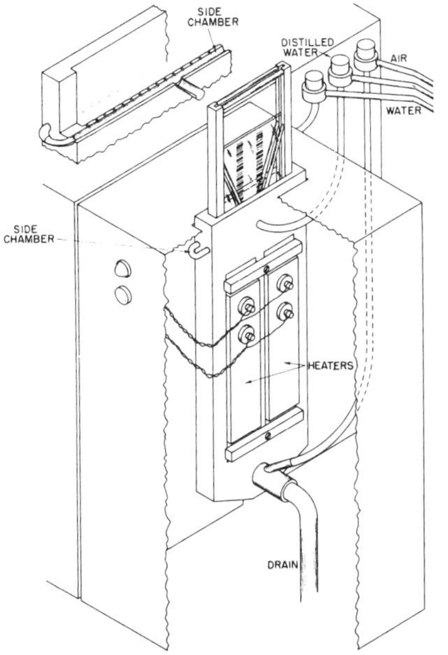

FIG. 1. PLATE WASHER-RINSER-DRYER

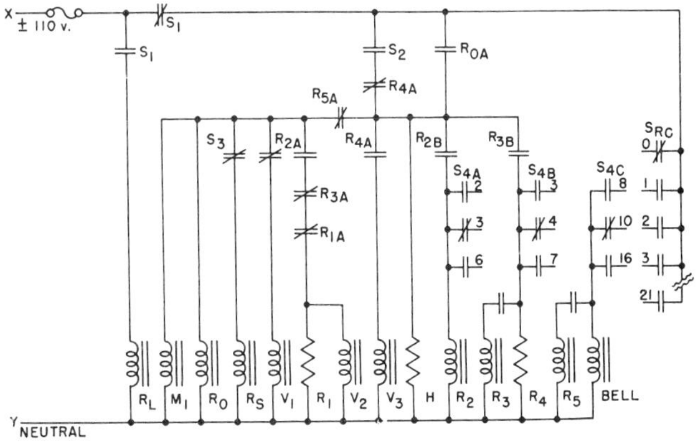

FIG. 2. PLATE WASHER-RINSER-DRYER CONTROL CIRCUIT

rinsing, the stepping contact moves to step 4 and the circuit operates relays R_3 and R_4 through switch circuitry S_{4B}. Contact R_{3B} locks R_3 to the line while R_{3A} de-energizes valve V_2 ending the rinse period. Delay relay R_4 allows the rinse water to drain for three sec. prior to the opening of the compressed air valve V_3. The strip heaters were energized at the start of the cycle and remain energized until the end of the operation. As shown in Figure 2, nine min. after the start of the processing step 10 or S_{RC} operates relay R_5 through switch S_{4C}. Contact R_{5A} then opens to stop the timing motor. The end-of-cycle bell simultaneously sounds recalling the operator to the darkroom. The operator depresses switch S_1 which de-energizes the bell and relays R_2, R_3 and R_4 and also pulses the return coil R_L of the stepping relay. The instrument is then ready to be used again.

Literature Cited

(1) L. E. Owen, Spectrochim. Acta **12,** 99 (1958)

1.34 Photo Processing Tank for Spectrographic Plate Development

M. L. Gonshor and S. E. Hausknecht

Kennecott Research Center, Kennecott Copper Corporation, Salt Lake City, Utah

In response to the need for a photo processing unit that would economically fulfill the need for uniform plate or film development, a device was built employing advantages of simplicity, versatility, and ruggedness. Figure 1 shows the unit itself, and the developing tray, plate, and solution beakers are shown in place in Figure 2.

The processor is essentially a stainless steel tank, 18″ x 13″ x 8″ with a 1 in. outlet pipe. This tank can be mounted adjacent to the ordinary darkroom sink or drain.

FIG. 1. PLATE DEVELOPMENT TANK

A stainless steel wire tray, 10½″ x 11¼″ x 1″ is attached to the tank with adjustable holding rods to permit depth placement in the water bath as desired. Oscillation of the tray to keep the developing and fixing solution in motion is carried out by means of a synchronous motor* geared down to 5.5 rpm. The oscillation axis is off-center to eliminate the formation of standing waves which could cause Eberhard effect. The motion of the tray serves to give some mixing of the constant-temperature bath water without undue violence. The oscillation stroke is readily adjusted by changing the effective arm length on the motor drive.

Provision is made for controlling the temperature within developing limits. This is accomplished by passing a slow stream of cold water through the bath, and using a bimetallic switch,† to activate a 750 watt enclosed heating unit as needed. The tank is large enough to contain a

*Reversible motor No. PYAZ928-A-1, Barber Coleman Company, Rockford, Ill.

†Thermoswitch Cat. No. 17502-0, Fenwal Inc., Ashland, Mass.

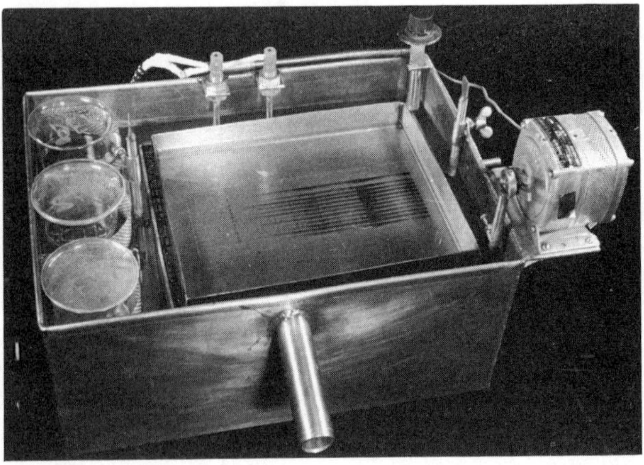

FIG. 2. TANK WITH TRAY, PLATE, AND SOLUTION BEAKERS

section where portions of each development solution may be maintained at the proper temperature. A wire screen divides this section from the developer proper to prevent tipping and spilling of solutions.

A single plate tray, 11½″ x 4¾″ x 1¾″, and a double plate tray, 11½″ x 9½″ x 1¾″, also of stainless steel, are used for the plate development. These trays permit the use of a minimum volume (about 150 ml for single plate and 300 ml for double plate) of developer, stop, and fixer. In our laboratory, these used solutions are discarded or used for cases where first quality development is not required.

The depth of the tank is great enough and the adjustment of the tray height is sufficient to permit the accommodation of film development, if desired.

Constant Temperature Photographic Processing 1.35

Alvin Bober

U. S. Customs Laboratory, Baltimore, Maryland

The advisability of using temperature controlled photographic processing for spectrochemical emulsions has long been recognized as proper procedure. The commercial or professional photographer applies this concept of temperature controlled processing to include all rinses and washes of a negative or print, but the spectrochemist appears to feel that the temperature controlling of the developer and fixer is enough. The precision of certain of our work required us to apply the principle of complete temperature control to all the solutions, rinses, and washings in the development of our spectrochemical emulsions.

A commercial photographic processing unit* was modified to include temperature controlled wash and rinse facilities. This unit normally requires a very small imput of chilled water (less than 68°F) to dependably control

*Catalog No. 3410, Jarrell-Ash Co., Newtonville, Mass.

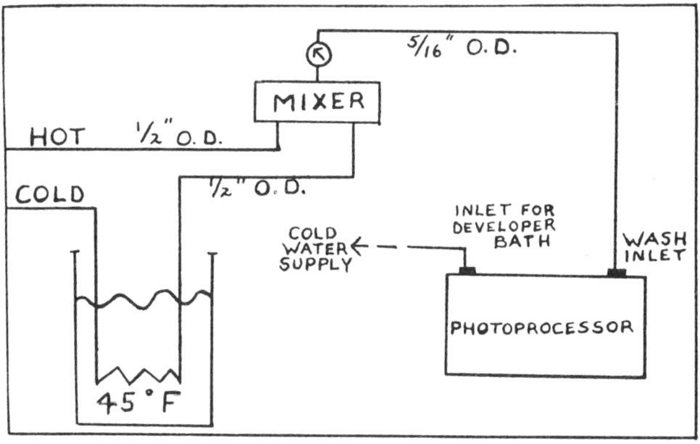

FIG. 1. DIAGRAM FOR THERMOSTATIC WATER MIXER

the temperature of the developer and fixer. It has no facilities for controlling the temperature of the rinse or wash water. To provide enough chilled water during the summer so that the rinse and wash water could be held to 68°F requires a large refrigeration capacity. Likewise, during the winter to provide 68°F water requires an extensive heating unit. The adoption of a thermostatic water mixer* solved this problem. The cold water supply is channelled to the mixer through ½ in. copper tubing submerged in 45° water (this reservoir of cold water is a water type soft drink cooler). The hot water line is tapped directly to the mixer through ½ in. copper tubing. The rinse and wash waters are now maintained at 68°F ± 0.5°F.

1.36 A Processor for Spectrographic Plates

J. M. McCrea

Applied Research Laboratory
United States Steel Corporation
Monroeville, Pa., 15146

Photographic plates used as ion detectors in mass spectroscopy were originally processed manually by rocking with the appropriate solution in stoppered glass cylinders *(1)*. This practice has been continued by many mass spectroscopists because it is simple and requires only the simplest apparatus. On the other hand use of mechanical equipment to aid in standardizing processing conditions has become the accepted practice in emission spectroscopy *(2)*. Commercial processors are available for plates up to 14 inches in length, but none will satisfactorily accept the 2″ x 15″ size frequently used in mass spectrography. A custom-made processing apparatus for such plates has been described by Owens *(3)*. As an alternative to custom-

*Powers Fotoguard Supply Fixture No. 894-2950 Model, The Powers Regulator Co., Skokie, Ill.

FIG. 1. VIEW OF TOP OF PROCESSOR

made apparatus, a suitable processor has been constructed by modification of a standard laboratory bath of suitable dimensions. The Reid Vapor Pressure Bath (Precision Scientific Company, Catalog No. 74893) is designed to meet ASTM specifications for testing petroleum products but is relatively simple to convert to a processor for spectrographic plates *(4)*. It can readily be made movable by setting it on one of the standard caster rings used for 25-l liquid-nitrogen containers.

Figures 1 and 2 show the top of the converted bath. The 100°F fixed-temperature thermoregulator was replaced by an adjustable wire-to-mercury unit and guard (Catalog Nos. 15-180-5 and 15-180-10, Fisher Scientific Company). The clips on the pressure-cylinder support bar were removed, and the bar was remounted on right-angle brackets at the same points on the bath. Appropriate holes were drilled in the support bar, and three 20″ x 5″ x 1¾″ stainless-steel trays were secured to the support bar.

Over two of the trays were mounted 117-v, 60-cycle synchronous motors (Type 117P, ten-rpm-right, Cramer Division, Giannini Controls Corporation). An additional toggle switch was located beside the stirring-motor switch to control power for the synchronous motors.

Plate hangers for two in. plates were made by cutting an offset section from the handles of hangers supplied by National Spectrographic Laboratories (Catalog No. 430-4) and reattaching the end pieces. Counterweighted pivot

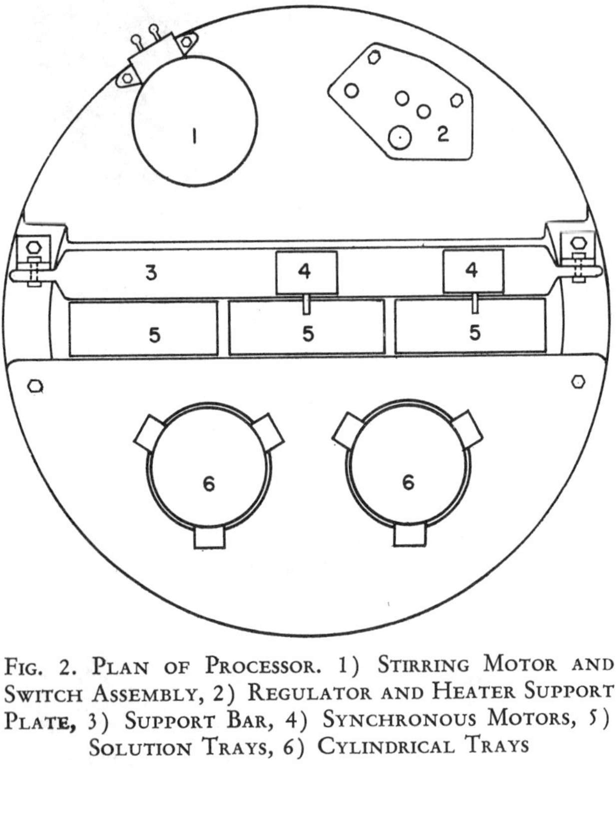

FIG. 2. PLAN OF PROCESSOR. 1) STIRRING MOTOR AND SWITCH ASSEMBLY, 2) REGULATOR AND HEATER SUPPORT PLATE, 3) SUPPORT BAR, 4) SYNCHRONOUS MOTORS, 5) SOLUTION TRAYS, 6) CYLINDRICAL TRAYS

arms were designed to raise and lower pendant plate hangers in the solution trays by using the synchronous rotation of the motor shafts. To prevent the motors from slipping, the counterweight on each arm must be adjusted to make unbalanced torque about the same whether or not the arm is loaded with the hanger and plate. The radius of the circle in which the pivot for the hanger moves is typically 1.25 in. Some slight perturbing motions occur at the pivot but the approximate locus of each point on the suspended plate is a circle of the same radius. Plates either 14 or 15 in. long can be processed conveniently by this system. Shorter hangers would be desirable if shorter plates were to be processed.

When the processor is not in use, plastic covers are used on the solution trays to reduce evaporation. Stainless-steel covers retard evaporation of water from the bath, and the front cover also supports two cylindrical trays used variously for washing, for stop-bath solution, or for cooling the bath below ambient temperature. These trays are made of thinwall stainless steel and are 3.50 in. o.d. and 22 in. long.

The processing apparatus described has been successfully used for processing Ilford Type Q plates. The normal processing temperature of 25°C (77°F) is slightly above ambient, and thermostatic control of the electric heater supplied with the bath yields excellent temperature stability. Temperature stability below ambient temperature can be achieved by inserting a large glass tube filled with crushed ice into one of the cylindrical trays. Relatively poor heat conduction across the air gap and through the glass enable a single filling of crushed ice to act as heat sink for the bath for periods as long as two hours.

Although this processor can be used to process certain types of plates in an eminently satisfactory manner, the processing of plates sensitive to longitudinal drainage results in streaky, unevenly fogged backgrounds. As such drainage is inherent in any vertical design processor, more satisfactory results can be obtained by processing such plates with horizontal rocking trays.

The writer acknowledges the cooperation of F. N. Hodgson, Monsanto Research Corporation, and W. L. Baun, Aeronautical Systems Division, Wright-Patterson Air Force Base, in arranging for some of the tests that determined the sensitivity of SWR plates to drainage.

Literature Cited

(1) F. W. Aston, *Mass spectra and Isotopes,* Edward Arnold Co., London, 1933, p. 91

(2) *Photographic Processing in Spectrochemical Analysis,* ASTM E115-59T, *1965 Book of ASTM Standards, Part 32,* Amer. Soc. Testing Mater., Philadelphia, 1965, p. 562

(3) E. B. Owens, Rev. Sci. Inst. **32,** 1420 (1961)

(4) *Vapor Pressure of Petroleum Products (Reid Method),* ASTM D323-58, *1965 Book of ASTM Standards, Part 17,* Amer. Soc. Testing Mater., Philadelphia, 1965, p. 143

1.37 Film Washer

Edwin S. Hodge

Mellon Institute, Pittsburgh 13, Pa.

A very satisfactory film washer has been built using a piece of stainless steel tubing and a base plate. Type 304 stainless steel has been recommended for photographic processing containers where water and photographic processing liquids are used. Figure 1 shows the necessary details of construction. The film is hung inside the washer by a stainless steel film clip (*Kodak* Jr. Film Clip), one side of which is welded to the center of a stainless steel rod. Slots filed in the top of the washer tube keep the rod in a fixed position during use. A small dental x-ray film clip serves as a weight at the bottom of the film to hold it down

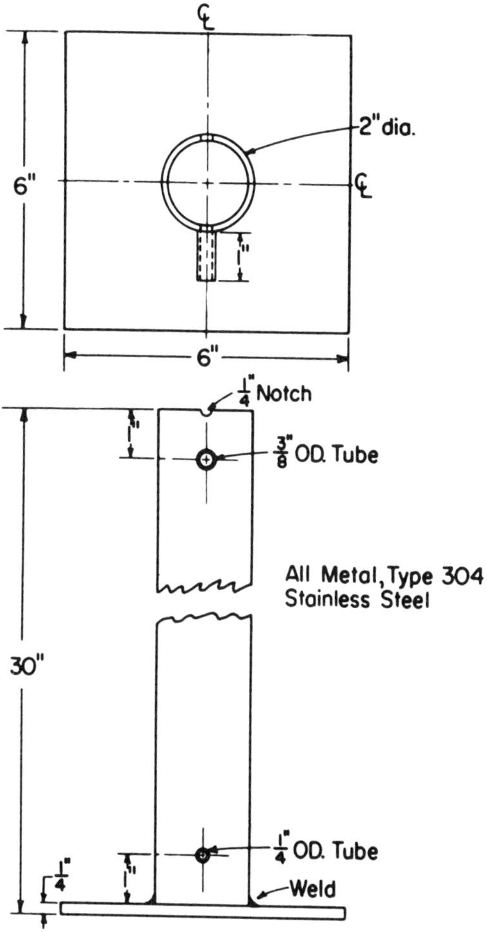

FIG. I. FILM WASHER

during washing. The washer is easily fabricated in a machine shop and has proven to perform rapidly and satisfactorily.

1.38 Modifications to Spectrum Plate Comparator to View Overlapping Wavelength Ranges

H. P. Rothbaum and H. J. Todd
Dominion Laboratory, Wellington, New Zealand

With spectrographs of high dispersion it is impractical to record the whole spectrum from 2,000—10,000 A on

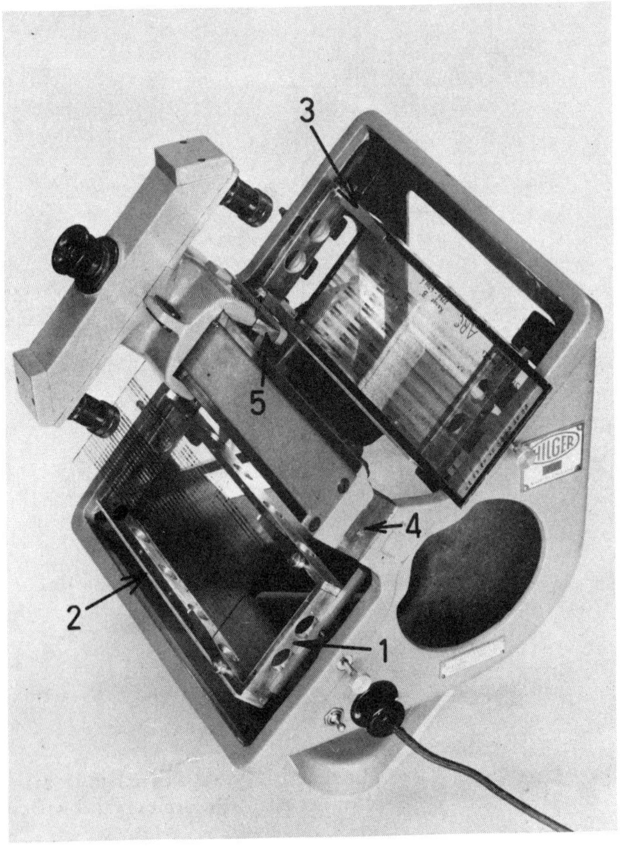

FIG. 1. ATTACHMENT IN POSITION

one continuous photographic plate or film. For this reason many large spectrographs are made readily adjustable to focus any selected wavelength range on to a standard size photographic plate, generally 10″ x 4″. The situation can arise where plates exposed on different but overlapping wavelength ranges have to be compared, but the lateral adjustment on standard comparators is insufficient. In this laboratory an early model Judd-Lewis Comparator* has been permanently adapted and used for a number of years for this purpose. Figure 1 shows the attachment in position on a current model.

Lightweight open frames made of 1″ x ¼″ aluminum bar (1) replace the 10″ x 4″ spectrum plates in the Judd Lewis Comparator. The spectrum plates rest on these frames, each being supported by a strip of aluminum (2) attached to the bottom of the frame. The plate is loosely clamped to the frame by microscope stage clips (3) fitting in holes drilled at regular intervals along the bars. To retain the same focal plane, the optical housing of the comparator is raised using two distance pieces of the same 1″ x ¼″ bar (4) and to give clearance the mirror assembly must be lowered by a similar amount (5). The frames can move vertically and the plates slide horizontally at least 4 in. in each direction. Plates of other sizes, e.g., quarter-plate and cracked or broken 10″ plates can readily be compared with standard plates. The body of the comparator prevents the lower exposures from entering the field of view so that the plate must be turned over for complete coverage. The small changes in dispersion when the same spectral region is exposed on different spectrograph ranges can be easily compensated by adjustment of one field lens.

*A. Hilger, London, Engl.

1.39 A Simple Densitometer for Semi-Quantitative Analysis

Daphne B. de Villiers and Diana van Wamelen

National Physical Research Laboratory
Council for Scientific and Industrial Research
Pretoria, South Africa

When using visual methods of estimation for semi-quantitative analysis, the intensities of the analytical lines are generally compared with a series of lines of standard intensity *(1-3)*. It has been found in this laboratory that the use of a translucent screen simplified the intensity comparisons, but that the use of double projectors having two projection lamps, was a distinct disadvantage *(4)*.

A double-beam densitometer has been designed and built. The design incorporates a system for background

FIG. 1. A. DENSITOMETER

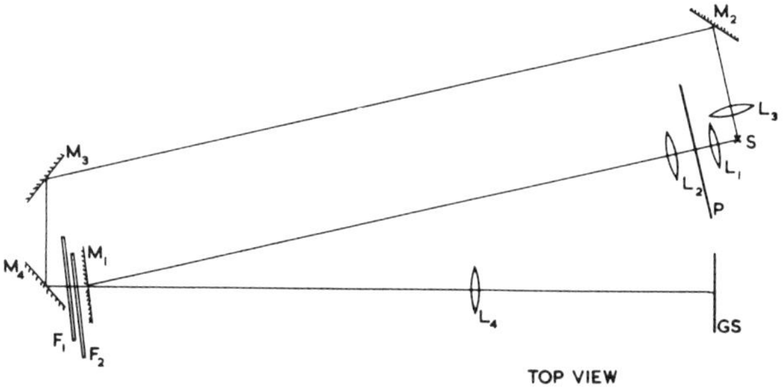

FIG. 1. B. OPTICAL DIAGRAM OF DENSITOMETER

S—projection lamp, L_1-L_4—lenses, P—photographic plate, M_1—mirror with hole, M_2-M_4—reflecting mirrors, F_1—background filter series, F_2—line filter series, GS—ground glass screen, C—controls for operating filters.

correction and includes a feature which greatly simplifies the visual comparison of intensities. The densitometer together with its optical diagram is illustrated in Figure 1. S is a single projection lamp. By means of the lens system, L_1 and L_2, an image of the spectrum on the photographic plate, P, is focused on the mirror, M_1. This mirror is front surface aluminized and has a small hole (approximately 1 mm in diameter) in it, bevelled from behind. The image on mirror, M_1, is focused by means of L_4 on to a ground glass screen, GS. As a result of the hole in the mirror, a small spot appears on the screen. By adjustment of the photographic plate, which can move laterally and vertically, the spot can be made to fall on, or next to, any given spectral line. A second light beam from the projection lamp, S, passes through lens, L_3, and is reflected by means of front surface aluminized mirrors, M_2, M_3, and M_4, so as to give a spot of light on the back of mirror, M_1. The mirrors, M_2, M_3, and M_4, are so adjusted that the small light spot caused by the hole in mirror, M_1, coincides with the black spot on the screen, GS. Two sets of filters, F_1 and F_2, of varying densities are inserted behind mirror, M_1, so that the intensity of the

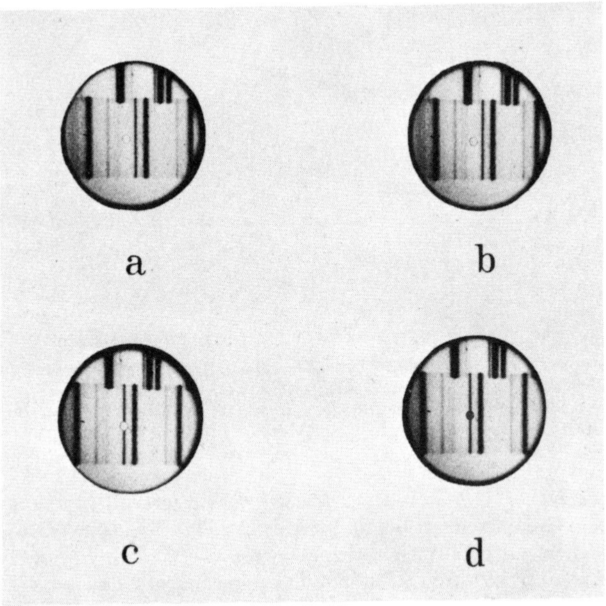

Fig. 2. Viewing Screen of Densitometer

a—spot on background, b—spot matched to background, c—spot on line, d—spot matched to line.

light spot on the screen can be altered by adjustment of the filters. The instrument is so designed that the operator sitting in front of the screen can adjust both the photographic plate and the filters.

The filters were made by exposing portions of photographic plates for varying periods. Fine grain plates (Ilford Thin Film Halftone) were used for this purpose. The first series of filters, F_1, is used for background correction, while the second series, F_2, is used for line intensity determinations. Each series consists of thirteen different filters, the background series having transmission values varying from approximately 17 to 90 per cent and the line series having transmission values varying from approximately 1 to 90 per cent.

The procedure for measurement is as follows. With filters and the photographic plate set on clear plate, the apertures of lenses, L_2 and L_3, are adjusted so as to match the spot to clear plate. The photographic plate is then moved so that the spot falls next to the analytical line of interest. The background filter, F_1, is adjusted to match the spot to background. The line is then moved across the spot and the line filter, F_2, adjusted so as to match the spot to line intensity. The number of the line

TABLE I. DENSITOMETER READINGS FOR BACKGROUND CORRECTION TESTS

(Values represent filter numbers)

Line 1		*Line 2*		*Line 3*		*Line 4*	
No Corr.	*With Corr.*	*No Corr.*	*With Corr.*	*No Corr.*	*With Corr.*	*No Corr.*	*With Corr.*
8	10	5	7	4	5	2	3
7-8	10-11	5	7	4	5	2	3
7	10	4-5	7	3-4	5	2	3
6-7	10	4-5	7	3	5	2	3
5	10	4	7	3	5	1-2	3
4-5	9-10	3-4	7	3	5	1-2	3
4	9	3-4	7	3	5	1-2	3

LINE FILTER VALUES

Filter Number	*% Transmission*	*Filter Number*	*% Transmission*
1	1.3	8	53.6
2	4.8	9	62.8
3	8.8	10	70.2
4	17.0	11	79.5
5	26.2	12	85.2
6	36.1	13	90.3
7	43.2		

TABLE II. DENSITOMETER READINGS FOR IRON LINES WITH CHANGE IN PROJECTION LAMP INTENSITY

(Values represent filter numbers)

	Operator A			Operator B		
Line No.	*Full Light*	*Reduced Light*	*Green Filter*	*Full Light*	*Reduced Light*	*Green Filter*
1	1-2	2	2	2	2	2
2	2	2	2	2	2	2
3	3	3-4	3-4	4	4	4
4	7	7	7	8	8	8
5	3-4	3-4	4	4	4	4
6	12	11	11	12	12	12
7	8	8	8	10	10	10
8	11	11	11	12	12	12
9	9	9	9	10	10	10
10	5	5	5	7	6-7	6
11	3	3	3	4	4	4
12	3	3	3	3	3	3

filter (or its transmission value) is then recorded. This value gives intensity above background.

Figure 2 illustrates the four steps of an estimation. a) Adjustment of the spot (which has previously been matched to clear plate) on background; b) The correct background filter in position; c) Adjustment of the spot on to the analytical line; and d) The correct line filter in position.

An enlargement of the spectral lines of approximately fifteen times is used on the viewing screen. Greater enlargements than this caused difficulty in matching the comparatively grainless spot to the lines of coarse grain plates, when these were used.

In order to test the efficiency of background corrections, a plate was prefogged in strips by varying amounts. A series of identical spectra from a mercury lamp were superimposed on these strips. Estimations of the intensity of four different lines of varying intensity were done both with and without background correction. The values obtained for each individual reading are given in Table I.

It is evident from the table that the importance of background correction increases as the lines become lighter.

To test the effect of changes in the projection lamp, a series of twelve iron lines of varying intensity were measured, the apertures of lenses, L_2 and L_3, (Figure 1) being adjusted both to match the spot to clear plate and to give maximum light intensity. The same lines were measured with the apertures of the lenses adjusted to cut down the light intensity by approximately 20 per cent. A third series of readings were taken on the same lines using the maximum intensity setting but introducing a green filter into each light path. The readings are given in Table II. It can be seen from these values that results should be unaffected by the gradual deterioration of the lamp, or by its replacement.

The reproducibility of readings (see Table II) taken by any one operator over a period is good. The differences in readings recorded by different operators indicate that even with the improved method of visual comparison, standardization tables or curves can still only be used by the operator responsible for their construction, unless some correction factor for each alternative operator is introduced. Not only is this method of intensity comparison less strain on the eyes than was the case with line intensity comparisons, but it makes possible the use of much darker lines.

The instrument is potentially capable of functioning as a densitometer for quantitative work and this possibility is at present being investigated.

The authors are indebted to Dr. A. Strasheim, Director of this laboratory, for suggestions and encouragement, to Mr. L. R. P. Butler for useful discussion, and to Messrs J. J. Erasmus, E. A. Hecker, F. van den Boom, and C. van Schaik for technical assistance in the manufacturer of the prototype. They also wish to thank one of the referees, Dr. M. Slavin, for drawing their attention to the Gaertner densitometer *(5)*, the optical arrangement of which was somewhat similar to the instrument now described.

Literature Cited

(1) N. W. H. Addink, Spectrochim. Acta **4,** 36 (1950)
(2) C. L. Waring and C. S. Annell, Anal. Chem. **25,** 1174 (1953)
(3) E. S. Hodge and W. K. Baer, APPLIED SPECTROSCOPY **10,** 150 (1956)
(4) A. Strasheim and Daphne B. de Villiers, J. S. African Chem. Inst. **XVI,** 5 (1963)
(5) S. Jacobsohn and W. H. Kliever, J. Opt. Soc. Am **25,** 244 (1935)

1.40 A Disk Calculator

Edwin S. Hodge
Mellon Institute, Pittsburgh 13, Pa.

Frederickson *(1)* and Goldspiel and Conner *(2)* have described circular calculators for computing intensity ratios and determining composition. One factor discouraging the use of such a calculator is the difficulty in preparing an exact circular two-cycle log scale of sufficient size and accuracy. This problem has been circumvented by the "zerox" (or photostatic) enlargement of the A scale of a 8-in. circular slide rule to a 10-in. diam. The reproduced scale is attached to an aluminum disk, 1/16-in. thick. Relative intensity values for each unit mark of % transmission are tabulated from the customary emulsion Seidel calibration curve. These data are laid out as a circular Seidel % transmission scale on the circumference of a smaller disk 9-in. diam. A special ruler made from rigid transparent plastic is cut so that a radius at the outer end serves as a ruling edge when the two disks and ruler are held concentrically by a bolt, nut, and washer. With the two disks being held together the Seidel % transmission values are marked on the smaller disk at relative intensity positions indicated on the outer log scale.

In use, the ruling edge is replaced by a similar piece of plastic having a ruled mark for an indicator. It has been necessary to prepare one scale for each emulsion lot. The device has proved to be a great time saver and is more convenient to use than the customary calculating boards or conventional linear scales. No originality is claimed for this calculator except the convenience and accuracy of using an enlarged finely divided circular log scale*.

Literature Cited

(1) L. D. Frederickson, Jr., ANAL. CHEM. **24**, 2019 (1952)
(2) S. Goldspiel and I. Conner, APPLIED SPECTROSCOPY **6**, 23 (1952)

Working Curve Shifter 1.41

Edwin S. Hodge

Mellon Institute, Pittsburgh 13, Pa.

Some laboratories performing a variety of analyses do not find it convenient to prepare working scales for quantitative analysis but prefer to use working curves drawn up as needed or already on file. A curve shifter has been devised and found to be useful for several reasons. Working curves are drawn on conventional log-log co-ordinate paper and traced on to a transparent matte, shifting it horizontally when necessary to avoid confusing overlaps where curves may naturally fall close together. The use of the curve shifter is based on the hypothesis that working curves do not change in slope but may shift in horizontal displacement with changes in working conditions of excitation, photographic processing, or some other factors. Corrections for working curve shifts can be made easily and quickly.

*Reproductions of the log scale are available from the author upon request.

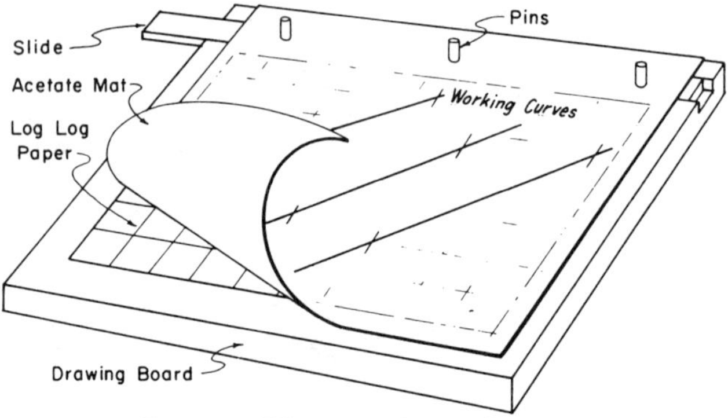

FIG. 1. A WORKING CURVE SHIFTER

A drawing board (Figure 1) was recessed so that a meter stick or similar rule would slide horizontally near the upper edge and be flush with the top surface of the board. Three 1/4-in. dowel pins, about 1-in. long and sharpened in a pencil sharpener, were set into the flat side of the rule about 8-in. apart. A matte finish cellulose acetate sheet, 12-in. x 20-in., 0.005-in. thick*, was punched to fit on the pointed dowel pins and may be easily removed. This material may be readily marked by pencil or ink and erased in the same way as tracing paper but is much more durable. In use, working curves are plotted in the customary manner on the usual log-log co-ordinate paper, after which the paper is fastened to the drawing board and overlaid with a piece of Draft Film. The working curves are traced and identified with colored pencils on the matte writing surface of the film, shifting the film sufficiently so that there is no confusion due to overlapping curves. The position of some concentration on the working curve is marked and each curve is identified as it is copied. Also, the position of log intensity ratio = 1.0 is marked on the Draft Film at each end of the concentration axis. One

*Material of this type is manufactured by Eugene Dietzgen Co., New York, under the name of Draft-Film No. 157M-5.

sheet may contain all the working curves for one particular sample type, and a separate sheet may be used for each kind of sample. The graph paper on the drawing board containing the original working curves is replaced by a clean sheet of the same kind of paper positioned vertically so that the log intensity ratio = 1.0 line of the ordinate is exactly under the same mark on the transparent sheet.

A set of working curves superimposed on log-log paper is shown in Figure 1. In use, the curves are set so that the index mark would fall on the indicated concentration, and concentrations read from the intensity ratio values. Alternatively, curve shift may be corrected by placing the working curve on a point determined by an averaged intensity ratio obtained produced by a known concentration of a secondary standard.

This device enables one to make working curve shifts in the same manner that is done with linear scale calculators without laying out the scales or plotting new working curves for each run.

Calculating Board for Spectrochemical Analysis 1.42

D. R. Stoss

Materials & Processes Laboratory, Large Steam Turbine-Generator Department, General Electric Company, Schenectady, New York

A spectrochemical calculating board* designed for two-step data evaluation has been modified to reduce data evaluation to a single operation without the use of special concentration scales for each analytical line pair investigated. The board is similiar in application to the calculator described by Dewey *(1)*, but is simpler to manipulate and utilizes the Seidel density function.

A Seidel density scale has been inscribed on the left

***Applied Research Laboratories* calculating board, Model 2375

edge of the vertical cursor (B) in addition to the two cycle log scale provided on the right edge (Figure 1)). Using this scale, Seidel calibration curves can be drawn on the plotting surface directly from transmittance data. A family of calibration curves was constructed and projected onto narrow plastic strips. These cover a wide range of emulsion contrast variations in small increments. Two sliding metal blanks (I′, T′) at the bottom of the plotting surface carry, respectively, a two cycle log scale and one of the calibration scales. Windows were cut in these metal blanks so that an index line (F) drawn on the plotting surface can be aligned with values on either the log scale or the calibration scale. These scales can be moved independently to perform all the calculations required in data evaluation. After calibrating a specific wavelength region of a specific spectrographic film or plate by conventional calibration techniques, the calibration scale from this calibration curve is secured to the metal blank. An index line (F) is drawn on the plotting surface and is used as the reference point in establishing the arbitrary intensity value for transmittances of internal standard lines. Working curves are drawn on the plotting surface in relation to the index line and concentration values are plotted as ordinates using the vertical log scale on the cursor. If it is desired to record the numerical value of I_a/I_s ratios, unity on the horizontal log scale must be aligned with the index line. In applications to routine analytical programs, it is convenient to plot the day-to-day working curves on a clear plastic overlay covering the plotting surface, and compare these to a set of "monitor" curves inserted beneath the overlay.

Background corrections can be made using the index line and a single horizontal log scale as follows: Align unity on the log scale with the transmittance value of the background on the calibration scale. Note the relative intensity value on the log scale corresponding to the transmittance value of line plus background. Move the vertical cursor (B) to this relative intensity value minus one, and the corresponding value on the calibration scale is the corrected transmittance value of the line. Positioning the calibration scale in relation to the plotting surface is de-

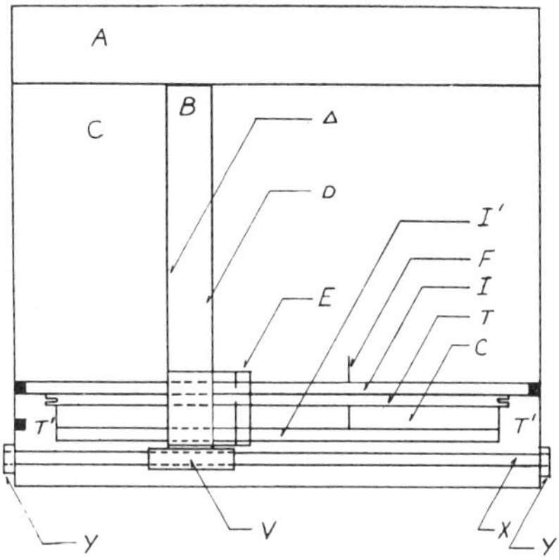

FIG. 1. CALCULATING BOARD

A — Storage for calibration scales, B — Vertical cursor (Δ — Seidel scale, D — 2 cycle log scale), C — Plotting surface of clear plastic, E — Polystyrene support for cursor hairline, F — Index line on plotting surface, I — 2 cycle log scale, I′ — Metal blank supporting I, T — Seidel calibration scale, T′ — Metal blank supporting T, V — Bearing block for vertical cursor, X — Horizontal guide bar for B,I, and T, Y — Support blocks for X.

pendent upon the nature of the background correction. If the correction is on the internal standard line only, align the corrected transmittance value with the index line after the correction is made. If the correction is on the analysis line only, align the observed transmittance value of the internal standard with the index line before the correction is made. If corrections are required on both members of the line pair, first make the correction on the internal standard line, and, with the corrected transmittance value aligned with the index line, make the correction on the analysis line. If it is desired to record the numerical value of I_a/I_s, unity on the log scale must be aligned with the index line after the correction is made.

The board can be used for two-step data evaluation for special cases by replacing the Seidel calibration scale with another 2 cycle log scale.

Literature Cited

1. R. A. Dewey, Applied Spectroscopy **7**, 87 (1953)

See also 8.2, 8.4, 8.5, 8.6, 8.7, 8.8.

1.43 A Graph for Calculating Weighing Errors in the Preparation of Standards for Quantitative Spectrochemical Analysis

H. Tavera-Beltrán, Y. Díaz-Hernández, A. Carrillo-García, and J. Ramírez-Muñoz*

Research Division†, Industrial University of Santander, Bucaramanga, Colombia, South America

Solid powdered standards used for calibration in quantitative spectrochemical analysis have to be prepared by careful weighing of known quantities of substances that contain the elements under analysis and dilution with the appropriate matrix. This matrix contains the internal standard in some cases. In other cases the internal standard is added to the mixture prior to dilution with the matrix.

It may easily be understood that accuracy of the spectral procedure will depend on the accuracy of the preparation of standards.

To avoid long grinding periods to homogenize the final mixture it is advisable to weigh the smallest quantities of substances possible keeping in mind that the greatest percentage in weight of the whole usually corresponds to the

---

* Present address: Beckman Instruments, Inc., Fullerton, California, U.S.A.

†This procedure has been developed at the Department of Spectrochemistry of the Institute of Pure and Applied Research of the above mentioned Division.

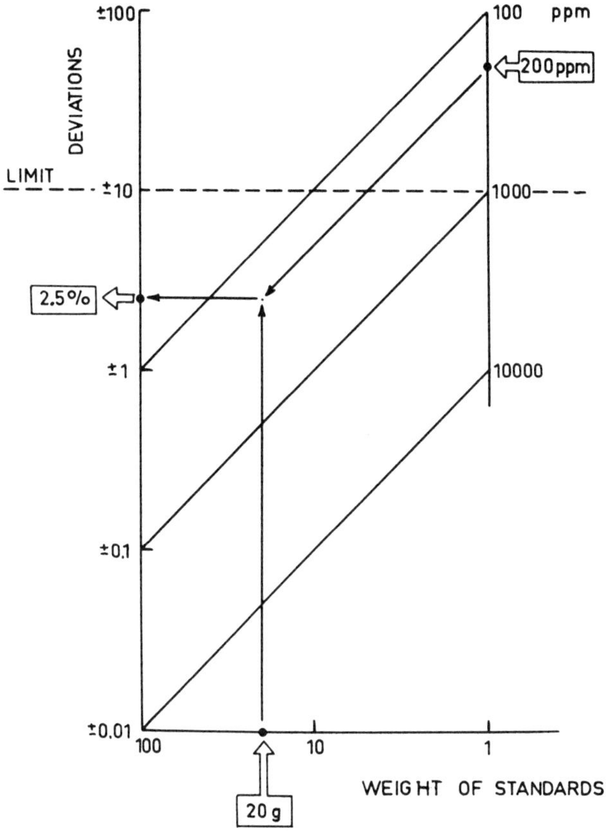

FIG. 1. USE OF THE GRAPH TO CALCULATE DEVIATIONS IN THE PREPARATION OF 20 g OF A STANDARD HAVING ADDED 200 ppm OF A COMPOUND CONTAINING THE ANALYSIS ELEMENT. LIMIT AT ±10%. DEVIATIONS (%), WEIGHT OF STANDARDS (g)

weight of the matrix especially in trace analysis where minimum quantities of analysis elements are included in the series of standards.

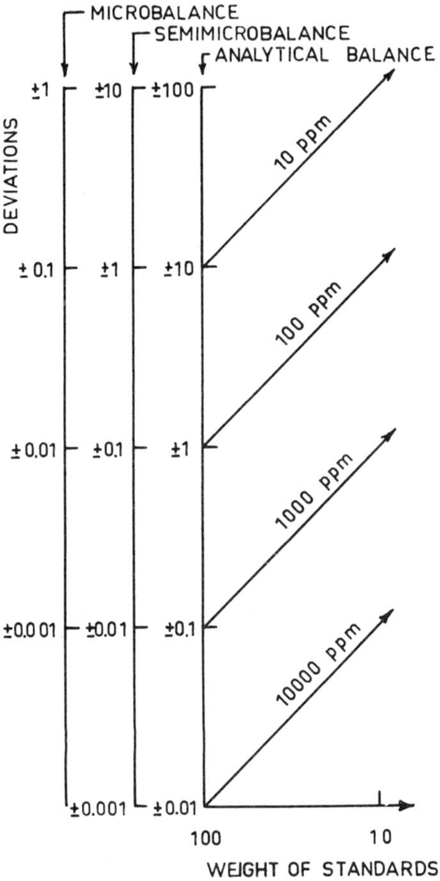

FIG. 2. AUXILIARY SCALES ON THE ORDINATE SCALE FOR DEVIATIONS IN PERCENTAGE

Standards are usually prepared by means of an analytical balance to obtain weights with a precision within ±0.1 mg, and sometimes a semimicro or a microbalance is used (±0.00001 g or ±0.000001 g, respectively).

It would be interesting to have a simple graph where, without calculations, the weighing errors to be achieved for a given total weight of standard and for a given concentration of substance containing the analysis elements might be known in advance.

In this note a graph is proposed for this purpose.

Logarithmic scales with the same unity have been used for all variables in the graph. There are three principal scales: one, abscissa, for weights of the standard, a second, ordinate, for deviations in percentage, and a third, vertical scale at the right, for concentrations of the added compound (Figure 1).

This graph has been built on the basis that deviations to be found in the standard, as a function of the deviations given by the balance, depend only on the magnitude of the standard and the concentration of the compound added, under the supposition that the percentage error in weight is due only to the error of the added compound and not to that of the matrix. Concentrations of the compound added are given in ppm. The ordinate scale has been traced far enough to include deviation values that may be admitted in some special cases.

The graph has the following uses: 1) to calculate deviations due to weighing for a given weight of standard and for a given concentration, 2) to calculate the smallest concentration to be added to a given final weight of standard to have deviations not greater than a defined percentage, 3) to calculate the smallest final weight of a standard for a given concentration to have deviations not greater than a defined percentage.

Actually, even in trace analysis, deviations should not be greater than a defined percentage e.g., 10%. Thus, cases yielding points over the dotted line (Figure 1) may render deviations that are too high, and consequently this type of standard should not be prepared and used.

If a semimicro or a microbalance is used, two auxiliary scales may be added to the ordinate scale (Figure 2). In these cases deviation may be less, but there should be a limit in the abscissa scale depending on the maximum load of the balance used.

SECTION 2
INFRARED SPECTROSCOPY

Sublimation of Inorganic and Addition Compounds for Infrared Spectroscopy 2.1

Herman A. Szymanski and Paul Peller
Canisius College, Buffalo, New York

A technique which permits rapid sublimation was developed during the study of the infrared spectra of inorganic salts and addition compounds.

The apparatus consists of a *Lepel* 15 KW* induction furnace in which a platinum boat is placed inside the copper induction coil of the furnace. When the coil is matched to the furnace, the boat can be heated to white heat in approximately one second. The sublimation technique consists of placing the compound in the boat with a salt plate suspended above it. An extremely fine powder is sublimed onto the salt plate which remains at room temperature. The current can be stopped when a white smoky deposit is seen on the salt plate.

The particle size of the deposit is quite small since the amount of scattered light is low as indicated by the spectra

*Lepel High Frequency Laboratories, New York, N. Y.

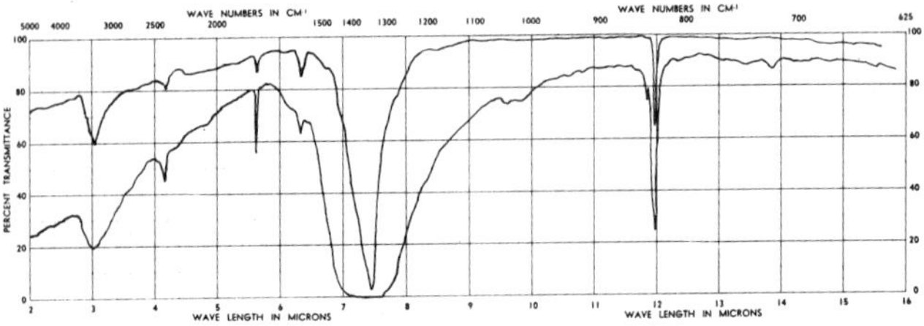

FIG. 1. SUBLIMED $Cu(NO_3)_2 \cdot 5\ H_2O$

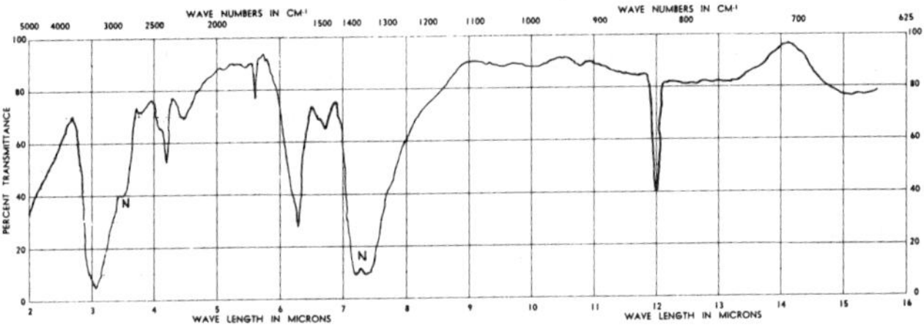

FIG. 2. $Cu(NO_3)_2 \cdot 5H_2O$ IN NUJOL MULL

at short wavelengths. Occasionally, a trace of water, as shown by a small peak near 3 microns, is present. Experiments with closed cells operating under vacuum and inert atmospheres show that this procedure eliminates water which would be condensed from the atmosphere.

Copper nitrate* is an excellent compound on which to use this technique because its anhydrous form is extremely difficult to obtain. Spectra of this compound showing small amounts of water present, have been obtained. The spectra of two thicknesses of the sublimate are shown in Figure 1 and the spectrum of this compound in *Nujol* is given in Figure 2. These spectra agree quite well except for the peak which is present in the Nujol spectrum near 2200 cm^{-1}. Apparently the spectrum of the compound prepared by the new sublimation technique is correct since

*This compound was suggested by Dr. S. H. Bauer.

this peak has not been assigned to any vibration *(1,2)* and may be an impurity.

This technique has been used to sublime addition compounds such as amine and dioxane complexes of arsenic, antimony, and titanium halides. Surprisingly, the organic part of the complex does not appear to decompose under the sublimation conditions. Comparison of the spectra of about twenty complexes obtained from sublimates, KBr discs, and mulls agree quite well. When the spectra do not match exactly, it is observed that some peaks are missing from the sublimate spectra. This is attributed to the elimination of impurities. This technique appears to give purer sublimates than the convenional sublimation procedure. For example, N,N-dimethylaniline arsenic trichloride was sublimed very slowly using the conventional sublimation apparatus and the spectrum run at various intervals. Bands due to N,N-dimethylaniline and oxidized aniline appeared when the sublimation was not controlled or was continued too long. These impurity bands did not appear in the spectra obtained by this new technique.

Literature Cited

(1) F. Vratny, APPLIED SPECTROSCOPY **13**, 59 (1959)
(2) F. A. Miller and C. H. Wilkins, ANAL. CHEM. **24**, 1253 (1952)

2.2 Arsenic Trichloride and Arsenic/Antimony Chlorides as Solvents for Infrared and N.M.R. Spectroscopy*

Herman A. Szymanski, Alvin Bluemle
and William Collins

Canisius College, Buffalo, New York

While somewhat difficult to handle due to its corrosive character, arsenic trichloride has certain solvent properties which make it a useful addition to the list of spectroscopic solvents. Conductiometric titrations have been made using this halide as a solvent *(2)*. The hydrolysis of this chloride to arsenous acid is a reversible reaction unlike the behavior of such a related halide as phosphorus trichloride. It is possible to steam distill arsenic trichloride and it forms no basic salt on hydrolysis. We have found that a clear solution in water can be formed with the halide up to 0.5 per cent by volume of water. Concentrated hydrochloric acid solutions in arsenic trichloride have been found to give spectra similar to that of water in the halide.

The spectra of concentrated hydrochloric acid in arsenic trichloride for two solution path lengths is shown in Figure 1. The position of the bands, as well as those of heavy water dissolved in the halide, indicates that water is dissociated in the solution. The observed bands can be assigned as the asymmetric and symmetric stretch and bend of the water molecule at 3650, 3550, and 1600 cm^{-1}, respectively. Weak bands in the spectra may be

*The use of $AsCl_3$ as a solvent was first reported at the Seventh Ottawa Symposium on Applied Spectroscopy, Ottawa, Ontario, September 1960; the mixed solvent $AsCl_3$-$SbCl_3$ was first reported at the Pittsburgh Conference on Analytical Chemistry and Applied Spectroscopy, March 2-6, 1964.

indicative of the H_3O^+-ion and these authors are examining this possibility.

One strong and one weak signal is found in the proton magnetic resonance spectra of water in arsenic trichloride. The position of the strong signal is variable and dependent on the amount of water dissolved in the halide. The range in which it appears is between that observed for water run neat and that of water vapor. The weak signal is found to the low field side of the signal found for water run neat and is presumably an acidic OH signal. It is obvious that the proton exchange reaction which would be expected for this solution is occurring at a rate where two distinct signals, rather than one, are seen. We are examining this equilibrium at present. The behavior of both signals with varying water concentration indicates the strong signal is that of liquid water partially dissociated. The weak signal moves to lower fields when hydrogen chloride is added to the solution verifying it is

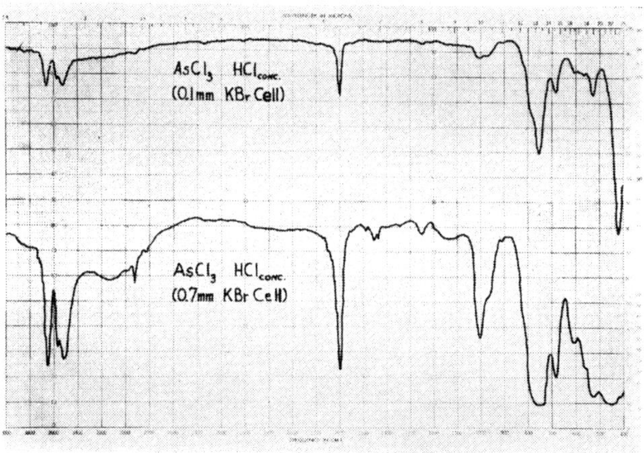

FIG. 1. THE INFRARED SPECTRA OF CONCENTRATED HYDROGEN CHLORIDE IN ARSENIC TRICHLORIDE

an acidic OH signal. The water signal moves to higher fields when hydrogen chloride is added indicating increasing dissociation is occurring.

It is apparent that hydrogen-bonded substances dissociate in arsenic trichloride and this author has examined a number of such substances to verify this. For example, ethanol gives an OH signal which moves to higher fields as more dilute solutions of it in arsenic trichloride are examined.

Mineral acids such as sulfuric acid and hydrobromic acid in wet arsenic trichloride give two concentration-dependent signals similar to hydrochloric acid.

Organophosphorus and carboxylic acids are also dissociated in arsenic trichloride solutions. In Figure 2 the spectrum of *n*-valeric acid in arsenic trichloride is presented. The top curve represents a solution containing

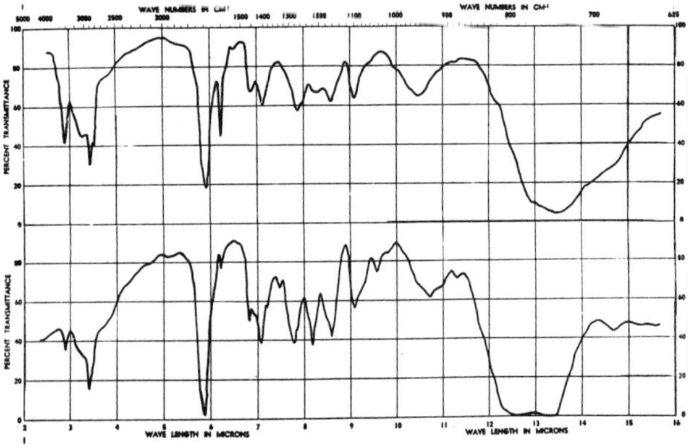

FIG. 2. THE INFRARED SPECTRA OF n-VALERIC ACID IN ARSENIC TRICHLORIDE

Top spectrum represents a solution containing 0.5% water. Bottom spectrum represents a solution where most of the water has been removed.

0.5 per cent water in addition to the acid, while the bottom curve is the same acid in fairly dry halide. The amount of water present in each sample can be estimated from the intensity of the water bands near 3500 and 1600 cm^{-1}. The out-of-plane O-H deformation of carboxylic acids appears in the 900 to 940 cm^{-1} *(3)*. In the monomeric form of these acids this band is at lower frequencies, although the only extensive study of the shift of this band has been of formic acid *(3)*. Examination of the spectra shown in Figure 2 indicates this band does shift from its position when run neat to lower frequencies in dry arsenic trichloride. The position of this band is similar to that found for the pure liquid in arsenic trichloride solutions where the water content is near 0.5 per cent. The same shift has been obtained with acetic and butyric acids and further studies of this behavior are planned.

In the organophosphorus acids a band near 1200 cm^{-1} shifts to lower frequencies in dry halide. This band is the P=O stretch and has been shown by other workers to shift with dissociation of the acid *(1)*.

The authors have examined a number of polymers in arsenic trichloride. These include phenolics, polyesters, polyimides, polyamides, and polyvinyl chlorides *(4)*. For PMR spectra, where nonprotonated solvents are important, the strong solvent properties of arsenic trichloride are quite useful. As an example, the PMR spectra in Figure 3 is that of a series of model compounds and the polymer *Novolak*, which contains the structural groups present in the model compounds. The spectra will not be discussed in detail except to call attention to the sharp spectra of the polymer in arsenic trichloride. The assignments are given on the spectra. In this work the OH groups were identified by passing hydrogen chloride gas through the solution and noting which peak shifted.

The presumably intractable polyimide polymer, H, of the E. I. DuPont Company was found not to be soluble in arsenic trichloride, but it will dissolve in molten antimony trichloride. In addition an equimolar mixture of

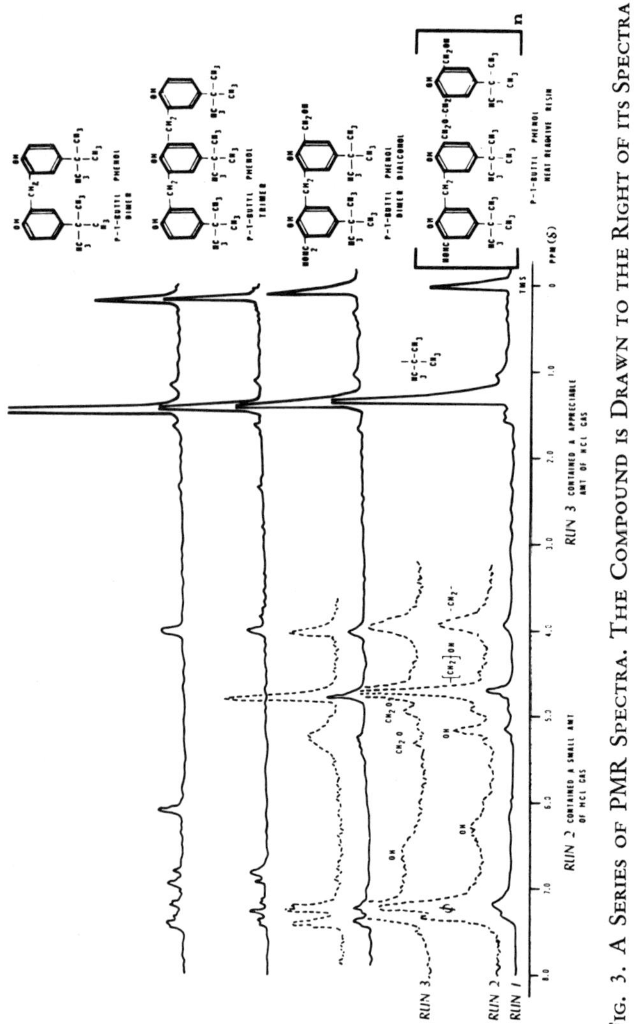

FIG. 3. A SERIES OF PMR SPECTRA. THE COMPOUND IS DRAWN TO THE RIGHT OF ITS SPECTRA

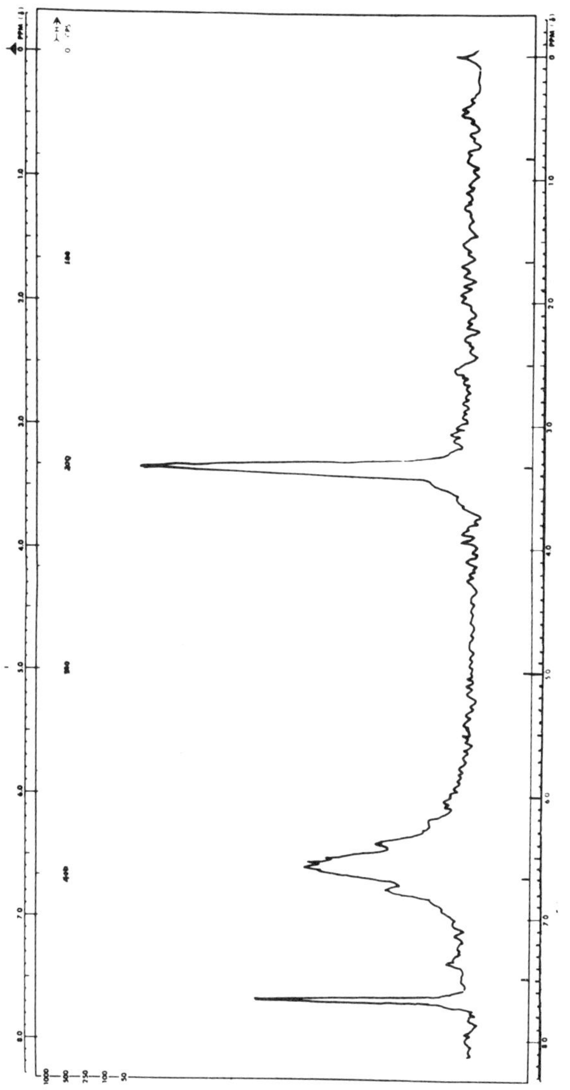

FIG. 4. A PMR SPECTRA OF POLYMER H IN A 1:1 MIXTURE OF ARSENIC AND ANTIMONY TRICHLORIDES

arsenic and antimony halides which is liquid at room temperature will dissolve polymer H. The PMR spectrum of this polymer is shown in Figure 4. The aromatic protons of the polymer give distinct signals in this mixed solvent. This author is examining mixed solvents of this type and will report on this work in later communications.

Literature Cited

(1) J. Ferraro in *Progress in Infrared Spectroscopy,* Volume 2, H. A. Szymanski Ed., Plenum Press Inc., New York, in press

(2) V. Gutman, Z. Anorg. U. Allgem. Chem. **266,** 331 (1951)

(3) G. C. Pimentel and A. L. McClellan, *The Hydrogen Bond,* W. H. Freeman Co., New York, 1960, p. 131

(4) H. A. Szymanski, W. Collins, and A. Bluemle, J. Polymer Sci., in press

2.3 KBr Discs for Liquid Samples

Robert E. Clark

Film Department, Experimental Station, E. I. du Pont de Nemours & Co., Inc., Wilmington, Delaware

In the qualitative infrared analysis of liquids and semi-liquids, this laboratory is frequently confronted with samples containing water, odoriferous materials, or highly viscous samples that would either be ruinous to standard liquid sample cells or cause costly or time-consuming cleaning and polishing operations. The use of cup-shaped KBr pellets for forming a cell that can be discarded after use provides a satisfactory solution to this problem

In Figure 1, the two KBr pellets (A) are shown in disassembly. A drop or more of the sample liquid is deposited in the recessed section (C), a standard flat pellet is then placed on top, and the assembly mounted in a

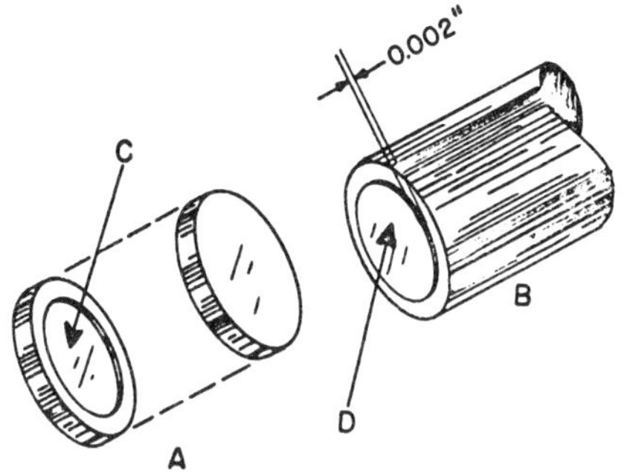

FIG. 1.
A—Exploded View of KBr Discs,
B—Modified Disc Forming Plunger

pellet holder for subsequent spectrophotometric measurement.

Construction of the die for making such pellets involves the machining of a hardened steel plunger (B) with a raised concentric section (D), 50μ (0.002 in) high (or other dimension as may be dictated by the absorption characteristics of the sample). The outside diam. of the plunger should be the same as that of the commercial die with which it is used. The machined surfaces of the plunger should be well polished. The pellets are then pressed in the usual manner, using approximately 200 mg of infrared quality potassium bromide. This results in a pellet thickness of about 2.4 mm when the diam. is 12.5 mm.

An alternate method involves the standard pelleting assembly and a disc of metal foil of selected thickness that is attached to the die plunger. It is suggested that a foil of hard metal be used, such as nickel rather than aluminum. Discs so prepared, however, have been found to be somewhat inferior to those prepared with the specially machined plunger since the foil causes irregularities in the surface of the KBr disc and is difficult to position properly.

2.4 KBr Pellet Holder

Robert A. Pittman

Southern Regional Research Laboratory, U. S. Department of Agriculture, New Orleans, La.

Recently, this Laboratory had reason to scan some KBr pellets, produced in a Beckman Die*, using a Model 14 Cary Recording Spectrophotometer. The problem of mounting the pellets in the instrument beam led to the design and fabrication of two brass holders according to the plans shown in Figure 1. When mounted in the instrument with the cell holders at the approximate center of the sample chamber, the pellet holder will pass the full beam of the instrument. Two pellet holders are used with one containing the sample pellet in the sample beam and the other a blank KBr pellet in the reference beam. Figure 2

*Catalog No. 4240, Beckman Instrument Co., Fullerton, Calif.

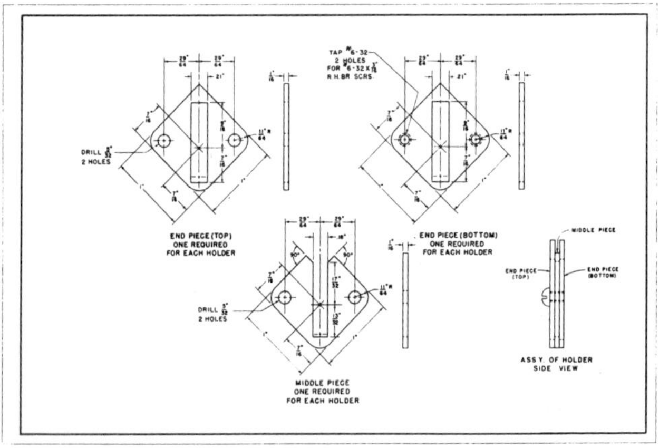

FIG. 1. PLANS FOR KBr PELLET HOLDER

FIG. 2. PELLET HOLDER MOUNTED IN SAMPLE CHAMBER OF INSTRUMENT

shows a holder mounted in the sample chamber of the instrument.

A Rectangular KBr Pellet Die and Holder* 2.5

George J. Edwards

Florida Citrus Experiment Station, Lake Alfred, Florida

In order to use the entire light beam area of a Beckman model IR-4 infrared spectrophotometer, a die has been constructed to make rectangular KBr pellets directly in the pellet holder. A description of the die and its use follows; comparisons were made between solutions, mulls,

*Florida Agricultural Experiment Stations Journal Series No. 1708

FIG. 1. DIE AND PELLET HOLDER

and pellets ground with and without a solvent. The pellets from this die were also compared to pellets prepared with a commercial die.

The die itself (Figure 1) consists of a ram, *A*, a pellet holder *B*, an anvil *C*, and a base *D*. The sample leveler, *E*, is also shown. The ram is 5″ x 1/2″ x 1″ and has a polished hardened projection of 1″ x 1/4″ x 1/16″. It is made the same length as the anvil in order to maintain a level pressure during pressing of the pellet. The anvil, 5″ x 1/2″ x 1″, with a polished hardened projection, 1″ x 1/4″ x 1/4″, is mounted in a 5″ x 4″ x 2″ base. After machining, the ram and anvil were hardened to withstand a total load of 40,000 lb hydraulic pressure. The rectangular hole, 1-1/64″ x 3/64″, of the pellet holder is milled so that the ram and anvil have minimum but adequate clearance. Too close a fit makes removal of the ram and anvil difficult. The rectangular hole is placed 7/8 in. from the edge and 1-1/8 in. from the bottom of the pellet holder.

The die is used by placing the pellet holder on the anvil, which is seated in the base, with the milled edges towards the anvil, or with the flat side up. A mixture of one to two mg of sample and 100 mg of infrared quality KBr is placed in the opening of the holder and leveled with the sample leveler. The ram is placed on the sample in the holder, and the die placed in a hydraulic press. A total hydraulic load of 40,000 lb is applied to the sample for five min with a Loomis 341 - 20 type press.* The pressure is slowly released, the holder removed and placed in the instrument as shown in Figure 2.

The sample mixtures were weighed directly into an agate mortar. Enough suitable solvent was added to wet the mixture, and it was ground until a paste was formed. The solvent was then evaporated using a hair dryer, and the mixture was transferred from the mortar into the pellet holder on the anvil using a rubber policeman.

In recording the spectra of these samples, a plain KBr pellet was used in the reference beam to cancel out any hydroxyl absorption in the three micron region. Three pellet holders were made in order to have an extra one for the sample being prepared, while the spectrum of another sample was being recorded.

Comparisons of spectra obtained using this die and technique are shown in Figure 3. A screen was used in the reference beam for curves 4 and 5. The spectrophotometer was set for an average run with a single beam double beam energy of 1-1, a 2 X slit program, and a wavelength speed of .1 micron/min. A comparison of curves 4 and 3 shows the advantage of grinding the sample and KBr with a solvent. The solvent appears to decrease the particle size and facilitate the distribution of the sample in the KBr, thus resulting in sharper absorption areas and better resolution. A comparison of curve 4 with curves 1 and 2 shows that there is no apparent change in the sample due to the pressure of 40,000 lb. Readability is increased in the KBr curves. The peaks marked by X's on curves 1 and 2 are due to solvent absorption. Curve 5, made from a sample using the Beckman die (Cat. No.

*Press made by Loomis Engineering & Manufacturing Company, Caldwell, N. J.

FIG. 2. PELLET HOLDER IN SAMPLE CELL HOLDER

4240), shows a loss in energy at the lower wave length. This die had been subjected to only 30,000 lb, which is 10,000 lb more than recommended. Evidently, this sample is thicker than the sample used for curve 4, and this re-

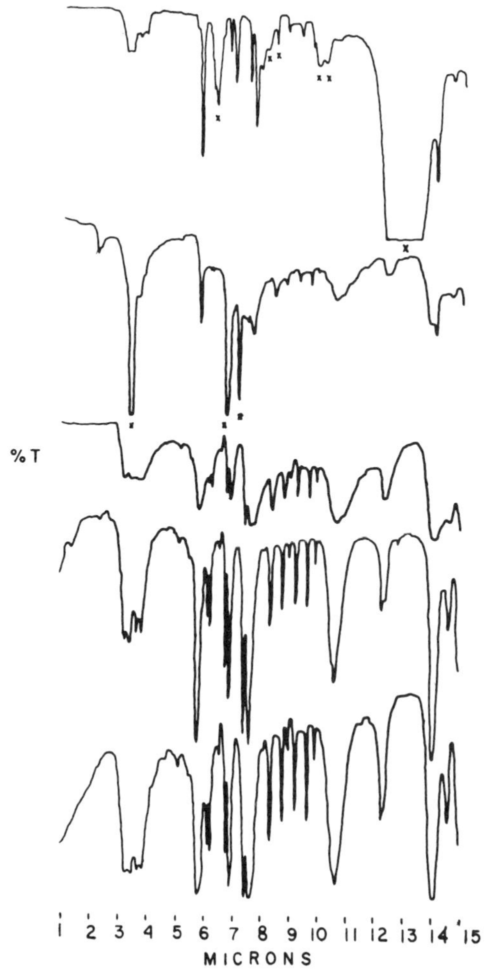

FIG. 3. SPECTRA OBTAINED BY DIFFERENT METHODS

1—1% solution of Benzoic Acid in CCl_4, 0.0925 mm cell, 2—Mineral oil mull of Benzoic Acid, 3—2 mg Benzoic Acid in 100 mg KBr, 4—2 mg Benzoic Acid in 100 mg KBr ground with CCl_4, 5—2 mg Benzoic Acid in 100 mg KBr ground with CCl_4 and pressed in Beckman Die. *Solvent absorptions sults in lower energy in the shorter wave length. One advantage of pressing the pellet in the holder is that the thinner pellet does not have to be transferred to a holder. Pellets of KBr alone, prepared using this technique, transmitted 70%, while those prepared using the commercial die with this technique transmitted 75%.

This die and technique constitute an improved procedure for making KBr pellets. The results are comparable to those obtained using a commercial die with the distinct advantage that the pellet does not have to be transferred to the holder. Also it is possible to press thinner pellets by using a larger total load on the die, and no vacuum is required to remove the entrapped air.

2.6 Preparation of Potassium Bromide Pellets of Unstable Materials

W. H. Price and R. H. Maurer

Climax Molybdenum Company of Michigan
14410 Woodrow Wilson, Detroit, Michigan

Infrared examination of solid materials that are unstable to atmospheric moisture or oxygen can be accomplished by the pressed-pellet technique only if precautions are taken to exclude these gases during sample preparation and scanning of the spectrum. A simple technique utilizing a dry box and an easily constructed sandwich-type cell has been developed in this laboratory and successfully used for obtaining the infrared spectra of many highly sensitive materials.

The dry box must be capable of maintaining an atmosphere of essentially pure, dry nitrogen or other inert gas during the several operations required and must be provided with an alternating current outlet for operation of a Wig-L-Bug amalgamator*. For hydrolytically unstable materials, it is recommended that a dew point of at least $-50°C$ be maintained throughout the procedure. In the case of substances unstable to oxygen, a sample of the atmosphere should be withdrawn and its oxygen content determined by gas chromatography before proceeding. The majority of samples may be safely handled if the concentration of oxygen does not exceed 0.04% by volume.

The cell used consists of two polished sodium chloride windows, 25.2 mm diam. x 5 mm thick, and separated by a Teflon gasket cut from 1/16-in. thick Teflon sheet with the aid of cork borers. Suitable dimensions for the inner and outer diameters are 14 mm and 22 mm respectively. A pellet of the usual 13 mm diam. size will fit snugly inside the gasket. When the latter is sandwiched between the two salt plates and clamped into a Perkin-Elmer demountable cell holder†, the assembly constitutes a virtually leakproof cell in which the sample will remain stable for a longer period than the time required to obtain a satisfactory spectrum.

All of the equipment ordinarily required for pellet preparation, with the exception of the hydraulic press, should be placed inside the dry box on the preceding day. The atmosphere of the box can then be prepared by such overnight treatment as may be required to bring it within the limits of dew point or oxygen content already prescribed. After the atmosphere has been checked, the sample ampoule is opened, and a portion of the sample is mixed with potassium bromide in a Wig-L-Bug amalgamator. The mixture is transferred to the inner compartment of the die assembly, which is then placed inside and near the bottom of a polyethylene bag made from 0.005 in. polyethylene sheet and of such depth that approximately one ft of the upper portion of the bag remains clear. This portion of the bag is then twisted into a "rope", which is folded back upon itself and held securely

* Crescent Dental Mfg. Co., Chicago, Ill.

†Cat. No. 012-0085, Perkin-Elmer Corp., Norwalk, Conn.

in place with a strong rubber band. The bag and its contents may now be removed from the dry box and placed in a hydraulic press so that no folds or creases are present in those portions of the polyethylene that are in contact with the surfaces of the press platens. It has not been found necessary to provide for evacuation of the die when it is surrounded by the atmosphere present in the bag, but this portion of the operation should, of course, be carried out with a minimum of delay. After pressing, the bag and its contents are returned to the dry box, and the die is removed from the bag and disassembled.

As an alternative to the polyethylene bag technique, the die assembly may be evacuated while in the dry box. In this case, one must employ suitable precautions to insure that the assembly does not develop a leak during the operations outside of the dry box.

After freeing the pellet from the die assembly, it is mounted inside the Teflon gasket, which is sandwiched between the two salt plates. After tightening securely in the demountable cell holder, the assembled cell may now be removed from the dry box, placed in the sample beam of the infrared spectrophotometer, and a spectrum recorded without fear of attack from the atmosphere of the room.

2.7 A Leveling Device for Alkali Halide Pressed Disk Preparation

H. W. Morgan

Oak Ridge National Laboratory, Oak Ridge, Tennessee

In the routine preparation of pressed alkali halide disks, difficulty frequently occurs in leveling the finely ground

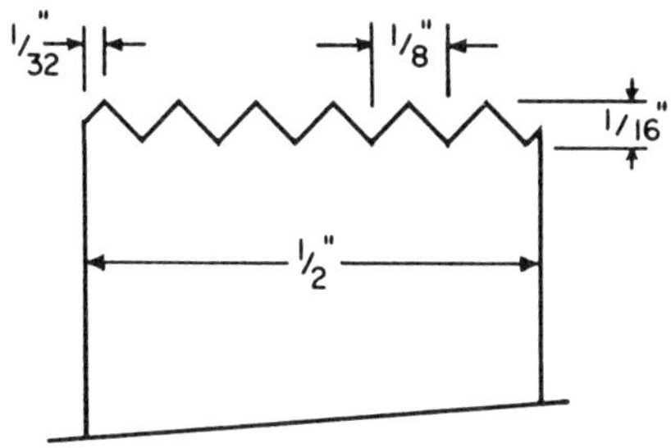

FIG. 1. SIDE VIEW OF A TYPICALLY GROOVED SURFACE

powder in the die. Low spots in the powder level produce, upon pressing, regions of reduced transmission. To insure clear, reproducible disks up to 3 mm in thickness, a leveling device has been in use for more than two years at this laboratory.

This device is made from a brass rod, roughly 5 inches long, having a diameter approximately 0.005-inch smaller than the i.d. of the die. On each end are milled two series of parallel V-shaped grooves, with walls cut at a 45° angle to the surface. The two sets of grooves are machined at right angles to each other, giving the surface a knurled appearance. On one end of the rod the grooves are 1/16-inch deep and 1/8-inch wide; at the other end they are 1/32-inch deep and 1/16-inch wide. Both sets are cut with the first groove 1/32-inch from one edge, so that the patterns are not symmetrical about the center. A typical profile view is shown in Figure 1.

In use, the finely ground salt is placed in the die and the coarse grooved end of the rod is slowly lowered, with continuous rotation, until it rests firmly on the packed powder. It is then rotated while slowly being raised about 1/8-inch. A gentle tapping removes any adhering particles, and the rod is removed. The same procedure is then followed using the smaller grooves. Final leveling is accomplished by pressing a flat-surface (the die face) against the powder. The entire operation can be performed in less than thirty seconds, and results in a powder of uniform density, spread evenly over the lower face of the die.

2.8 An Inexpensive Solid Sampling Technique for Infrared Studies

Leonard H. Ponder

Carrier Research and Development Co.
Carrier Parkway, Syracuse 1, N. Y.

A modification of the pressed potassium bromide pellet technique provides a rapid and inexpensive method for qualitative infrared studies of solid materials. The method of Dinsmore and Edmondson *(1)* for 0.4 to 0.7 mg pellets is easily adapted to give larger pellets suitable for use without condensing optics.

A ⅝-in. steel ball is pressed about one-third the way into a piece of Plexiglass to form a depression for the sample. Although a horizontal jaws bench vise is preferred, vertical jaws may be used if the ball is taped to the plastic. The depression is filled with the sample—KBr mixture and capped with the ball. Pressure is applied for about half a minute. The pellet may be pushed off the ball or removed from the depression by a glass rod.

The pellet may be held securely without danger of breakage by mounting between two thin sheets of polyethylene taped together. This package is taped in front of the entrance slit in the sample compartment. Compensation for the simple spectrum of polyethylene may be accomplished by taping polyethylene in the reference beam. Standard 13mm pellet holders which may be adjusted to provide only a small pressure on the pellet may also be used.

If the pellet is opaque, a screen or attenuator may be used in the reference beam to compensate for the reduction in transmitted radiation. The saucer shape of the pellet may cause some light scattering, but this has presented no difficulty in obtaining good spectra. Spectra as good as those obtained from pellets made in the conventional die using a hydraulic press and vacuum pump can be obtained by this method. The strong bands of some spectra may appear less strong, however. This is the principal difficulty of the method.

Interference from Plexiglas has not been observed even when the potassium bromide was "wet" with methyl ethyl ketone (which dissolves the plastic).

Literature Cited

(1) H. L. Dinsmore and P. R. Edmondson, SPECTROCHIM. ACTA, **11**, 1032 (1959)

The Use of Polyethylene Disks in the Far Infrared Spectroscopy of Solids* 2.9

Leopold May and Karl J. Schwing†

Department of Chemistry, The Catholic University of America
Washington, D. C.

In determining the infrared spectrum of a solid sample, alkali halide disks have been used to a great extent. The preparation of the disks involves the use of pressure, which with some material leads to alterations in the spec-

*This work was sponsored in part by the College Teacher's Research Program sponsored by the National Science Foundation.

†Department of Chemistry, Upsala College, East Orange, N. J.

trum *(1)*. Potassium halides do not transmit past 28 microns. Cesium bromide disks can be used in the far-infrared region but also require pressure. However, polyethylene is transparent throughout the far-infrared region *(2)*, and disks can be prepared simply by melting the mixture of the substance and polyethylene powder under suitable conditions.

The method of preparing the polyethylene disk consists of mixing the sample with the powdered polyethylene and melting the mixture between two glass cover slips on a hot plate. Approximately 2-3 mg of sample is thoroughly mixed with 50 mg of the polyethylene in the Wig-L-Bug mixer (Crescent Dental Mfg. Co., Chicago, Ill.) or ground in a mullite mortar. The mixture is placed between the two cover slips and inserted onto the heating block of a melting point apparatus (Fisher-Johns Melting Point Apparatus, Fisher Scientific Co.). The temperature of the block is raised until the mixture melts (approximately 100° C). When the mixture melts, slight pressure is exerted upon the top cover slip with a proper sized cork until a uniform film has formed between the cover slips.

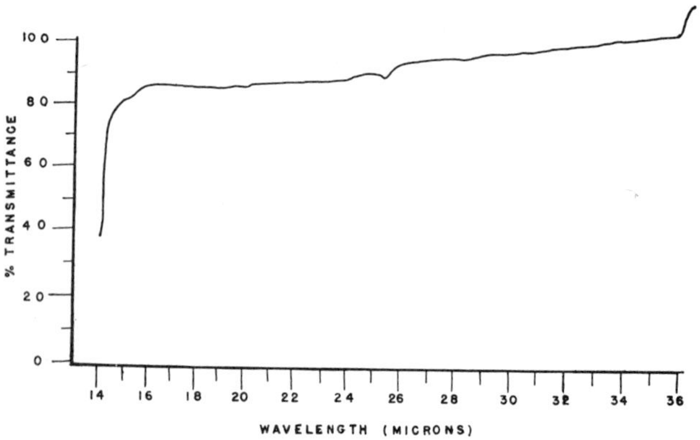

FIG. 1. FAR-INFRARED SPECTRUM OF A POLYETHYLENE DISK

The cover slips are now moved from the hot plate and allowed to cool. The top cover slip is then pried apart with the help of an ordinary safety razor blade. The film adhering to the other cover slip can then be peeled off using the blade. The disk appears translucent but is transparent in the region from 16-38 microns (Figure 1). They are about the size of potassium halide disks and can be placed in the potassium bromide disk holder when the spectrum is run. The disks can easily be attached to filing cards by the use of a small piece of cellophane tape when filed for future use. A distinct advantage of these polyethylene disks is their inertness. They are nonhygroscopic in marked contrast to potassium halide disks, which have to be stored under anhydrous conditions.

A good grade of powdered polyethylene can be prepared from low melting polyethylene pellets, such as Epolene C, (Eastman Products, Inc., Kingsport, Tenn.) by dissolving the pellets in hot organic solvents such as the xylenes, letting the solution cool to room temperature, and then precipitating the polyethylene with ethanol. The filtered product is washed with ethanol and dried. It appears somewhat cleaner and drier than commercial polyethylene powders. It is stored in a desiccator until used. Microthene, 620 (U. S. Industrial Chemical Co., Tuscola, Ill.) can be used directly without purification.

If the sample decomposes at a temperature below 120°, satisfactory disks can be prepared that melt at a lower temperature from mixtures of polyethylene and low melting (55° C) paraffin. The melting points and compositions

TABLE I. MELTING POINTS OF VARIOUS POLYETHYLENE-PARAFFIN MIXTURES

% Paraffin	*M.P. ° C*
0	100
30	78-82
40	72-78
46	70
60	68-69
80	55-57

are given in Table I. These samples were also transparent in the far-infrared region.

The authors thank Miss Benigna Smola for her assistance in performing the experiments with the various mixtures of polyethylene and paraffin.

Literature Cited

(1) For example, A. J. Baker, J. Phys. Chem. **61**, 450 (1957)
(2) E. K. Plyler, J. Res. Natl. Bur. Standards **41**, 125 (1948)

2.10 Cold Pressing of Polyethylene Disks. A New Technique.

C. Schiele and K. Halfar

Forschungsinstitut der Telefunken AG
Ulm / Donau (Western Germany)

Techniques for the preparation of polyethylene disks for the cesium iodide range were proposed recently in notes of May and Schwing *(1)* as well as Smethurst and Steele *(2)*. Both techniques apply heat to obtain translucent disks. Some disadvantages may result from heating during work with substances of low mp or with easily decomposed organics. For this reason we were in need of a highly linear polyethylene which would produce translucent disks at room temperature without application of heat. It has been found, that Vestolen A 120 powder of the Chemical Works Hüls (Western Germany) satisfies our demands fully. The data for this highly linear polyethylene in Table I were supplied by CWH.

For the preparation of disks, commercial Vestolen A 120 powder was recrystallized twice from boiling petroleum benzine, b. p. 100-140° C; the filtered product

TABLE I. DATA OF VESTOLEN A 120

Molecular weight	about 50.000
Crystallinity (X-ray analysis)	about 85%
Methyl groups	0.8-1.4 / 1000 C
Chain double bonds	<0.02 / 1000 C
Vinyl double bonds	0.05-0.1 / 1000 C
Vinylidene double bonds	0.03-0.05 / 1000 C

TABLE II. THICKNESS AND TRANSMISSION OF DISKS

Vestolen A 120 (mg)	*Thickness of the resulting disks (mm)*	*Transmission (%)* 250 K	300 K	500 K	650 K
40	0.15	82	89	87	84
50	0.17	82	88	86	84
60	0.21	80	87	86	83
80	0.26	80	86	85	80
100	0.31	78	86	84	78

washed with petroleum benzine, b.p. 50-70° C; and air dried. Using the recrystallized material in a 22 mm die and exerting about 300 kp/cm^2 for two min., the disks had the characteristics shown in Table II.

The transmission could be improved somewhat by exerting pressure for more than two min., as shown in Table III.

A comparison of spectra resulting from potassium iodide disks and Vestolen A 120 disks is shown in Figures 1 and 2. The equivalence of this new technique and the

TABLE III. TRANSMISSION OF 80 MG DISKS

Time (min)	*Thickness of the resulting disks (mm)*	*Transmission (%)* 250 K	300 K	500 K	650 K
2	0.26	79	86	84	80
5	0.26	81	88	85	81
15	0.26	82	89	86	82

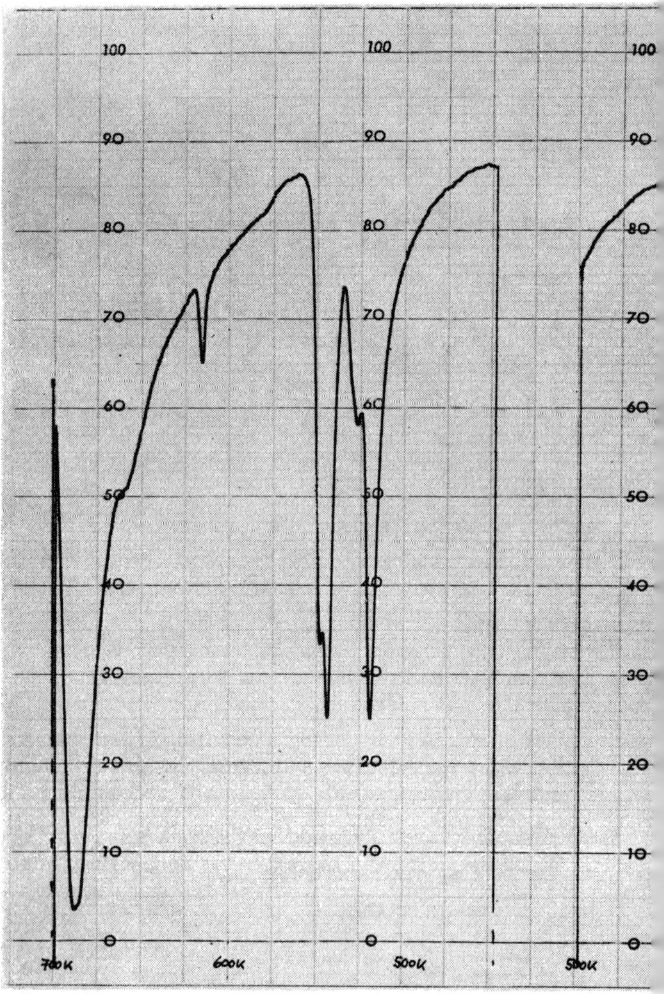

FIG. 1. SOLVENT: POTASSIUM IODIDE (120

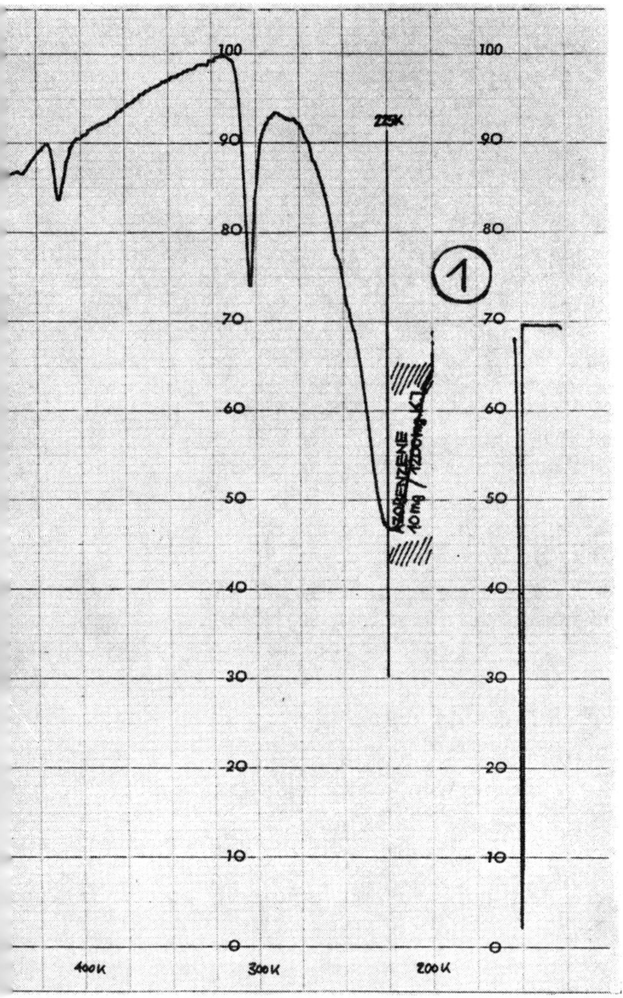

MG). SAMPLE: AZOBENZENE (10 MG).

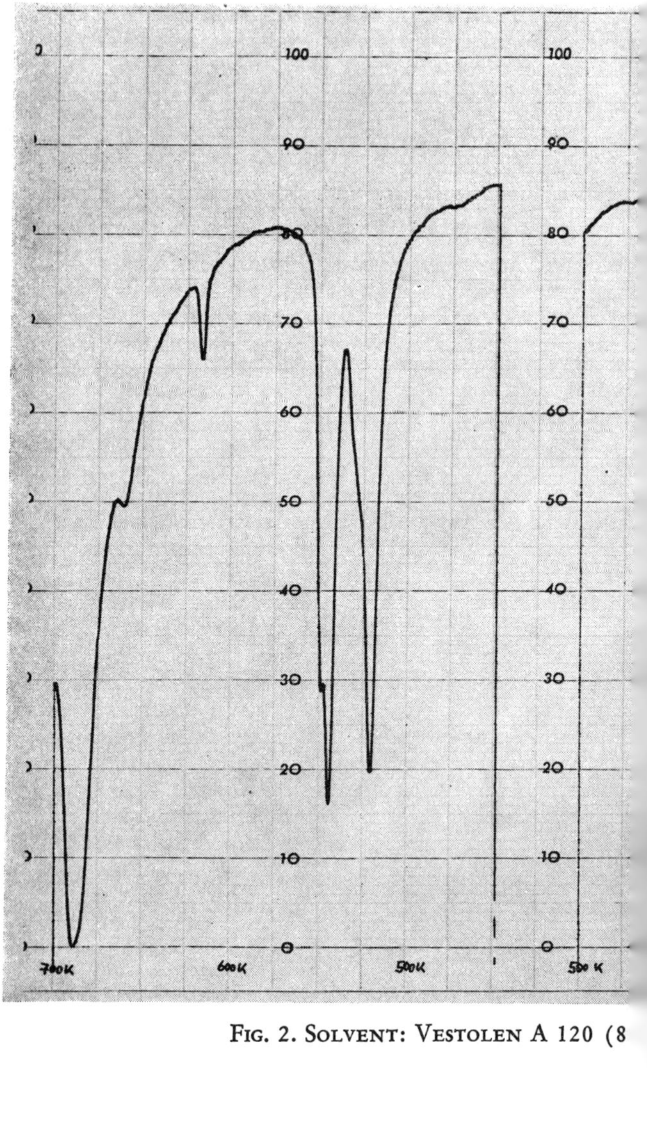

FIG. 2. SOLVENT: VESTOLEN A 120 (8

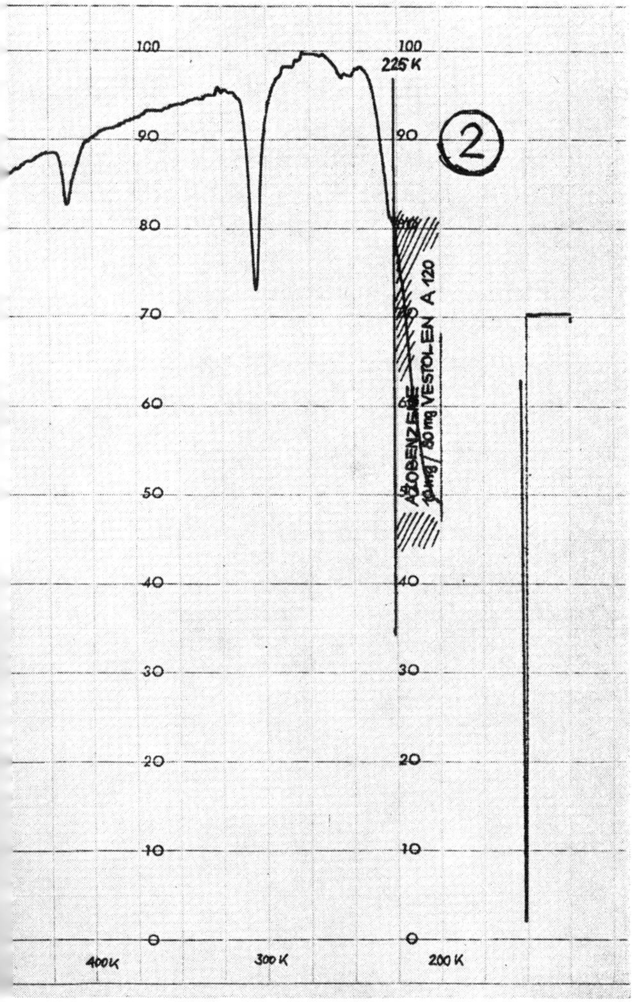

G). SAMPLE: AZOBENZENE (10 MG).

potassium iodide pellet technique may be clearly seen. The use of Vestolen A 120 or another suitable polyethylene yields a higher transmission in the 225-275 K range.

All spectra were scanned on a Beckman IR 7 spectrophotometer with cesium iodide prism-grating interchange.

We are indebted to Dr. O. Ambros for this brand of polyethylene.

Literature Cited

(1) L. May and K. J. Schwing, APPLIED SPECTROSCOPY **17,** 166 (1963)

(2) B. Smethurst and D. Steele, SPECTROCHIM. ACTA **20,** 242 (1964)

2.11 Polyethylene Cell Technique In Infrared Spectroscopy

Edward F. Ferrand, Jr.
The Cooper Union, New York 3, New York

Inexpensive polyethylene cells can be used to obtain the infrared spectra of mulls, liquids, aqueous solutions and commercial products. The precautions used for the safety of expensive cells are not needed with polyethylene cells.

In the preparation of sample cells from mulls of minerals, severe damage to salt windows sometimes occurs because of the presence of abrasive material in the mineral. To avoid this possibility a technique was developed which finds useful application with many types of samples.

Figure 1 describes the preparation of cells for mulls and for liquids. If cardboard is used for the holder, the hole may be cut conveniently by use of a cork borer. In the liquid-holding cell, heat sealing of the edges would be an improvement. The spectrum of polyethylene film is not too different from that of the paraffin oil mulling agent

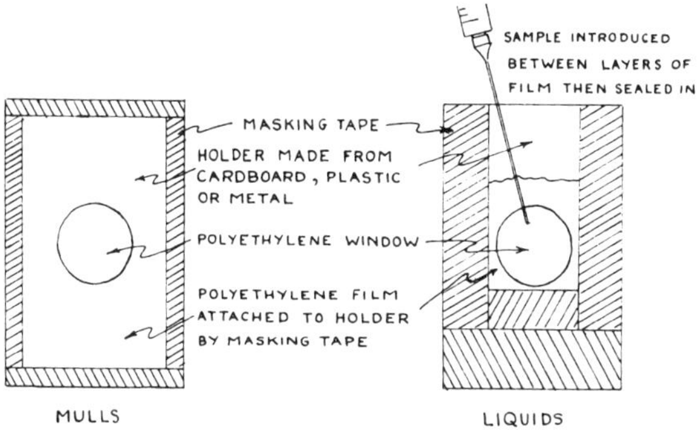

FIG. 1. POLYETHYLENE CELLS

(Figure 2*); however, each batch of film should be checked, and the possibility of additives contained in the film contaminating liquid samples should be considered. The film used to prepare the spectra presented was obtained from dry-cleaners garment bags.

*Spectra were measured with a Perkin-Elmer Model 221 Infrared Spectrophotometer.

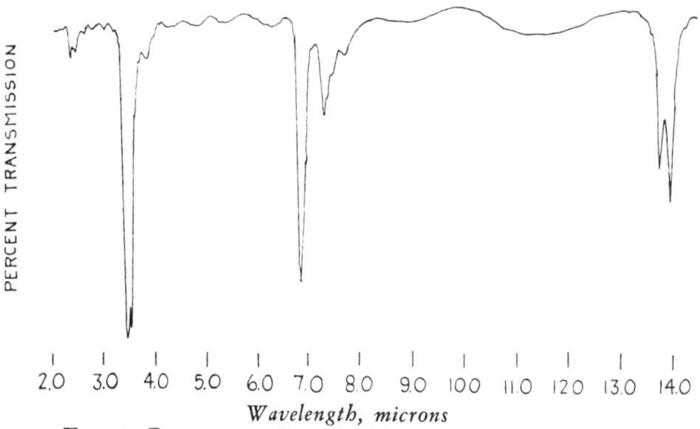

FIG. 2. PARAFFIN OIL ON POLYETHYLENE FILM

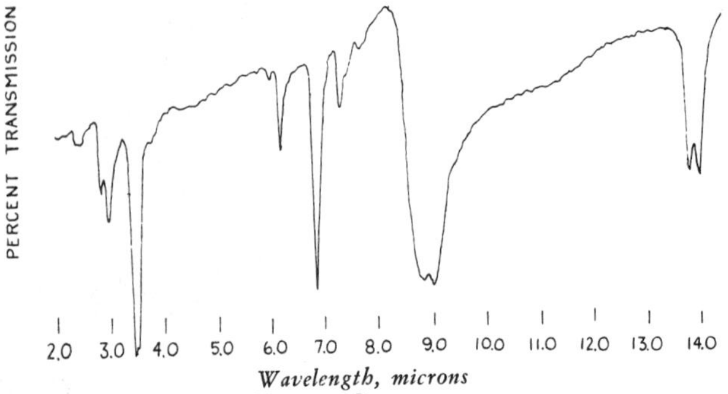

FIG. 3. SELENITE

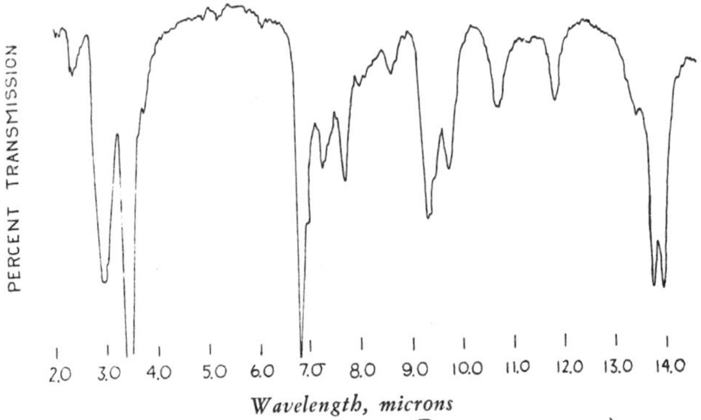

FIG. 4. 2-CHLORETHANOL (POLYETHYLENE)

The sample was mulled in the usual manner, and then transferred to the cell by means of rotating the pestle end with adhering mull against the window. The sample thickness can be readily adjusted after placing in the beam by further use of the pestle and absorbent tissue. A good starting point at 2.0 microns is 50% transmission. As usual the more evenly distributed the mull and the finer mulled the sample, the more detail will be found in the spectrum. The spectrum of minerals is particularly susceptible to improvement by further grinding. No difficulty from interference fringes was encountered. Figure 3 is an example of a mineral spectrum using the polyethylene cell technique.

The technique with liquids is slightly more difficult except with viscous liquids; however, all but the most

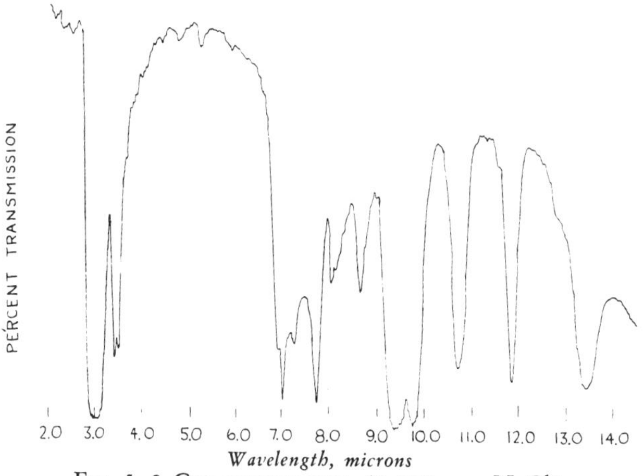

FIG. 5. 2-CHLORETHANOL (0.025 mm NaCl)

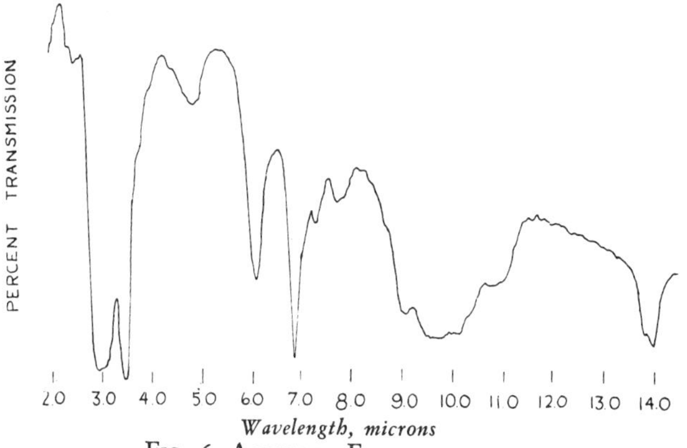

FIG. 6. AQUEOUS FORMALDEHYDE

volatile liquids can be used. With a little practice it is possible to adjust the cell thickness so as to get the type of spectrum desired. Figures 4 and 5 show 2-chloroethanol run on polyethylene and in a 0.025 mm NaCl cell. It is interesting to note the improved detail between 9.0 and 10.0 microns that was obtained with the polyethylene.

Figure 6 is a spectrum of 40% aqueous formaldehyde in a polyethylene cell. Using this technique, studies of infrared spectra of aqueous systems can be made with very little difficulty in cells so inexpensive that they can be discarded after use.

2.12 Polyethylene Microcells for Infrared Analysis

V. J. Filipic and D. Burdick

Eastern Regional Research Laboratory*
Philadelphia, Pennsylvania

Polyethylene film has been used recently for preparing cells for infrared analysis *(1, 2)*. We have successfully adapted this technique for samples as small as three μl for liquids and three mg for solids. Also, we have found that compensation of spectral bands for the polyethylene may be achieved by use of an appropriately made blank, thus increasing the spectral usefulness of the technique.

For liquid samples, polyethylene microcells, approximately 3 x 13 mm, were made as follows: A piece of Handi-Wrap†, approximately 10 x 40 mm, was folded to give a double sheet 10 x 20 mm. The sheet was then clamped between the narrow faces of two brass plates, 3 x 15 x 15 mm, with the folded edge perpendicular to

*Eastern Utilization Research and Development Division, Agricultural Research Service, United States Department of Agriculture

†Mention of a specific commercial product does not constitute endorsement by the United States Department of Agriculture.

the broad face of the plates and about two mm from one end of the butted faces. Both sides of the folded sheet were heat sealed with a small electric soldering iron set to an appropriate temperature by a variable transformer. The cell was removed from between the brass plates and the sample was introduced into the open end by means of a ten μl Hamilton (The Hamilton Co., Inc., Cat. No. 701-N) syringe. Finally, the top of the cell was gently held between the smooth jaws of small cutting pliers and sealed with the hot soldering iron.

Spectra were run at the fast scan on the Perkin Elmer model 237 infrared spectrophotometer. The KBr disc holder supplied with the instrument was adapted to hold the microcell by placing a metal shield (0.7 mm thick and 1.35 cm diam. with a 1 x 8 mm slit) into the recessed end of the holder. The microcell was then centered over this opening, and the holder assembled. The metal shield permits about 40% of the radiation to be transmitted. Since the KBr disc holder is placed close to the focal point of the incident light, a beam condenser is not necessary. Placing a similar polyethylene cell in another KBr disc

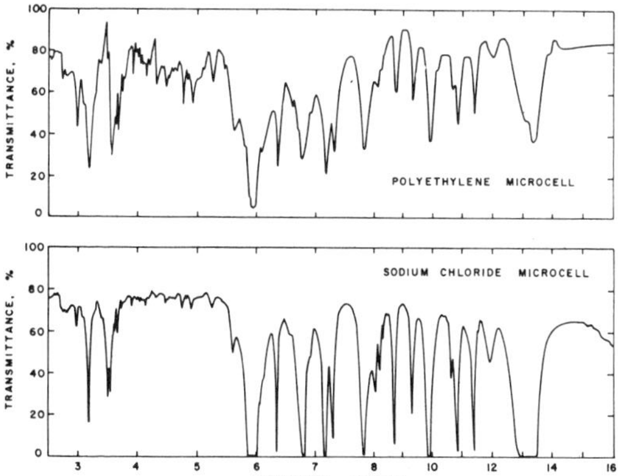

FIG. 1. INFRARED SPECTRUM OF FURFURAL IN POLYETHYLENE AND NaCl MICROCELLS

holder in the reference side of the instrument permits compensation for the few absorption bands resulting from the polyethylene. However, the I_0 line is somewhat irregular due (probably) to imperfections in the surface of the polyethylene film. All polyethylene used was taken from an adjacent area of a sheet of Handi-Wrap to obtain material of uniform thickness. It is advisable to run an I_0 line to insure that the polyethylene absorption bands are adequately compensated prior to filling the cell for analysis.

A second type of cell was used for solid and viscous liquid samples. A piece of polyethylene, approximately 4 x 4 cm, was stretched over the smoothly polished end of a brass pipe (7/16 in. o.d., 5/16 in. i.d., and one in. long) and held in place by a rubber "O" ring. The sample dissolved in a suitable solvent was placed dropwise on the stretched polyethylene surface and gently heated with an infrared lamp to remove the solvent. A second piece of polyethylene similarly mounted was butted against the film holding the sample and the edges of the two films were sealed with a soldering iron as described above. In attaching this cell to the KBr disc holder, a metal shield having a 5/16-in. diam. hole was used.

A spectrum of authentic furfural obtained on a three μl sample using a polyethylene reference cell is compared in Figure 1 with a spectrum using a conventional NaCl microcell.

Due to imperfect sealing or vapor permeability of the polyethylene, some loss of material may occur with liquid samples during spectral scanning. Except for relatively volatile material, the extent of the loss is small and major bands in a full 2.5 to 15.0 micron scan can be obtained.

The technique offers an inexpensive means of obtaining adequate spectra for qualitative purposes of samples as small as three μl of liquid or three mg of solid. In fact, recognizable spectra can sometimes be obtained with only one mg of sample.

Literature Cited

(1) I. Cohen, J. Chem. Educ. **39,** 262 (1962)
(2) E. F. Ferrand, Jr., APPLIED SPECTROSCOPY **16,** 22 (1962)

A New Technique for Preparing Films on Cell Window for Infrared Absorption Spectroscopy* 2.13

Huo-Ping Pan and G. J. Edwards

Agricultural Experiment Station, University of Florida
Gainesville, Florida

The preparation of films for infrared spectroscopy has previously been accomplished by adding dropwise a solution of the desired compound in a volatile solvent to the cell window. The difficulties encountered with this technique are: 1) during solvent evaporation the solute is concentrated along the edge of the film and consequently the film is not uniform in thickness; 2) the process of preparing the film is time-consuming and tedious; and 3) the compound is difficult to recover from the cell window. A new method was developed to eliminate these difficulties.

---

*Florida Agricultural Experiment Station Journal Series, No. 1479

FIG. 1. CAPILLARY PIPETTE PLUGGED WITH TWO COTTON WADS

This method employs a disposable capillary pipette (Figure 1) similar to that used by Barreto *(1)* for filtration. The pipette is prepared by pulling out an eight mm soft glass tubing in a Bunsen burner. The capillaries on both ends are about 1 mm i.d. One end is plugged with a slightly extruded wad of purified absorbent cotton, and the other end is open. The pipette is filled automatically by capillary action. The amount of solution filled is controlled by tilting the pipette. After the solution has been filled in the capillary, it is swabbed on the cell window under a hair drier.

If the solution contains insoluble material, the end is plugged with two successive wads. The wad near the tip captures the insoluble material. After the capillary is filled with the solution, the wad near the tip is broken off at a mark previously made with a file. The application of the solution onto the cell window is the same as described above.

Literature Cited

(1) R. C. R. Barreto, J. CHROMATOG. **6**, 278 (1961)

2.14 A New Way of Casting Polymer Films

J. J. Elliott and D. R. Winans

Esso Research and Engineering Company
Analytical Research Division
P. O. Box 121
Linden, New Jersey 07036

A new method has been developed for the casting of polymer films for infrared analysis. Existing methods, such as hot-pressing the solid polymer or placing drops of a solution on a salt-plate and allowing the solvent to evaporate, have a number of serious disadvantages. The former is impractical for very thin films, whilst the latter rarely gives a sample of even thickness. Recently, a more satisfactory method was reported *(1)* but even this appears limited if the solubility of the polymer is very low.

We have found that the use of an airbrush to spray a solution of the polymer onto a salt plate gives a highly satisfactory film. With a little experience, a very even sample can be cast and, in addition, it can be built up to any desired thickness. This is extremely useful when one wishes to compensate in the reference beam for a known component in a two-component polymer. Moreover, polymers of low solubility can be readily cast for large volumes of solution can be handled without difficulty.

The airbrush used is a Paasche Type H3 operated with dry nitrogen or air at about 30 psi. It is advisable to replace the small plastic gasket in the nozzle of the brush with one of Teflon. Films have been successfully cast using a wide variety of solvents, including chloroform, carbon tetrachloride, carbon disulfide and cyclohexane. The solution used should be sufficiently dilute to be readily mobile for too high a viscosity may not give the very fine spray required for an even film. Most of the solvent evaporates during the spraying; however, to remove the last traces, it is still advisable to warm the film beneath an infrared lamp for about 15 minutes.

Literature Cited

(1) Hou-Ping Pan and G. J. Edwards, APPLIED SPECTROSCOPY, **17**, 74 (1963)

2.15 An Optical Accessory for Obtaining the Infrared Spectra of Very Thin Films

R. W. Hannah*

Aluminum Company of America, Alcoa Research Laboratories
New Kensington, Pennsylvania

In 1959, Francis and Ellison *(1)* described a procedure for obtaining the infrared spectra of monomolecular and thicker layers of fatty acids and fatty acid salts on various metallic substrates by a multireflection technique. To accommodate the accessory optics and the associated increase in length of optical path between the source and photom-

*Present address: The Perkin-Elmer Corporation, Norwalk, Conn.

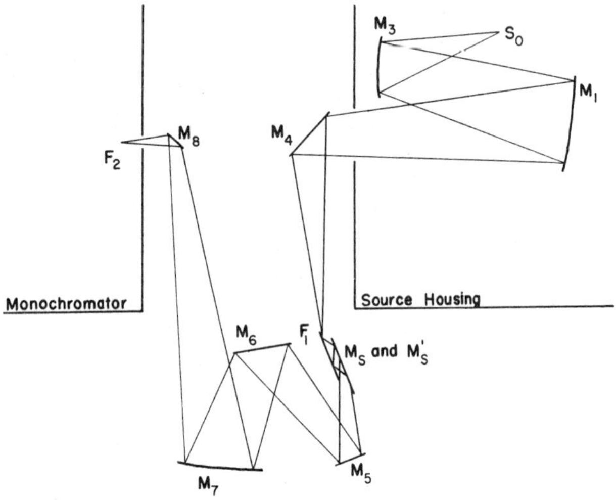

FIG. 1. SCHEMATIC DIAGRAM OF THE OPTICAL ARRANGEMENT FOR THE MULTI-REFLECTANCE ACCESSORY

eter section of a Perkin-Elmer Model 21, the source optics were modified. Such a modification is undesirable if the instrument is to be used for transmission or specular reflectance measurements. Therefore, an optical design was derived which would permit installation and removal of the accessory without requiring undue changes in the basic instrument.

Although some theoretical knowledge has been obtained with regard to the properties of extremely thin films, the primary applications have been directed toward the identification and, in particular instances, determination of the thicknesses of films present on aluminum. The minimum thickness for organic coatings has been found to be in the neighborhood of 200 A if one wishes to identify the species and approximately 100 A if the thickness of a known material is to be determined.

The theory is well developed in the paper by Francis and Ellison *(1)* and the associated references and need not be discussed in detail here. Their general conclusions indicate that only the transition moment perpendicular to the surface will interact with the incident radiation to produce an absorption spectrum and that the amount of absorption will be significant only at high angles of incidence. Francis and Ellison have demonstrated experimentally the veracity of these conclusions for organic films.

These conclusions and the size of the sample space of the Perkin-Elmer model 21 for the most part determine the optical design. One additional characteristic was considered necessary. The optical arrangement must be capable of routine installation and removal with no modification of the basic instrument.

Figure 1 is a schematic diagram of the sample half of the resulting accessory, while Figure 2 shows the resulting unit mounted in the Perkin-Elmer model 221. In Figure 1, M_4, M_5, M_6, and M_8 are 38 mm x 45 mm plane mirrors, mirror M_7 is an 80 mm diam. spherical mirror having a radius of curvature of 294 mm, and M_s and M_s' are the sample. Points F_1 and F_2 are conjugate focal points for

FIG. 2. PHOTOGRAPH OF THE MULTI-REFLECTANCE ACCESSORY MOUNTED IN THE PERKIN-ELMER MODEL 221

M_7 and are 294 mm from the center of M_7. All mirrors and mounts except the sample mirrors and mounts may be obtained from the instrument manufacturer.* The sample mount (Figure 2) is of special design incorporating

*Perkin-Elmer Corp., Norwalk, Conn.

the prerequisites that the samples be reproducibly parallel and ⅛-in. apart, and that horizontal, vertical, and angular adjustments within limits be available. All mirrors are mounted on a ¾-in. aluminum plate held in position in the instrument by ¼-in. countersunk Allen-head bolts, which pass through brass support posts and placed to fit the tapped holes for the Perkin-Elmer specular reflectance accessory. Leveling and bracing legs have been added to the plate at four locations (Figure 2).

As Francis and Ellison indicate, a polarizer will increase the sensitivity appreciably. A pile-of-plates polarizer similar to that described by Bird and Shurcliff *(2)* was

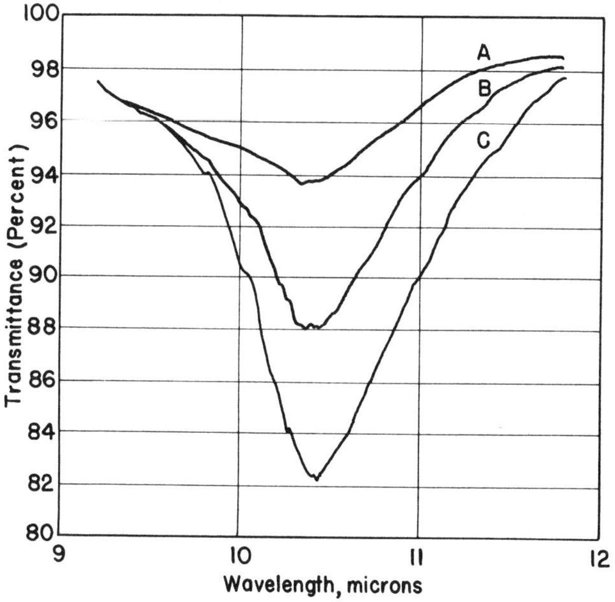

FIG. 3. REFLECTION CURVES FOR BARRIER TYPE OXIDE ON ALUMINUM

Ordinate Scale Expansion, 5X; A—28 A, B—56 A, C—84 A

constructed and when in use is mounted on the mask immediately in front of the entrance slit. In addition, the infrared instrument must be equipped with the ordinate expansion accessory, since the absorbance levels are, in general, less than 0.1 unit.

If the samples were heavy enough to support themselves, approximately 2″ x 2″ samples were cut and placed in the sample mount. Foil samples, however, were mounted with the aid of two-sided masking tape, on 2″ x 2″ photographic slides, which were then inserted into the sample holder. Spectra were obtained at 1X and at ordinate scale expansion factors of 5X, 10X, or 20X, depending upon the intensity of the band or bands at 1X.

Samples of barrier-type, anodically-formed oxide of known thickness were prepared by the method of Hunter and Fowle (3) in ammonium tartrate electrolyte. According to their work, the thickness of the oxide layer produced is directly proportional to the anodizing voltage. For the electrolyte mentioned, 14 A of barrier-type oxide are produced per applied volt. Several samples were prepared by removing all natural film and then applying 2-, 4-, and 6-v coatings on the surfaces of two 2″ x 2″ specimens and the spectra determined. Only one band near 10.4 microns was observed in the spectra. Reflection curves for several thicknesses of barrier oxide are shown in Figure 3. The plot of absorbance at 10.4 microns is linear and passes through the origin.

Monomolecular and thicker layers of barium stearate were prepared on aluminum sheet using a hydrophil balance. Oleic acid, which yielded a driving force of 30 dynes was employed as the piston oil. The pile-of-plates polarizer was used in obtaining the spectra. Figure 4 is typical of the spectra and is indicative of the sensitivity.

The sensitivity, versatility, and convenience of the accessory are quite satisfactory. Under well-defined conditions, the lower limit of detection has been shown to be near 50 A for organic films and near 10 A for barrier type anodically formed oxide, assuming a film having about the same density as the bulk solid. If identification of an un-

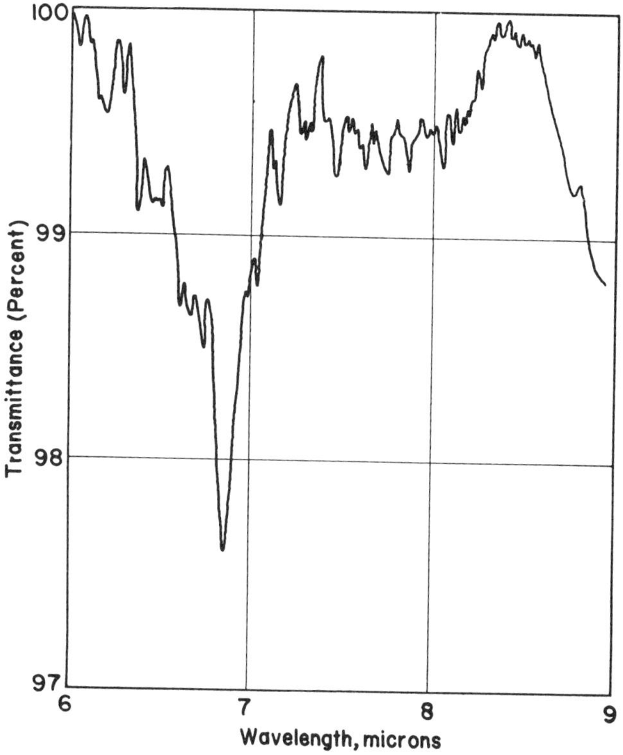

FIG. 4. THREE MONOLAYERS OF BARIUM STEARATE ON ALUMINUM

Ordinate Scale Expansion, 20X

known coating is to be made, the lower limit is somewhat higher, depending on the system, and approaches 200 A.

The accessory is limited to those substrates having reasonably high reflectivities in the infrared; this includes most of the metals. It can be seen that sampling involved in the determination or identification of very thin coatings is reduced to a minimum. The principal precaution which must be observed involves maintaining the cleanliness of the samples.

The band observed for barrier-type, anodically-formed oxides is not assigned. No other bands were observed in these spectra in the 2 to 25 micron region except for comparatively thick, 300 to 500 A, barrier anodic coatings, when bands characteristic of the electrolyte may be observed. It is believed, however, that the band near 10.4 microns is related to an Al-O vibration and is characteristic of barrier oxide on aluminum.

In conclusion, direct observation of the infrared spectra of extremely thin films is a useful technique for both analytical and fundamental studies. Modification of the basic instrument according to Francis and Ellison's design has possibly restricted its use. The design presented here overcomes this objection, with no sacrifice in sensitivity, and makes the observations nearly as routine as obtaining a transmission spectrum.

The author acknowledges the assistance of Mr. James R. Ryan and Mr. M. S. Hunter and the support and encouragement of Dr. M. L. Moss.

Literature Cited

(1) S. A. Francis and A. H. Ellison, J. Opt. Soc. Am. **49,** 131 (1959)

(2) G. R. Bird and W. A. Shurcliff, Ibid. **49,** 235 (1959)

(3) M. S. Hunter and P. Fowle, J. Electrochem. Soc. **101**, 481 (1954)

An Infrared Cell Assembly for Volatile Solids 2.16

George J. Janz and Steven S. Danyluk

Department of Chemistry, Rensselaer Polytechnic Institute, Troy, N.Y.

In the course of studies in progress on the properties of the hydrogen halides in anhydrous polar organic solvents*, crystalline substrates have been isolated which frequently are unstable on exposure to the atmosphere, decomposing rapidly with the evolution of the hydrogen halide and reformation of the solvent. The conventional pressed window techniques are thus not applicable for the study of such solids. To meet the need for a controlled atmosphere cell suitable for study of readily volatile solids, the infrared assembly described in this note was designed.

---

*Part of a program of study on the properties of simple electrolytes in polar organic solvents, supported in part by the Atomic Energy Commission through the Division of Chemistry under Contract No. AT (30-1)-1999.

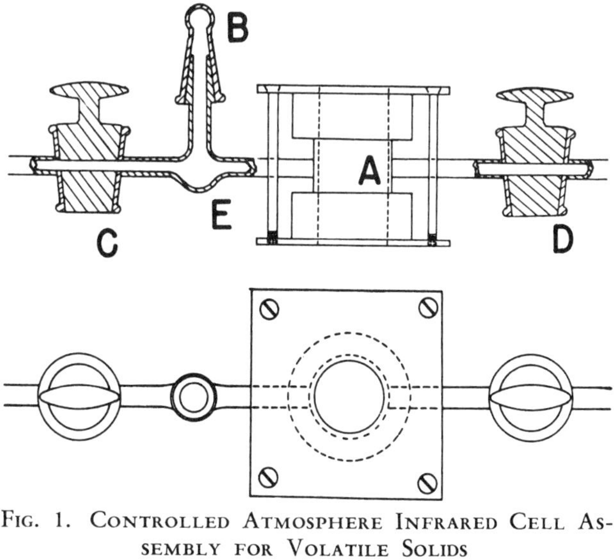

FIG. 1. CONTROLLED ATMOSPHERE INFRARED CELL ASSEMBLY FOR VOLATILE SOLIDS

Two views of the assembly, basically simple in design, are illustrated in Figure 1. It consists essentially of a 22 mm i.d. and 15 mm wide pyrex tube, A, closed at the optically flat ends by two polished salt windows mounted in a brass frame. In the work with the HBr solids, for example, KBr windows are used. The contact between the windows and glass cell body is coated with glyptal cement to give a vacuum tight seal. Two 6 mm outlet tubes from A as shown were sealed by the one-way stopcocks, C, and D. A 7/25 standard taper cone and socket joint, B, sealed on a T arm above the small receptacle, E, blown on the lower portion of the sidearm outlet tube completed the design.

The assembly is flushed with dry nitrogen prior to each measurement. The pure anhydrous solvent is added via B to cover the bottom of the receptacle (0.10 ml). Atmospheric contamination is minimized in this operation by closing D and venting the positive flow of nitrogen from C through B. With B sealed by the cap, a stream of the hydrogen halide, diluted with nitrogen, is admitted through C, and vented at D through a drying tube to the atmosphere until the formation of the crystalline addition compound at E is complete. The flow of the hydrogen halide is discontinued and the excess vapors are flushed away with a slow nitrogen stream. Stopcocks C and D are then sealed. A fine film of the compound is next sublimed onto the windows of the infrared cell, A, by gently warming the solid in E. After the spectrum has been obtained, the film on the windows can be readily removed by a nitrogen gas sweep, and a fresh layer can be formed for further study as described above. The assembly thus enables formation of the solid *in situ*, eliminating the hazards of atmospheric moisture contamination attendant with the conventional technique.

In this laboratory, the assembly has been used quite successfully for a study (1) of the infrared absorption spctrum of acetonitrile dihydrogen bromide, $CH_3CN \cdot 2HBr$, m.p. 86°C (sealed tube), which volatilizes rapidly on exposure to the atmosphere at room temperature with the reformation of HBr and CH_3CN. The method is generally applicable to volatile solids where strictly anhydrous conditions and controlled atmospheres are essential, and has the advantages of basic simplicity and inexpensive design.

Literature Cited

1. To be published elsewhere in detail

A Demountable Infrared Gas Cell 2.17

M. P. Brash, B. W. Burrell, J. S. Perkins

Avco RAD, Wilmington, Massachusetts

It is often desirable to determine what volatile products are evolved when materials are heated to moderate temperatures (about 250°C) in a controlled atmosphere. The present method accomplishes this analysis *in situ* in an infrared gas cell without the necessity of trapping, transferring, or handling the gases after they are evolved.

A standard 10-cm, glass body gas cell is modified to make a vacuum demountable cell as follows: The salt windows are removed from the cell, and the edges of the glass are ground smooth, flat, and parallel to each other. The windows are resealed to the body of the cell using Fluorolube H G wax, manufactured by Hooker Chemical Company, Niagara Falls, New York. Hanst *(1)* observed that cells sealed in this manner maintain a 0.01 micron vacuum. Since fluorolube is a grease and not a cement, the salt windows can now be readily removed to permit the introduction of a sample, and then resealed prior to evacuating or introducing an inert atmosphere. The cell can be heated with a heating tape wrapped around the glass body. Insulation should be used to prevent temperature fluctuations. The temperature can be monitored with a thermocouple, and products volatilized determined with an infrared spectrophotometer. After the scan is completed, the windows are taken off the cell, the sample removed, and the body and windows cleaned. The cell is then ready for the next material or can be reassembled for use as a regular gas cell.

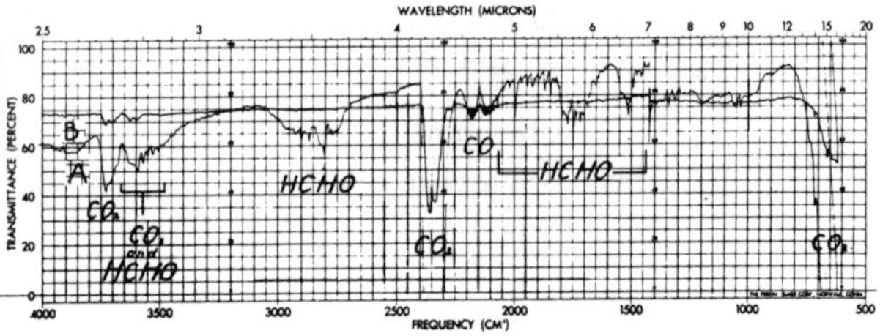

FIG. 1. INFRARED SPECTRA OF VOLATILES FROM PHENOL-FORMALDEHYDE POLYMER USING THE DEMOUNTABLE CELL

A—Volatiles at 200°C, ordinate expanded five fold, B—Same cell after standing 16 hr at room temperature, normal ordinate

The illustrative spectrum shows the gases evolved when a phenol-formaldehyde polymer was heated in the above cell to 200°C. The sample was powdered and placed in the cell, which was then evacuated to approximately 0.05 mm mercury at room temperature. The evacuated cell was then placed in its usual sample beam position in the spectrophotometer, heated to 200°C using the insulated heating tape connected to a variable autotransformer, and the spectrum was recorded while at this temperature. To insure detection of minor decomposition products, the spectrum was recorded using a five-fold ordinate expansion, and this is shown as curve A of the figure. Carbon dioxide, carbon monoxide, and formaldehyde are identified using this technique. No C-F bands, which might be attributable to the Fluorolube wax used for sealing the salt windows, were detectible even at this elevated temperature and expanded ordinate scale. The cell was left overnight at room temperature and then rerun with an unexpanded ordinate to determine if the cell was gas tight. Curve B shows that the same components were still present.

Literature Cited

(1) P. Hanst, PERKIN-ELMER INSTR. NEWS **5,** No. 3 (1954)

Small Volume Long Path Infrared Cell for Liquids 2.18

D. S. Erley, B. H. Blake and W. J. Potts

Chemical Physics Research Laboratory, The Dow Chemical Company, Midland, Michigan

Stewart, et al *(1)* have described a method for the analysis of trace organic compounds in the blood. An absorption cell has been designed which is particularly useful in this type of work and which may be suited to other applications as well. The cell is easily assembled, is less subject to leakage than most infrared cells, and solution transfer losses are minimized by its use.

Figure 1 shows the construction details of the cell. Two crystal windows, *a*, are separated by a *Teflon* spacer, *b*, which is milled out in the center to form the sample chamber. If the windows and spacer are carefully flattened before assembly, a tight seal will form with the usual pressure clamp. However, if extreme flatness is not attained, thin polyethylene spacers between the teflon and the windows (not shown) will insure a good seal. In either case the cell assembly should be warmed under a heat lamp after assembly so that the polymer may flow slightly. A 6-inch syringe needle is cut about ½ in. from the syringe fitting, and the two sections thus formed, *c* and *d*, are inserted through opposite sides of the spacer into the sample chamber. A pressure fit has sufficient mechanical strength and there will be no leakage. The auxiliary spacers, *e*, form a cushion between the crystal windows and the brass frame, *f*. The area of the sample chamber is 1 inch x 11/16 inch, which will not vignette the sample beam of most instruments. Further reduction in area could undoubtedly be obtained with beam condensing units, but this size was felt to provide a reasonable compromise between small volume and convenience of use. The approximate volumes of cells of various thickness are; 2mm, 1ml, 4 mm, 1.9 ml, 8 mm, 3.7 ml, and 16 mm, 7.3 ml.

The cell is filled by inverting it, placing a syringe in the syringe fitting, and drawing the solution into the chamber through the long needle. The needle is then with-

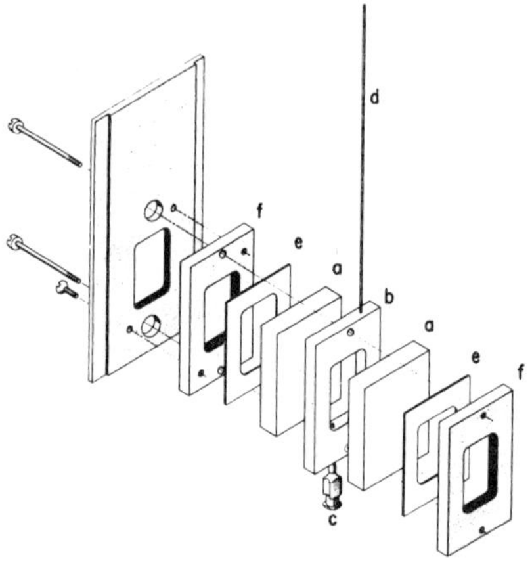

FIG. 1. LONG PATH INFRARED ABSORPTION CELL

a—Crystal windows, b—Teflon spacer, c—Syringe fitting, d—Filling needle, e—Cushioning spacer, f—Brass frame

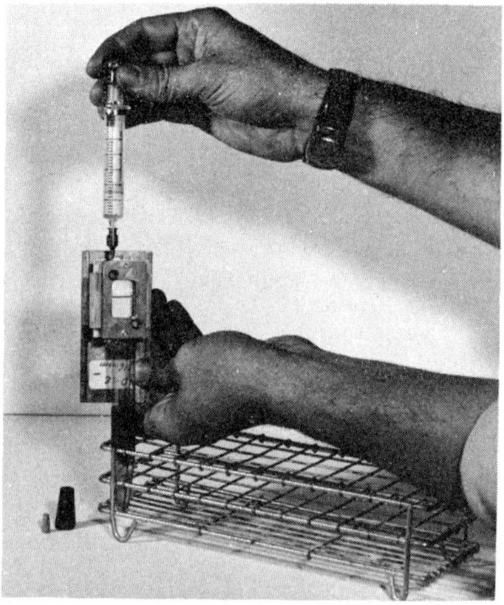

FIG. 2. FILLING ASSEMBLED CELL WITH CS_2 EXTRACT FROM BLOOD

drawn from the solution and inserted into a rubber stopper to prevent leakage. A small cork is placed in the syringe fitting. In solvent extractions of aqueous solutions such as blood, the needle may be inserted through the aqueous layer into the solvent layer as shown in Figure 2, and the solution drawn directly into the cell. In this way separation of the two layers is not necessary and transfer losses are minimized. The use of AgCl or BaF_2 as a window material reduces the possibility of cell damage if a few drops of the aqueous layer should be inadvertently drawn into the cell. Since the cell is filled directly through the spacer, no filling holes need be drilled in the crystal windows—a particularly time consuming job with hard crystals such as BaF_2. The associated problem of leakage around these holes is also eliminated.

The cell has proven to be most useful when extracting anesthetics and common industrial solvents from the blood where the ratio of sample to solvent must be kept high to insure adequate sensitivity and where the possibility of fractionation would be present at each transfer operation.

Literature Cited

(1) R. D. Stewart, D. S. Erley, T. R. Torkelson, and C. L. Hake, NATURE **184**, 192 (1959)

Long Path Infrared Microcell 2.19

D. S. Erley

Chemical Physics Research Laboratory, The Dow Chemical Company, Midland, Michigan

The increasing demand for the analysis of trace organic chemicals in blood and urine by the solvent extraction technique described previously *(1)* has led to an investigation of methods to facilitate sample handling and improve efficiency *(2)*. In order to extend the method to the smaller laboratory animals it was found necessary to reduce the sample volume from 5 ml to 1 or 2 ml. In addition, it was desirable to take serial samples from an animal or human subject during the course of a chemical exposure so that changes of its concentration in the blood could be measured. This, too, necessitated smaller samples so that the total volume of blood lost would be minimized. The cell described below has a length of 10 mm and requires only 0.5 ml of solution. This gives a sensitivity of 1 - 10 ppm (minimum amount detectable) for many organic chemicals in a 1 ml sample of blood or urine.

Figure 1 shows a machine drawing of the cell. A 7/8-in. diam. rod is recessed on both ends to accommodate a 5/8-in. diam. window. A slot milled thru the center of the rod forms a sample chamber which is 10 mm in length and 1/8″ x 1/2″ in cross section. The cell itself does not vignette the beam of a Perkin Elmer Model 137 spectrometer when inserted into the microcell holder, but some losses result from reflection and scattering of the windows. The filling holes in the top of the cell are offset to permit the cell to slide fully into the microcell holder and are stoppered with small teflon plugs.

Two types of windows were tried; KBr pressed plates and AgCl discs. The former were cemented in place with an epoxy resin*, but it was difficult to obtain a good seal without getting some of the resin into the beam area. They also became cloudy after a short time as the solutions were saturated with water.

AgCl windows were cut with a No. 11 cork borer from a 1 mm sheet. Since AgCl is somewhat plastic, it may be sealed to the cell body by tapping the windows gently around the edge so that they spread out to form a pressure seal. The change in path length caused by slight distortions of the window is negligible in cells of 10 mm total length. A silver or Teflon cell body is used to prevent reaction of the silver chloride windows with metals

---

*Araldite Type 102, with Hardener 951, Ciba Co., Inc., 627 Greenwich St., New York, N. Y.

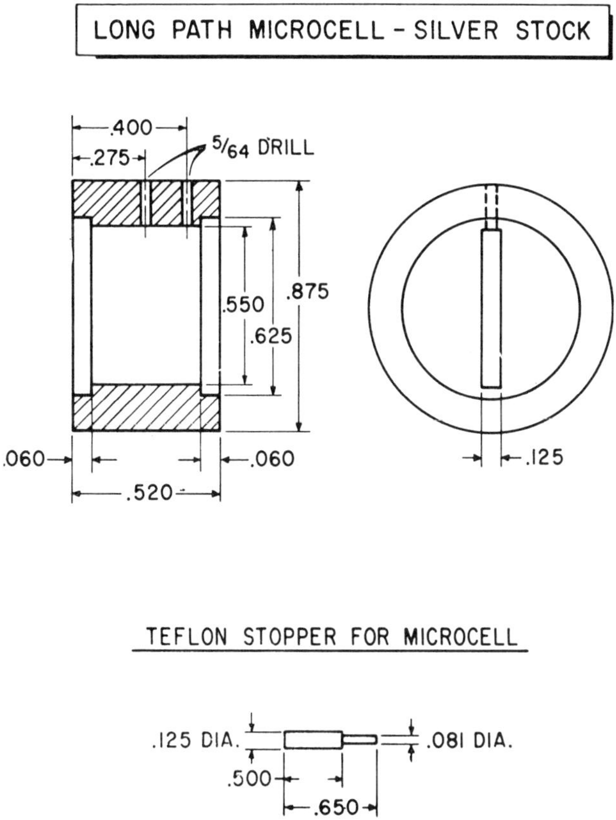

FIG. 1. MACHINE DRAWING OF MICROCELL. ALL DIMENSIONS IN INCHES.

higher in the electromotive series. Of these, silver (cost approximately \$3.25/cell) has been found more satisfactory as it acts as a heat sink and minimizes the tendency of the solvent to boil in the cell. If Teflon is used, or for extended scans a silver cell, boiling may be virtually eliminated by placing a standard 1 mm cell filled with solvent

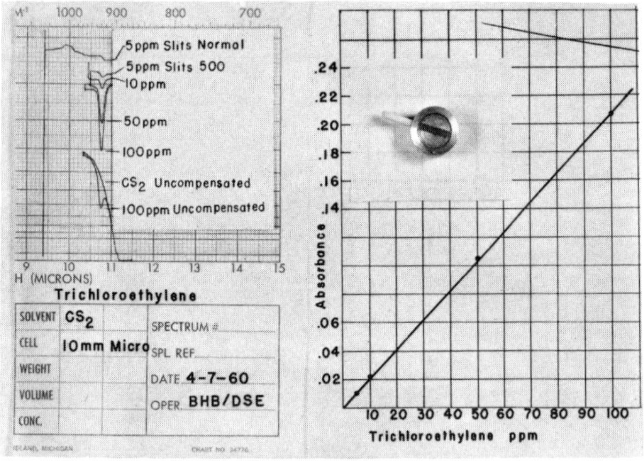

FIG. 2. SENSITIVITY AND ANALYTICAL PERFORMANCE OF MICROCELL USED WITH PERKIN ELMER MODEL 137 SPECTROMETER.

between the source and the sample cell. This acts as a filter to remove that radiation which is causing the boiling.

In practice a 2 ml blood sample is shaken for about 1 min with an equal volume of CS_2 and centrifuged to separate the layers. This yields enough solution to fill the cell twice. Satisfactory results can also be obtained using a 1 ml sample and 1 ml of solvent, but the agitation must be gentle to prevent excessive formation of emulsion. The spectra are usually obtained with a duplicate cell filled with solvent in the reference beam. This requires that the instrument slits be opened to regain the energy lost to solvent absorption. Figure 2 shows a series of standards scanned at the analytical wavelength for trichloroethylene, the resulting quantitative curve, and a photograph of the cell.

Literature Cited

(1) R. D. Stewart, D. S. Erley, T. R. Torkelson, and C. L. Hake, NATURE **184,** 192 (1959)

(2) D. S. Erley, B. H. Blake, and W. J. Potts, APPLIED SPECTROSCOPY **14,** 108 (1960)

A Sealed Infrared Absorption Cell of Variable Path Length 2.20

E. M. Banas and R. R. Hopkins

Research and Development Department, American Oil Company, Whiting, Indiana

A new infrared absorption cell of variable path length has been devised. As shown in Figure 1, it is similar in

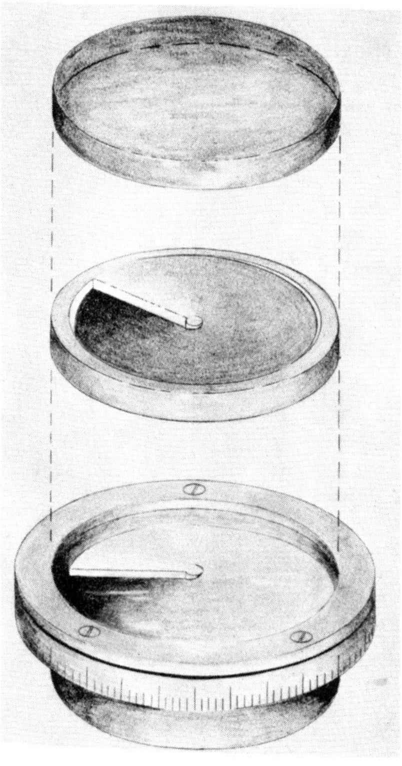

FIG. 1. CELL ASSEMBLY

construction to cells of fixed path length but has a sample volume in the shape of a circular wedge. The inner surface of one of the windows has impressed into it a circular inclined plane. The outer edge of this surface is flat so that it can be sealed to the flat surface of the other window. The infrared beam passes through the cell midway between its axis and the outside edge. Thus, the effective sample thickness varies as the cell is rotated about its axis. The rotation is measured by a graduated circular scale. No attempt is made to obtain a quantitative sample thickness because the window surfaces enclosing the sample are not parallel.

The depressed surface was obtained by a new technique: plastic deformation of a flat single crystal of an alkali halide. Crystal surfaces were first ground and polished. The crystal was then placed on a flat hot plate, and the temperature was raised at a rate 110°C/hr to 400°C. A metal die, heated to the same temperature as the crystal,

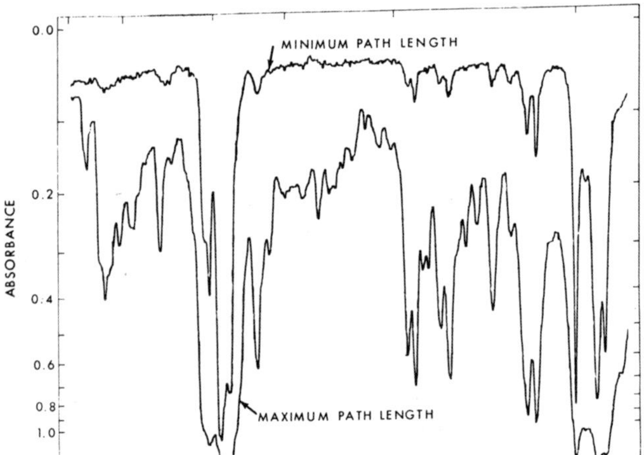

FIG. 2. INFRARED SPECTRUM OF TETRAHYDRONAPHTHALENE

was pressed into the crystal surface until the desired depression was obtained. Pressure was released, and the temperature was lowered 110°C/hr.

The cell has several advantages over equipment now in use. The absence of moving parts eliminates gasket seals and the resultant capillary spaces that make cleaning difficult. Spectra can be recorded, on a single filling, over a range of path lengths selected to emphasize details of band structure. Figure 2 shows a portion of the spectrum of tetrahydronaphthalene at the two extremes of path length.

An alternative cell design could be obtained by depressing the crystal surface into steps of different thickness. Such a cell would have a series of different but fixed path lengths and could be used for quantitative analysis. The novel technique of impressing crystals can be applied whenever a surface is desired that can not be obtained easily by grinding and polishing.

"O" Ring Gaskets For Infrared Cells 2.21

Bernard M. Mitzner

Instrumental Analysis Research Laboratory, International Flavor and Fragrances, Inc., Union Beach, New Jersey

The conventional infrared absorption cell utilizes two amalgamated lead gaskets. One of these gaskets is placed between two salt plate windows and serves as the cell spacer (i.e., determines the light path length of the cell). The other amalgamated lead gasket serves as a true gasket, providing a seal between the cell body and the upper salt plate. The cell normally is filled by passing the sample through a hypodermic hub, through a hole in the cell plate, through an opening in the amalgamated lead gasket, then through holes drilled in the upper salt plate, and finally the space between the two salt plates. When materials that tend to "mess" up the cell are used, it is necessary to frequently disassemble the cell for cleaning. The preparation of amalgamated lead gaskets is quite time consuming and in most instances does not give a leak-proof cell.

This difficulty has been partly overcome by employing "O" rings between the upper cell body plate and the upper salt plate in place of the lead gasket. The amalgamated lead spacer or a Teflon spacer may be used for determining the path length. Experiments with both Teflon* as well as Silicone† "O" rings have demonstrated that the latter always give a leak-proof cell because of their greater compressability. No deleterious chemical effects on the Silicone "O" rings have been observed after they have been in continuous use for nearly a year. No contamination due to the presence of the Silicone "O" rings has been observed when employing a large variety of organic solvents. Ordinary rinsing of the cell with solvent has been found sufficient to prevent contamination from sample to sample due to a somewhat larger than usual dead volume. If there is diffi-

*Nylon Molding Corp., 145 South Avenue, Garwood, N. J.
†Garlock Packing Company, 114 Liberty Street, New York 6, N. Y.

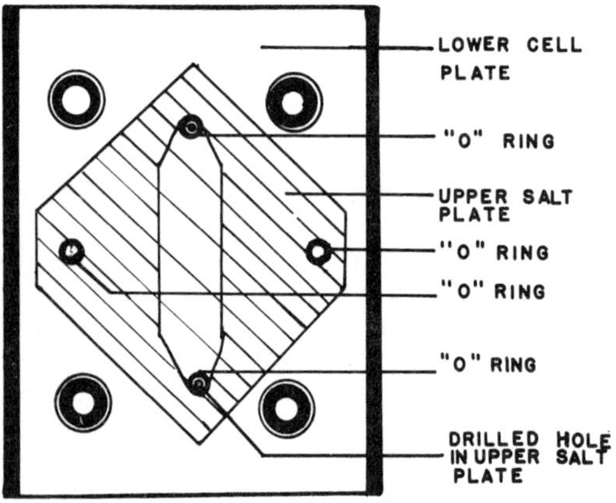

Fig. 1. Top View of Lower Cell Plate with "O" Rings Positioned

culty due to chemical attack on the Silicone "O" rings, the Teflon "O" rings should then be considered.

In practice, four 1/8 in. o.d. Silicone "O" rings are used. Two are placed over the drilled openings in the upper salt plate; the other two are placed midway between the holes on the periphery of the cell so as to equalize the pressure when the cell is tightened (Figure 1). In case the "O" rings move somewhat while assembling the cell, they can be positioned exactly by turning the cell over after it has been made finger tight, and then observing (through the salt plates) the position of the "O" rings opening relative to the opening in the salt plate. The "O" rings can be easily moved into their proper position with the aid of a thin spatula. The cell can then be tightened in the conventional manner. During the tightening procedure, the "O" rings are squashed and the dead volume is considerably reduced.

The leakage from this part of the infrared cell has been completely eliminated, and the customary inadvertant cracking of salt plates during cell preparation has become an unpleasant memory of the past.

A Liquid Ultramicrocavity Cell Holder For Use With An Infrared Beam Condenser 2.22

Patricia A. Estep and Clarence Karr, Jr.

Low-Temperature Tar Research, Morgantown Coal Research Center, Bureau of Mines, Morgantown, West Virginia

The development of many new methods for isolating micro-quantities of substances has emphasized the need for infrared microanalysis. The most common technique is the incorporation of the sample into a potassium bromide micropellet, using a beam condensing system with the spectrophotometer to concentrate the radiant energy on the sample. However, it is often more desirable to obtain spectra of microsamples in solution. In this laboratory, the fractionation of low-temperature coal-tar samples by various methods, followed by infrared spectrophotometry, has frequently demanded a rapid technique for obtaining solution spectra of micro-samples. This problem was solved with a holder designed for positionig a liquid microcavity cell into a 6x beam condensing unit in the infrared spectrophotometer.

The cell holder was analogous to the disc holder supplied by the Perkin-Elmer Corporation for use with their 6x microsampling unit. The Perkin-Elmer disc-holder was designed only for positioning a potassium bromide micropellet in the sample beam. No matter by what means a

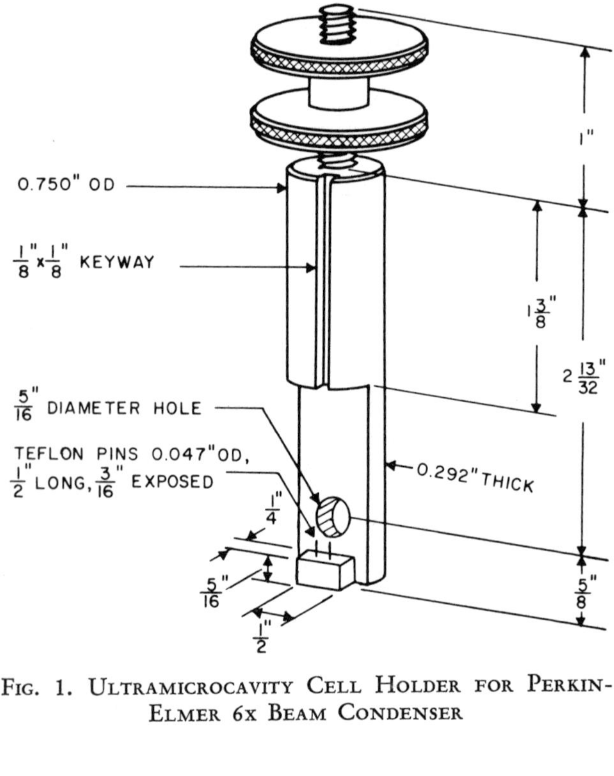

FIG. 1. ULTRAMICROCAVITY CELL HOLDER FOR PERKIN-ELMER 6x BEAM CONDENSER

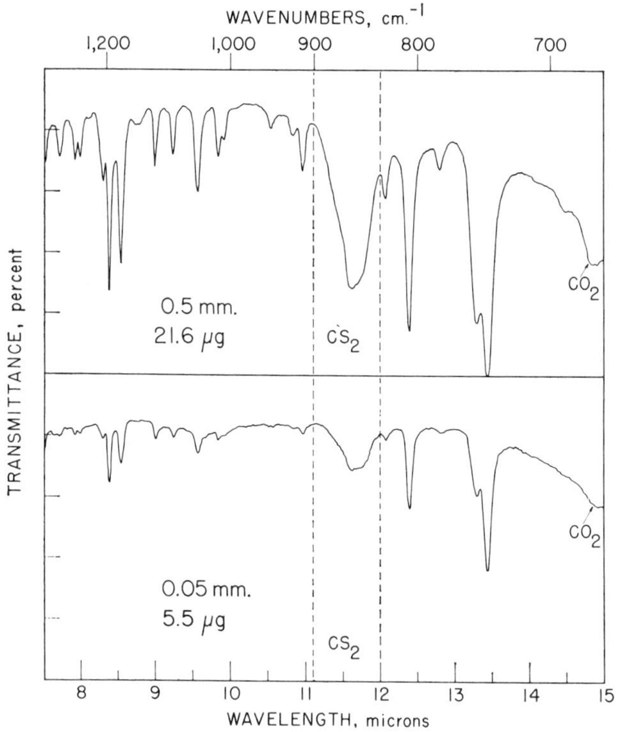

FIG. 2. INFRARED SPECTRA OF MICROGRAM QUANTITIES OF BENZO[B]NAPHTHO[2,1-D]FURAN IN CS_2 SOLUTION

liquid microcavity cell is fastened to the disc holder, the center of the cell, that is, the point midway between the optic faces, will be displaced considerably from the correct position, which is the point that would have been occupied by the micropellet, because the cell is much thicker than the micropellet. The holder designed in this laboratory made it possible to mount an ultramicrocavity cell (Type "D"—Connecticut Instrument Corporation, Wilton, Conn.) in the Perkin-Elmer 6x beam condensing unit in a reproducible position.

The cell holder, Figure 1, was machined from a single piece of type 304 stainless steel to the dimensions required to fit into the 6x disc-holder mount on the beam condensing unit. A keyway ⅛″ x ⅛″ was required to fit the mount. Two knurled thumb nuts (1¼-in. o.d.) at the top of the sample holder were added to a 5/16-in. x 18 N.C. screw (as on the potassium bromide disc-holder) for vertical sample positioning in the amount. The top nut served to lock the lower one in position, once the alignment was complete. The two other thumb screw adjustments on the holder mount, which allowed for optimizing the sample position horizontally along and across the sample beam, could be used in the usual manner.

The lower section of the holder was milled to 0.292-in. to give sufficient space for the cavity cell to be fitted onto two Teflon pins mounted on a platform at the bottom of the holder. These Teflon pins were made to fit the holes already drilled in the microcavity cells and were placed 0.113-in. from the rear of the platform, 3/16-in. apart. The two pins were held in place by inserting them in holes drilled to the bottom of the platform. It was necessary to recess the cell platform enough to clear the keyway projection when the holder was placed in the mount. A 5/16-in. diam. hole was centered in the face of the milled section of the holder. The cavity cell was mounted on the platform so that the center of the cavity fell on the center of this hole, which, in turn, corresponded to the same position of a 0.5-mm. potassium bromide disc mounted in the Perkin-Elmer disc-holder. This careful sample positioning was necessary for obtaining maximum transmittance.

Figure 2 shows the infrared spectrum of benzo[b]-naphtho[2,1-d]furan obtained in carbon disulfide solution. Curve I represents 21.6μg in a 0.5-mm. microcavity cell. Curve II represents 5.5μg in a 0.05-mm. microcavity cell. These were the amounts of material actually present in the cavity portion of the cell and did not include the total amount of sample needed for solution preparation. No effort was made to compensate for atmospheric water and carbon dioxide bands that appeared because of the increased path length in the sample beam. Also, no solvent compensation was made. In this regard it was helpful to run a solvent background curve on the same sheet of recording paper using a different color ink.

Low Temperature Infrared Cell* 2.23

C. M. Lovell and H. F. White

Research Department, Union Carbide Chemicals Company
South Charleston, West Virginia

Several low temperature infrared absorption cells have been described in the literature (*1-4*). The simplest one of these, by Janz and Fitzgerald (*3*), employs a sandwich cell surrounded with an aluminum foil housing and cooled with a liquid nitrogen reservoir. This cell, though well suited for obtaining spectra of non-volatile liquids at low temperatures, is not applicable for low boiling liquids. Two others (*1,2*), though suitable for low boiling liquids, are of complicated design requiring precision workmanship. The low temperature infrared cell to be described is unique in that any of the commercial infrared liquid cells may be used as the base component. The cell is especially suited for the study of materials which are unstable at room temperature. Also it affords a means of obtaining the spectra of low boiling liquids without resorting to the comparatively expensive pressure cells.

In essence this cell is a *Perkin-Elmer "Infracord"* liquid cell with sodium chloride windows and a redesigned back plate containing a reservoir for cooling. The *"Infracord"* cell was chosen because of its ease in filling; both inlet and outlet tubes are located at the top of the cell, enabling the cell to be filled while positioned in the cell

*Presented at *The Pittsburgh Conference on Analytical Chemistry and Applied Spectroscopy*, March, 1959.

compartment of the spectrophotometer. The cell is designed to be used in the *Baird-Atomic* infrared spectrophotometers, model 4-55 or AB2. Both of these instruments have an enclosed cell compartment which can be flushed with dry nitrogen to eliminate moisture condensation on the cell windows. With spectrophotometers not containing an enclosed cell compartment it would be necessary to enclose the cell with a suitable housing to provide a dry nitrogen atmosphere.

Figure 1 shows a schematic drawing of the cell. The back plate was machined from ¼-in. copper plate to replace the original back plate of the "*Infracord*" cell. The dimensions are 2¾ inches in width, the same as that of the *Baird-Atomic* liquid cell, and 6 inches in height, made reservoir 2 inches in diameter by 6 inches in height, made of 16 gauge copper tubing was tapered to a ¼ x 2¾-in. rectangle and soldered to this plate. The plate height of 6 inches allows the cell to be placed in the cell compart-

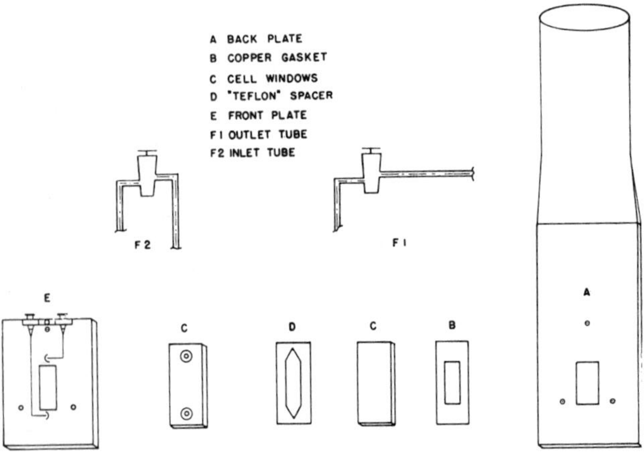

FIG. 1. LOW TEMPERATURE INFRARED CELL
A—Back Plate, B—Copper Gasket, C—Cell Window, D—Teflon Spacer, E—Front Plate, F1—Outlet Tube, and F-2—Inlet Tube

ment of the spectrophotometer with the reservoir on the outside. Previous work employing the Hornig cell (*4*) suggested a similar type of cooling reservoir for this cell. Some departure from the conventional was necessary in assembling the cell. The lead spacer between the cell windows was replaced with a spacer cut from 0.020 mm *Teflon*® sheet. This was necessary due to the corrosive action of some of the materials examined. Also, to obtain adequate thermal contact between the back plate and cell window, the cell was assembled with a thin annealed copper gasket in place of the original rubber gasket. The front plate was mounted without a gasket since adequate cushioning between the plate and cell window is obtained from the soft rubber seal around the inlet and outlet holes.

The temperature of the cell is measured with a thermocouple, the junction of which is placed in contact with the cell windows along one edge and secured with *Apiezon*® wax. As an alternate method, a hole may be drilled in one window to serve as a thermocouple well. The accuracy of the temperature measurement was checked by obtaining the freezing point of carbon tetrachloride; the range of −22 to −24°C obtained compares favorably with the theoretical freezing point of −22.9°C. The cell is cooled with a mixture of dry ice and isopropanol in the reservoir. Constant cell temperatures can be obtained by varying the concentration of dry ice in the isopropanol. Temperatures of 10, −3, −18, −24, and −35°C have been maintained for periods of 30 minutes or more.

Low boiling liquids are introduced into the cell by means of inlet and outlet tubes made of *Pyrex*® capillary tubing, each containing a stopcock. The tubes are connected to the cell with *Tygon*® tubing and the outlet tube is connected to a vacuum line. The cell is placed in the cell compartment of the spectrophotometer and cooled to the desired temperature while purging the cell compartment with nitrogen. The sample is cooled to approximately the same temperature as the cell and introduced through

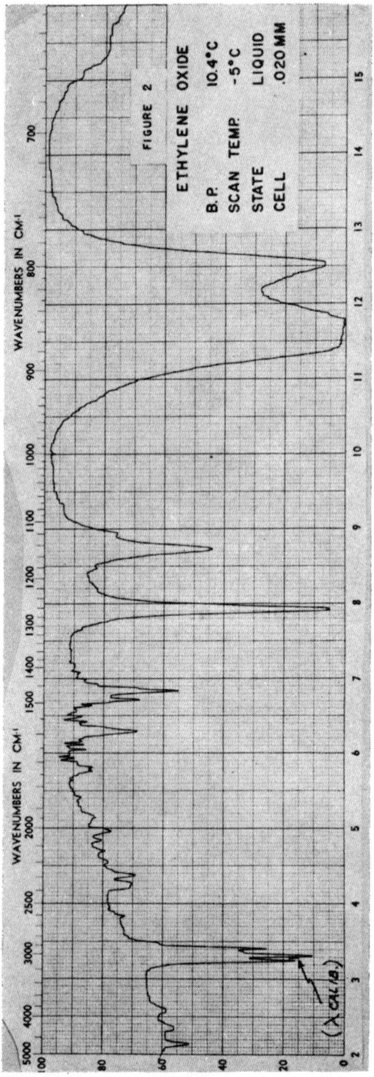

Fig. 2. Infrared Spectrum of Liquid Ethylene Oxide

the inlet tube into the cell by careful adjustment of the vacuum by the outlet tube stopcock to avoid slugging.

The spectrum of ethylene oxide as obtained in the liquid phase with this cell, is presented in Figure 2. The absorption band appearing at 4.25 microns is due to the presence of carbon dioxide in the nitrogen used for purging.

Literature Cited

1. W. H. Duerig and I. L. Mador, *Rev. Sci. Instr.* *23*, 421 (1952)
2. R. B. Holden, W. J. Taylor and H. L. Johnson, *J. Opt. Soc. Am.* *40*, 757 (1950)
3. G. J. Janz and W. E. Fitzgerald, *Applied Spectroscopy* *9*, 178 (1955)
4. E. L. Wagner and D. F. Hornig, *J. Chem. Phys.* *18*, 296 (1950)

Low Temperature Infrared Cell for Reaction Kinetic Studies 2.24

G. Nencini and E. Pauluzzi
Laboratori Riuniti Studi e Ricerche, S. Donato Milanese
Milano, Italy

In connection with the research program of this laboratory, it was attempted to apply infrared spectrophotometry to the study of the kinetics of liquid phase reactions at low temperature. Several low temperature cells have been described, for example (*1*), but are not applicable for low boiling liquids when they are introduced at room temperature. An apparatus has been developed which allows a continuous circulation of a liquid reaction mixture from a reactor to the absorption cell at a low temperature. The apparatus can be fitted into the sample space of the *Perkin-Elmer* Infrared Spectrophotometer, Model 21.

The general layout of the apparatus is shown in Figure 1. The reaction takes place in A which is a 400 ml stainless steel cylinder provided with a screwed cover carrying two ground joints and a mercury seal stirrer. The reaction mixture flows through a filter to the absorption cell (B) and it is then pumped to the top of A by the pump (C). All are immersed in a constant-temperature bath (D) which supports the whole apparatus. A cross section of the cell and the reactor is shown in Figure 2. The cell mount is soldered to the bath walls, and two NaCl plates, 50 mm diam., 0.1-mm width, are fixed in the center by means of a retaining ring and *Teflon* gaskets. Smaller diam. can be

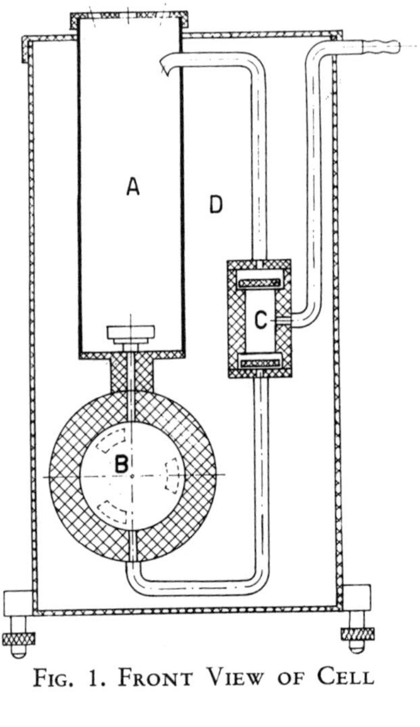

FIG. 1. FRONT VIEW OF CELL

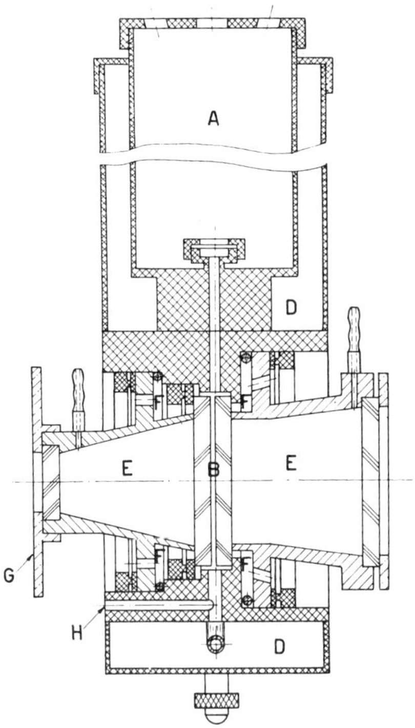

FIG. 2. SIDE VIEW OF CELL

used with a suitable ring adapter. Three small spacers maintain the desired gap between the plates (Figure 1). The fluid circulates between the plates but the major part bypasses the spaces around these plates. Two cone-shaped *Plexiglass* spacers are pressed against the plates separating the two vacuum chambers (E) inside and the two rings (F) outside. These can be filled with mercury through a small hole closed with a screwed plug to maintain a seal. Two NaCl plates, 25 and 50 mm diam., 0.1-mm width, are sealed with *glyptal* at the ends of E that are evacuated through a suitable vacuum connection. The endplate (G) rests against the cell side on the monochromator cover.

The fluid flows to a push-pull stainless steel pump through a 6 mm diam. tube (Figure 1). This pump is operated by a piston which is controlled by a motor as shown in Figure 3. The connection is made through a U tube filled with mercury that minimizes contamination of the reaction mixture and the lubricating oil in the piston. A small tube (H) contains the thermocouple and is fitted at the exit from the cell. D is a stainless steel box, 77 mm x 170 mm x 312 mm, which rests on three bolts that permit the alignment of the cell with the light beam. The constant-temperature fluid is circulated through the inner compartment. Rough thermal insulation is provided by means of a 2 cm glass wool layer applied to the outer walls of D.

The cell has been tested at temperatures between —60° and 100° C without *Plexiglass* spacers. It could be extended to below —100° C. The absorption peaks of a

FIG. 3. GENERAL ASSEMBLY

soluble substance added to the circulating fluid are observed to reach their maximum value about 30 sec after its addition. Thirty sec is the time that must be allowed for the mixing of liquids in the reactor and the passage of the solution through the cell and is considered the time-lag of the apparatus. The transmittance of the empty cell is above 80% and it can be assembled in about 1 hr.

The valuable assistance of Mr. R. Vitali is acknowledged. The authors wish to thank the management of the L.R.S.R. for permission to publish this report.

Literature Cited

(1) W. Brügel, "*Einfuhrung in die Ultraotspektroskopie*", Steinkopff, Darmstadt (1954)

A Versatile Low Temperature Spectral Attachment 2.25

H. H. Richtol and F. H. Klappmeier*

Department of Chemistry
Rensselaer Polytechnic Institute
Troy, New York

The use of low temperature spectra *(1)* is likely to become an increasingly important analytical tool. Infrared bands are sharpened considerably and frequently split at liquid-nitrogen temperatures. Luminescent intensities are enhanced, and phosphorescence is frequently measureable only in rigid media at low temperatures. This communication describes a versatile spectral attachment for making low temperature absorption measurements routinely in the infrared, visible, and ultraviolet regions, as well as luminescence measurements in the visible and ultraviolet regions.

*Esso Educational Foundation Fellow, 1962-1963

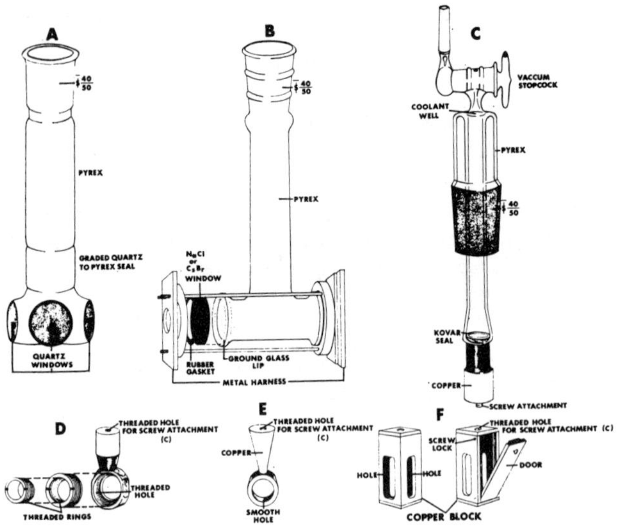

FIG. 1. DIAGRAM OF THE LOW TEMPERATURE SPECTRAL ATTACHMENT

A and *B* in Figure 1 are the outer jackets with the optical windows, which are quartz in *A* and either rocksalt or cesium bromide in *B*. The windows in *B* are held on the ground glass lip with stopcock grease and tightened by the metal harness. *C* contains the reservoir for the coolant and a standard tapered vacuum stopcock for evacuation when *C* is attached to either outer jacket.

The sample holders, *D*, *E*, and *F*, (Figure 1) may be used for a large number of applications. The sample holders are all readily interchangeable with the coolant reservoir. Sample holder *D* is used for solid samples, *e.g.*, KBr pellets or evaporated films on rocksalt or cesium bromide windows. Sample holder *E* is used for rigid room temperature samples that can readily be shaped to the size of the smooth hole, *e.g.*, boric acid glasses. Sample holder *F* is used to hold one cm^2 spectral cells containing solutions that become rigid at liquid nitrogen temperatures *e.g.*, a mixture of ether, isopentane, and ethyl alcohol. Strips of copper foil are placed inside the door of *F* to give a snug fit to the sides of the copper block. There are three holes in the copper block that allow both absorption and luminescence measurements to be made on the same sample.

Evacuation prior to cooling is advantageous when using holders *D* and *E* with solid samples. Solvent loss when using liquid samples in holder *F* is prevented by first cooling with liquid nitrogen until the sample is rigid and then evacuating the cell. Frost accumulation on the exterior quartz windows of *A* is easily removed by warming with the hands or a stream of air after evacuation. The solidified sample is easily maintained by periodic addition of coolant to the well.

Fitted wooden blocks or a metal harness and slight modifications of sample compartment housings, enable this spectral assembly to be reproducibly positioned with many standard instruments.

Literature Cited

(1) E. L. Wagner and D. F. Hornig, J. CHEM. PHYS. **18,** 298 (1950)

Heated Cell for Thermal Stability Studies of Polymers Using Infrared Spectroscopy*† 2.26

Robert T. Conley and Joseph F. Bieron
Department of Chemistry, Canisius College, Buffalo, New York

In the course of studies on the thermal stability of polymeric materials, it was of interest to follow the course

*Presented at the 137th National American Chemical Society Meeting, Cleveland, Ohio, April 1960 and abstracted from the Masters' thesis of J. F. Bieron.

†This work was supported under Contract #DA-30-069-ORD-2626 and Grant #DA-ORD-31-124-60-G51 from the Office of Ordnance Research, U. S. Army.

of oxidative and non-oxidative degradation reactions of various functional groups in the polymers using infrared spectroscopy. In general, the method available for this type of investigation has been limited to heating the polymer sample in an oven followed by cooling of the specimen and determination of its infrared spectrum *(1)*. By successive heating and cooling cycles with intermittent spectral evaluation a series of spectra are obtained which are indicative of changes of functionality taking place under the degradative conditions. Recently *(2)*, the use of a heated wire cell has been reported for infrared studies of polymers up to 145°C. The advantage of this type of unit is that continuous monitoring of the sample is possible at the reaction temperature.

Sometime ago, in an effort to obtain kinetic data on polymer degradation reactions it was necessary to develop an infrared cell unit which could be used at temperatures from 100 to 400°C. The cell described here was constructed to the port dimensions of a Baird Model AB-2, double-beam, recording infrared spectrophotometer. However, using the same cell design, rectangular units have been constructed and used with equal success on other instruments.

As indicated in Figure 1, the entire cell unit is constructed of tempered asbestos. The heater unit is constructed from an aluminum tube (2½ in. dia., 1¼ in. long) covered on both sides with a thin layer of asbestos and wrapped with 9 ft. of chromel 'A' heating wire and an additional outer covering of asbestos tape. It has been found that the inner layer of asbestos is necessary in order to isolate the NaCl plate from the metal tube to prevent cracking of the salt plate on rapid heating and cooling. Although the cell ends can be fashioned from metal, such as brass or steel, asbestos markedly reduces the cost of the unit. In units for instruments which require a rectangular cell, a thin metal backing plate is necessary for repeated proper positioning of the cell on the instrument port.

The cell temperature is controlled and indicated through a single thermocouple positioned at one-half the radius of the salt disc. By using a proportioning controller-

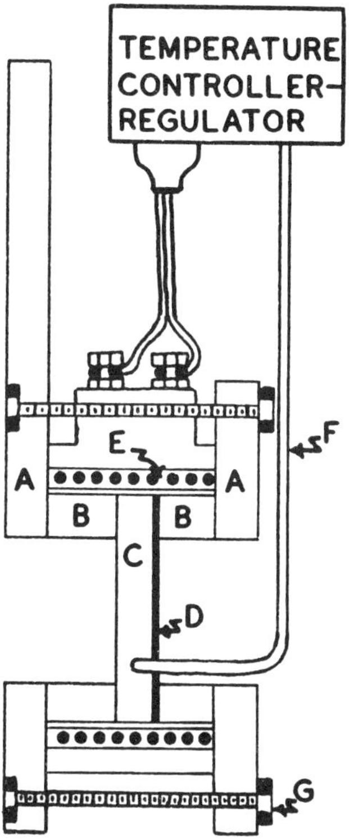

FIG. 1. CELL ASSEMBLY

A—Asbestos cell ends, B—Asbestos spacers, C—Salt plate, D—Polymer, E—Heating wire, F—Thermocouple, G—Retaining bolts.

regulator unit with a 500 watt light bulb in the heating circuit in addition to the heater coil, temperature control is accurately maintained within $\pm 2\,^{\circ}C$ temperature range.

In the study of oxidative reactions in air, the cell was heated to reaction temperature under a cover of inert gas to prevent oxidation prior to the initial determination of the spectrum of the sample. Thereafter, the spectrum could be recorded of particular regions of interest as rapidly as desired. For example, on examination of the thermal degradation of polyacrylonitrile at 200°C the 4—7 micron region was scanned every 4 min for 6 hrs. At high temperatures, it has been found that it is necessary to adjust the base line with the sample inserted in the instrument at the reaction temperature in order to obtain good spectral data.

The same cell can be used for controlled atmosphere studies. The spacers, B, (Figure 1) are removed and a single spacer of asbestos is used between two salt discs. The polymer is on the inner face of the front plate. The gaseous atmosphere is passed through the chamber at a slow rate. The only modification is the insertion of two gas ports in the heater body. Using this technique it has been possible, for example, in helium atmospheres to trap out volatile degradation products for vapor phase chromatographic examination. This allows monitoring of both the gas and solid phases of the system during the degradation.

Literature Cited

(1) B. D. Achlammer, M. J. Reiney, and F. W. Reinhart, J. Research Natl. Bur. Standards **47,** 116 (1951); A. L. Smith, L. H. Brown, L. J. Tyler, and J. M. Hunter, Ind. Eng. Chem. **49,** 1903 (1957)
(2) J. L. Luongo, J. Polymer Sci. **42,** 139 (1960)

2.27 A Capillary Trap for the Collection of Gas Chromatographic Fractions for Infrared Spectrophotometry

S. S. Chang,* K. M. Brobst, C. E. Ireland, and H. Tai
A. E. Staley Manufacturing Company, Decatur, Illinois

The characterization of chemical compounds by the use of gas-liquid chromatography and infrared spectrophotometry has become an important research technique.

---

*Present address: Department of Food Science, Rutgers, The State University, New Brunswick, N. J.

In this method, the mixture is chromatographed, the pure fractions collected, and then identified by their infrared spectra. A difficult step in this technique is the collection of the micro amount of sample from the gas chromatograph and its transfer into a suitable cell for spectrophotometric study.

A gas cell suitable for the collection of low boiling fractions and the determination of their infrared spectra without further transfer has been reported *(1)*. The present paper describes a capillary trap for the collection and identification of the micro amounts of higher boiling fractions separated by gas-liquid chromatography.

The trap body is made using ₮ 10/30 borosilicate glass joints as shown in Figure 1. The open outer joint is the gas inlet. One end of the inlet tube is drawn into a tip, 10 mm long and 3 mm o.d. The capillary attached to the tip is made from polyethylene tubing of ¼ in o.d. by softening in a micro burner flame and drawing it out to a capillary of approximately 0.03 mm i.d. An 18 cm portion is cut off in such a manner that one end fits tightly to the tip of the inlet tube. At 7 cm from this end, a section of the capillary 7 mm long is pressed with a hydraulic press using a ram force of 35,000 lbs. A flattened area, (2.5 mm wide, 7 mm long, and 0.09 mm thick) is thus formed and is shown in the cut off section of Figure 1. After the pressing, the sides of the flattened area may stick together. They can be opened easily by a stainless steel wire of 0.001 in. diam.

The outlet of the cell body is a ₮ 10/30 outer joint, which is fitted with a drying tube and a flow meter constructed from a ₮ 10/30 inner joint. The lower 5.5 cm of this joint is made into a drying tube, while the upper 5.5 cm is replaced with a piece of borosilicate glass tubing, 5 mm o.d.

A Teflon flow meter float stop* is placed at the contraction point using a glass ball as the float. The top of the tube is fitted with another Teflon float stop.

The capillary trap is connected to the effluent port of gas-liquid chromatograph either through a ₮ 10/30

*Cat. No. 3575, Ace Glass Inc., Vineland, N. J.

inner joint or through 15 gauge stainless steel tubing* fitted with a one hole type silicone seal†. The cell body is then immersed in a Dewar Flask filled with solid carbon dioxide or liquid nitrogen. Multiple fractions may be collected in a series of traps attached to a manifold. The flow meter in each trap constantly indicates whether the effluent gas is passing through the right trap at the set rate. As many as 16 traps were used by the authors to collect the components of a food flavor.

After the sample is collected, the inlet ₮ 10/30 joint is closed with a drying tube, and the whole trap is centrifuged. The polyethylene capillary is then disconnected from the trap body, and the sample is gently sucked into the flattened area by attaching a micro syringe at one end of the capillary. Both ends are then sealed with a micro burner flame. The sample is now ready for infrared study.

A Beckman Beam Condenser Assembly (Cat. No. 18601) was used and the sealed capillary was mounted on a Beckman Micro Pellet Holder (Cat. No. 24497) with the fattened section over the window. The spectrum of the sample was then obtained with a Beckman IR-4 spectrophotometer using a polyethylene film (0.06 mm thick) in the reference beam. The use of the capillary as a cell for infrared spectrophotometry has been reported previously by Molnar and Yarborough *(2)*.

If the sample collected in the capillary is sufficient for transfer with a micro syringe, an infrared spectrum free from polyethylene absorption bands can be obtained with the use of a cavity cell. The sample was transferred into a cavity cell of 0.1 mm light path (Connecticut Instrument Corp., Wilton, Conn.) with a 10 μl Hamilton micro syringe. The spectrum was again determined using a Beckman Variable Thickness Cell (Cat. No. 28701) in the reference beam to compensate for the absorption of the solvent.

With the present technique, only 0.1-0.2 μl of a sample is needed to fill the flattened section of the polyethylene capillary. When a solution of 1% *n*-propyl

*Cat. No. 344-25-01, Burrell Corp., Pittsburgh, Pa.
†Cat. No. 261-9, Burrell Corp., Pittsburgh, Pa.

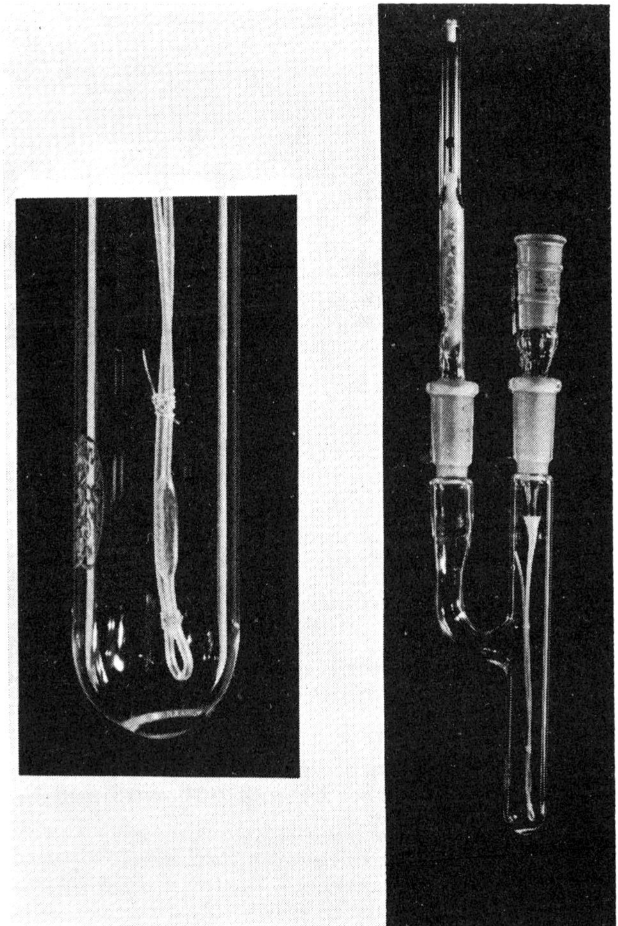

FIG. 1. CAPILLARY TRAP FOR DIRECT COLLECTION OF GAS CHROMATOGRAPHIC FRACTIONS

acetate in ethyl ether was chromatographed with a Burrell K-2 instrument using a Carbowax 20 M Column and a helium flow rate of 50 ml/min, 90% of the propyl

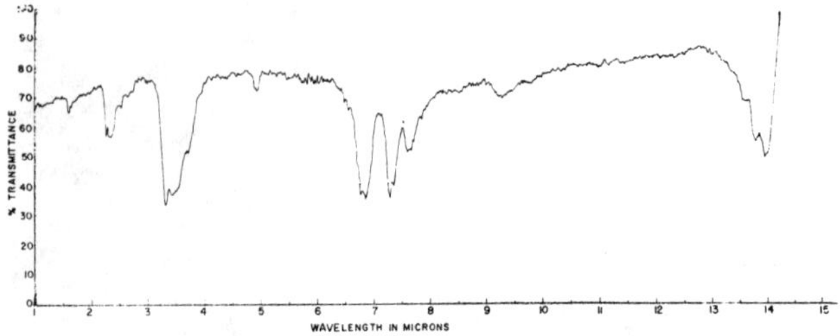

FIG. 2. INFRARED SPECTRUM OF THE POLYETHYLENE CAPILLARY

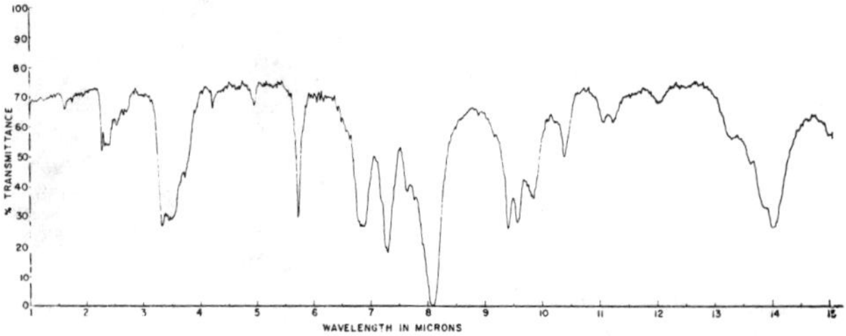

FIG. 3. INFRARED SPECTRUM OF N-PROPYL ACETATE IN THE CAPILLARY

acetate was recovered with the use of this trap as measured with a Hamilton Syringe of one μl capacity. The spectrum of the flattened section of the polyethylene capillary is shown in Figure 2, and that of *n*-propyl acetate as obtained by this technique is shown in Figure 3.

The present capillary trap therefore serves two purposes. One, it efficiently collects a sample from the gas chromatograph. Two, the flattened section of the polyethylene capillary can be used as a spectrophotometric cell for the determination of infrared spectrum.

Literature Cited

(1) S. S. Chang, C. E. Ireland, and H. Tai, ANAL. CHEM. **33,** 479 (1961)

(2) W. S. Molnar and V. A. Yarborough, APPLIED SPECTROSCOPY **12,** 143 (1958)

Sampling Technique for Obtaining Infrared Spectra of Gas Chromatographic Fractions 2.28

B. H. Blake, D. S. Erley, and F. L. Beman

Chemical Physics Research Laboratory and
E. C. Britton Research Laboratory
The Dow Chemical Company, Midland, Michigan

Infrared spectroscopy, with its high specificity, is an ideal way to identify gas chromatographic fractions *(1)*, but the size of sample available as a column effluent often demands the use of micro techniques for obtaining spectra. The present Trick describes a method for collecting and obtaining the infrared spectra of gas chromatographic fractions in the 10 to 100 μg range. Although it is a micro technique, the equipment is simple, inexpensive, and can be made in most laboratory machine shops. No beam condenser is required, and the spectra may be scanned on a "table top" infrared spectrophotometer.

Fractions are collected in a V-shaped capillary tube (1.0 mm i.d.), Figure 1, which is attached to the chromatograph by inserting it through a silicone rubber washer inside the exit-port nut. The small bubble in the bottom of the trap swirls the carrier gas for more efficient

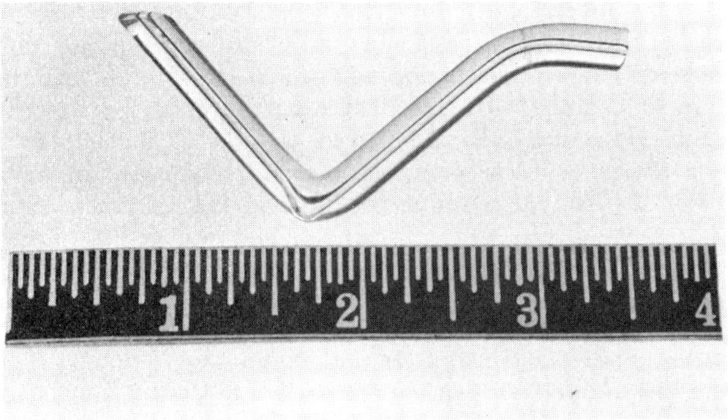

FIG. 1. CAPILLARY TRAP FOR COLLECTING CHROMATOGRAPHIC FRACTIONS

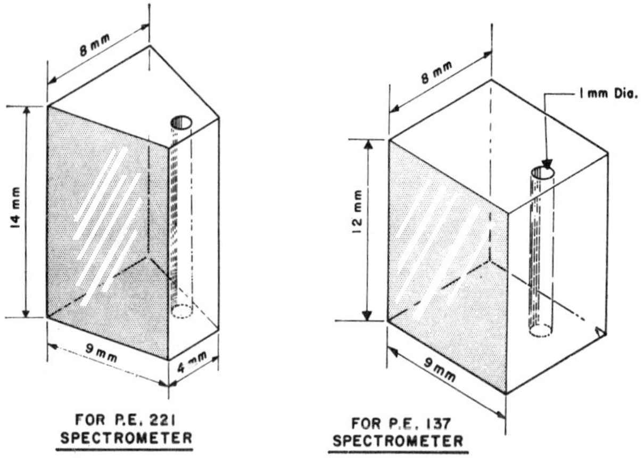

FIG. 2. SLIT-IMAGE MICROCELLS FOR USE WITH PERKIN-ELMER SPECTROPHOTOMETERS

condensation. The trap may be cooled for collection of lighter fractions. After the fraction has collected, ten μl of solvent is added, and the trap is tipped slowly several times to wash the walls thoroughly. A ten μl syringe is inserted to the bottom of the trap to draw out the solution and transfer it to the infrared cell. Recovery and transfer efficiencies average about 70%.

The infrared cell is a cavity cell of our own design, made from a scrap NaCl crystal (Figure 2). A 1.0 mm hole drilled* close to one edge of the crystal forms the sample chamber. It is drilled near the edge so that the sample chamber may be placed as close as possible to a *slit image* or focal point of the infrared beam. In most cases the sample beam is focussed on the trimmer comb just beyond the sample chamber, and the cell is placed as close to this point as possible. However, the slit-image cell may also be placed directly behind the entrance or

* Drilling may be done on a standard drill press, but the drill should be lifted frequently from the hole or the crystal may crack from the buildup of NaCl powder.

exit slit to the monochromator if these are conveniently accessible.

After the cell is filled with solution, it is clamped in the cell holder (Figure 3) by means of the L shaped slider. A small piece of rubber cemented to the bottom of the slider seals the cell during the scan (alternatively, it may be sealed with a small piece of masking tape). This cell holder is designed to fit a Perkin-Elmer model 137 infrared spectrophotometer and is held in place by the small spring clip on the chassis of the instrument. The cell is then carefully positioned in the holder to give maximum transmission at some wavelength free of sample or solvent bands to assure maximum interception of the light by the sample chamber. If the cell is properly positioned, totally absorbing sample (or solvent) bands should fall close to the zero percent transmittance line on the chart. During the scan, volatile solvents such as

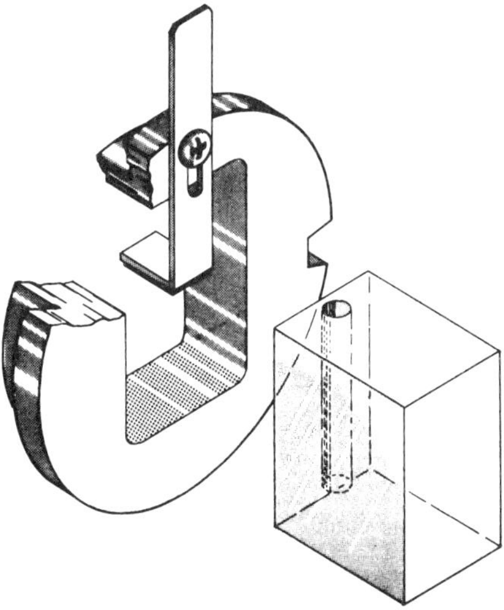

FIG. 3. CELL HOLDER FOR USE WITH PERKIN-ELMER MODEL 137 SPECTROPHOTOMETER

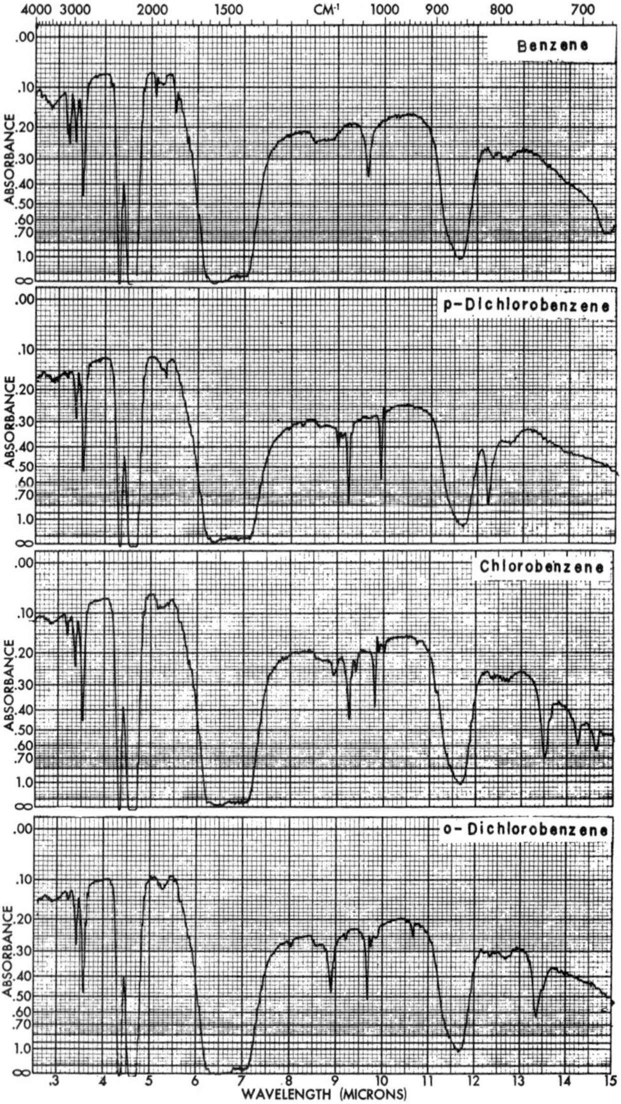

FIG. 4. INFRARED SPECTRA OF FRACTIONS COLLECTED FROM TEST SOLUTION

Each spectrum represents ~50 μg of material

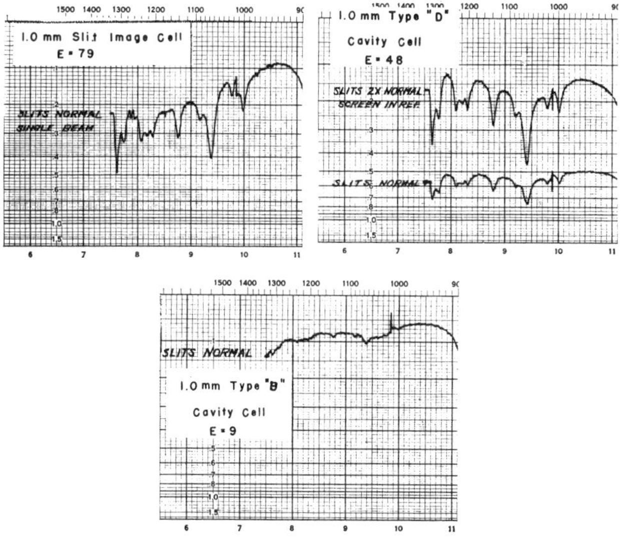

FIG. 5. INFRARED SPECTRA OF TEN MICROGRAMS OF 1,1-DICHLORO-2,2-DIFLUORO ETHYL METHYL ETHER IN THE SLIT IMAGE MICROCELL AND IN TWO COMMERCIAL MICROCELLS

CS_2 may evaporate, so it is sometimes necessary to place a second (standard sized) cell filled with solvent between the slit-image cell and the source to filter out that radiation which causes the boiling *(2)*. An alternative method for avoiding the problem of solvent boiling is to place the cell at the exit slit of the monochromator where the radiant energy is greatly reduced. The sides of the cell must then be rough ground to a wedge shape so that the sample chamber may be positioned close to the slits. The slit jaws on the Perkin-Elmer model 221 spectrophotometer will accept the cell without need of a holder. In this position the cell is in the optical path of both beams, so the instrument must be operated single beam.

Infrared spectra of the four fractions obtained from a methylene chloride solution containing 0.75% (w/v)

each of benzene, chlorobenzene, *p*-dichlorobenzene, and *o*-dichlorobenzene are shown in Figure 5. Ten μl of solution were injected to give a theoretical load of 75 μg/fraction. Recovery and transfer losses reduce this to ~50 μg; nevertheless, the spectra obtained are readily identified and could probably be recognized at considerably lower concentrations.

The performance of the slit-image cell is compared with two commercially available cells in Figure 5. This shows the spectrum of a ten μg fraction of 1,1-dichloro-2,2-difluoro ethyl methyl ether as obtained in the slit-image cell, and 1.0 mm type D cavity cell†, and a 1.0 mm type B cavity cell*. Cell efficiencies were calculated from E = cell length (mm) × % Transmittance/cell volume (ml). The transmittance value (usually measured at 10.0 micron) includes losses in any auxiliary device used with the cell such as a beam condenser. Note that the spectrum obtained in the slit-image cell equals that obtained in the 1.0 mm type D cavity cell. The latter required the use of a beam condenser, a 2X slit program, and a filtering cell to prevent solvent boiling. These spectra were obtained on a Perkin-Elmer model 221 infrared spectrophotometer modified in our laboratory for single beam operation.

The slit-image cell described above can provide a convenient, economical way to obtain infrared spectra of gas chromatographic fractions. The idea of placing a sample at the slit image where the beam is very narrow and only useful radiation passes through the sample may open up many new possibilities for micro-sampling without beam condensing equipment. For example, a KBr pellet in the shape of a 1 mm (diam.) x 1 cm rod placed behind the exit slit of the monochromator might provide good solid state spectra in the sub microgram range. This, and other extensions of the slit image idea, are being investigated further in this laboratory.

---

*Connecticut Instrument Corporation, a subsidiary of Barnes Engineering Company, Wilton, Conn.

Literature Cited

(1) J. G. Grasselli and M. K. Snaveley, APPLIED SPECTROSCOPY **16,** 190 (1962)
(2) D. S. Erley, IBID. **15,** 80 (1961)

Infrared Spectra of Small Samples Without Beam Condenser **2.29**

Seymour Glassner
General Foods Corporation, Tarrytown, New York

A new infrared micro cell manufactured by the Connecticut Instrument Corporation for the direct collection of small fractions from a gas chromatograph has a volume of less than one μl and is designed for use with a beam

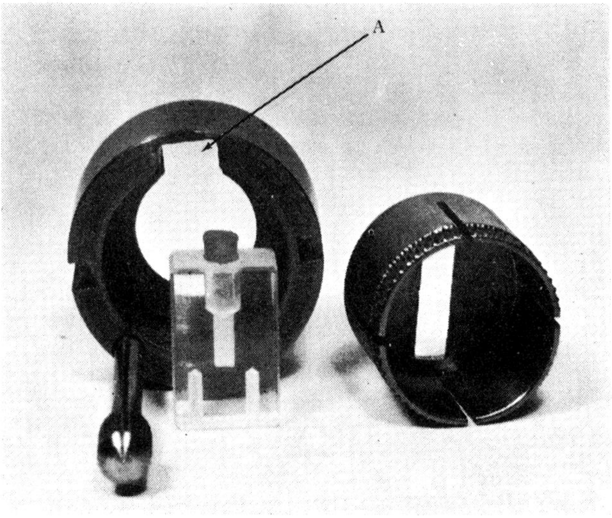

FIG. 1. CAVITY CELL AND DISC HOLDER

FIG. 2. CAVITY CELL POSITIONED IN HOLDER

condenser. In this laboratory, a Perkin-Elmer KBr disc holder has been modified for use with this Type "D" micro cell. Excellent spectra may be obtained on a Perkin-Elmer Model 21 spectrophotometer without a beam condenser.

The micro cell fits into the disc holder without any trouble except for the cover on the cell. To allow enough space for the cover to fit, it is necessary to cut out a section 0.5 cm wide at position *A* (Figure 1). The micro cell is then positioned in the disc holder as shown in Figure 2. The disc holder is placed in the instrument in the same manner that one normally uses it for KBr discs. Reference beam compensation may be accomplished by any standard method, and a wire screen is sufficient for qualitative purposes.

A test solution of 10% ethyl acetate in CCl_4 gave an absorbance reading of 0.22 at the carbonyl stretching wavelength, 5.75 microns. It is possible to identify 0.1 μl

samples without the aid of a beam condenser. It is necessary to use an ordinate expansion of 5X or 10X for the identification of such small samples. It has been found that trapping, and in cases where material has condensed above the cell, transfer of sample are limiting factors. A 0.5 μl sample injected into the vapor fractometer is the smallest amount that has produced a meaningful spectrum.

Modified Infrared Salt Plate for Liquid Microliter Samples Without Beam Condenser 2.30

G. L. K. Hunter

Fruit and Vegetable Products Laboratory*
Winter Haven, Florida

Although it is possible to handle liquid microliter samples in infrared spectrographic analyses using a beam condenser, it is more expedient to avoid its use whenever possible. In the present work excellent spectra have been obtained repeatedly on 0.3 μl liquid samples. Liquids can be applied directly from the gas chromatograph onto the salt plate or transferred from traps using a syringe.

In order to accomplish this, salt plates were modified so that samples were confined to the beam image, thereby substantially reducing the amount of material needed for a good infrared spectrum.

A Connecticut Instrument Company D-4 salt disc was used because its diameter, 13 mm, was the same as the height of the entrance slit in the Perkin-Elmer Infracord Model 137 spectrometer being used. The width of

*One of the laboratories of the Southern Utilization Research and Development Division, Agricultural Research Service, U. S. Department of Agriculture. Mention of brand names is for identification only and does not constitute endorsement by the U. S. Department of Agriculture.

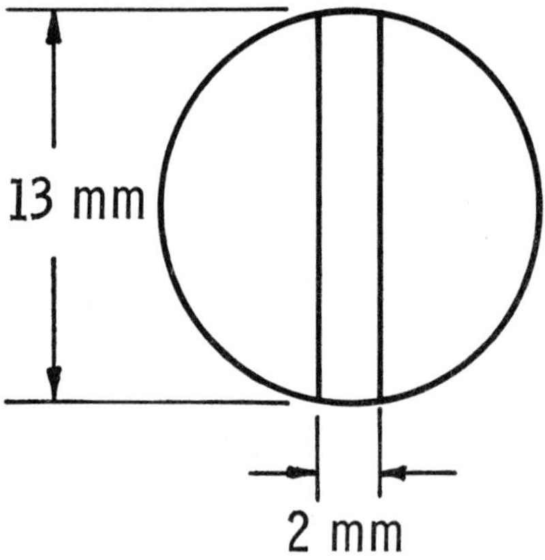

FIG. 1. DISC WITH DIMENSIONS

the slit in this instrument is 2 mm, and to confine the sample to this width two parallel lines 2 mm apart were etched across the entire surface of the plate. A round edge joint Swiss file was used to make the line to obviate the production of sharp edges which might serve to initiate cracks in the crystal. The disc is illustrated in Figure 1.

The sample of liquid is placed or condensed on the area between the etched lines, and an ordinary cover placed deftly against the liquid to prevent the formation of air

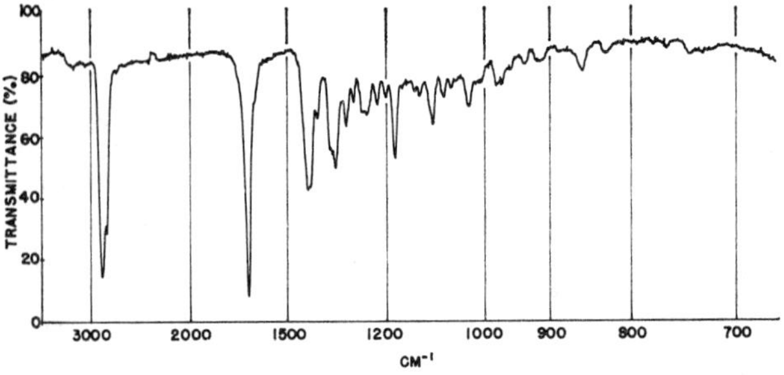

FIG. 2. INFRARED SPECTRUM OF 0.3 μl OF MENTHONE

pockets. Pressure is avoided to prevent spreading of the sample. There is sufficient capillary attraction so that clamping is unnecessary. It was found convenient to place the 13 mm discs in a KBr pellet holder that had been arranged to support the plates aligned in the beam.

Figure 2 shows the infrared spectrum of a 0.3 μl sample of menthone using the above described modified plate. The spectrum was obtained on a Perkin-Elmer Model 137 Infrared Spectrophotometer.

Continuous Reference Beam Attenuator for Infrared Spectrophotometry 2.31

J. P. Luongo
Bell Telephone Laboratories, Inc., Murray Hill, New Jersey

In the course of infrared studies on polymers and other materials, one is often interested in weak absorption bands that may be significant in the structural determination of the sample. In order to increase the intensity of these bands, the operator generally increases the sample thickness and thereby frequently decreases the background transmission. However, some samples such as certain mulls or samples containing inorganic fillers or even inorganic samples themselves are quite dense and require the attenuation of the reference beam in order to record the spectrum properly. Thus it is often desirable to compensate for the fixed energy losses in the sample beam (or in effect, to expand the scale by attenuation of the reference beam). This has been accomplished through the use of wire mesh screens or slotted shutters. These methods are inconvenient since they either produce a "step-by-step" attenuation, have only a limited attenuation range, or the degree of attenuation can not be easily adjusted. A reference beam attenuator that will compensate the energy losses in the sample beam from 0 to 100% transmission in a continuous manner and can be adjusted to energy differences as small as 1% is shown in Figure 1. This attenuator was constructed for use with the *Perkin-Elmer* Model 21 Spectrophotometer and its mounting is shown in Figure 2.

The brass vane structure was constructed of a rectangular frame 1⅝ in. x 2 in. into which the 4 mil thick brass vanes were positioned by slotting the upper and lower sections of the frame. The vanes are 5/16 in. wide and are spaced 5/16 in. apart so that when the frame makes an angle of more than 45° with the reference beam there is no transmission. At an angle of 0° with the beam there is about 96% transmission. The metallic frame and the vanes were blackened with an oxide coating and placed as close as possible to the reference beam exit port of the source housing in order to minimize reflection and shadow effects.

A pointer, fastened to the shaft sweeps over a circular scale which was divided into ten arbitrary equal spaces (actually about ½-in. apart) with the center of the circular scale at the point where maximum transmission of the reference beam occurs. A vertical hole was drilled into the cylindrical phenol fiber block to give a snug but smooth running fit for the shaft of the vane structure.

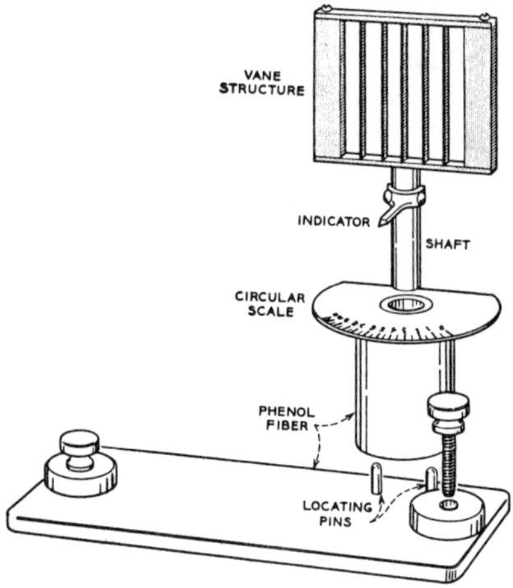

FIG. 1. EXPANDED VIEW OF ATTENUATOR

FIG. 2. ATTENUATOR MOUNTED ON SPECTROPHOTOMETER

In order to mount this unit securely to the instrument, a flat piece of phenol fiber $3\frac{5}{8}$ in. x 6 in. x $\frac{1}{4}$ in. was fastened with thumb screws to the base casting of the instrument between the monochromator and the source housing using the holes already tapped for the reflectance accessory. The vane structure and its fiber block base are positioned on the base with locating pins so that the optical axis passes through the center of the vane assembly. This permits easy replacement of the attenuator.

It has been found that by manual adjustment this device can attenuate the reference beam from 0 to 100% to a precision of 1% and the circular scale permits reproducible settings. In actual use the attenuator is left on the instrument most of the time, for even with the vanes "open" there is only a loss of approximately 4% in the reference beam. This attenuator has been found useful in recording spectra of polymer films containing dispersed carbon and for such samples as dark oils, resins and inorganic materials.

The author wishes to express his appreciation to C. R. Geith for his help in the design and construction of the attenuator.

2.32 Preparation of Selenium Polarizers for the Near Infrared Region

K. Buijs

National Physical Research Laboratory, C.S.I.R., Pretoria, Union of South Africa

Unsupported selenium films with a thickness of a few microns, which are used for infrared and near infrared transmission polarizers *(1,2,3)*, are generally very fragile. The use of this type of polarizer has accordingly been rather restricted. For application in the near infrared, the removal of the formvar® films used by Ames and Sampson *(2)* as a support for the formation of the selenium films has been found unnecessary. The procedure for preparing such polarizers is described in this note.

The outside perimeter of a brass support to which a polarizer film is to be fixed is traced with a colored pencil on a piece of glass plate (about 2 x 3 inches). This glass plate is then turned over and four drops of a 1% solution of formvar* in dioxane are placed within the traced area and spread uniformly to fill it. After the drying of the formvar film, a support is placed on the film and the whole assembly is immersed in water for a minute; the support prevents the film from curling during the immersion process. This step allows the formvar film to shrink slightly and in this way the breaking of films on final assembly due to high tension is eliminated. After this step, the formvar film is allowed to dry on the glass plate with the support removed. Upon drying, the formvar film will again adhere firmly to the glass and a support is then glued onto it with acetone collodion. Some pressure is exerted on the frame for about half an hour after which the pressure is then removed and the whole assembly allowed to dry for another hour. The support with the film is then stripped from the glass under water. On drying, the formvar film shrinks slightly and becomes perfectly flat.

---

*Grade 15/95, Shawinigan Ltd., London, England

Selenium is evaporated onto the formvar film in the usual way *(1)*. About 200 mg of black selenium* is evaporated from a source at a distance of about 200 cm and at a pressure of 0.3 mm of Hg. This process takes about two min. The distances of the different frames from the source are varied slightly. In this way, slightly different thicknesses of selenium are evaporated on the films and interference effects in the final assembly are avoided. In the method described above, the selenium is deposited on both sides of the formvar films. The deposit on the side farthest away from the source is thus thinner than the side exposed to the source.

With formvar films of about 0.3 μ thickness, the transmission of a pile of five films at an angle of 65° to the light beam is 30-36% in the region of 1.8-3.2 microns. Only at 2.8 microns does the transmission decrease to 28% (due to the absorption of formvar) and the degree of polarization is 95-98%. At 3.5 microns and higher, more absorption occurs. Selenium films of this kind are quite durable and can even be dropped from a small height without breakage. It has been found advisable to store the films in a desiccator to prevent development of absorption bands due to water.

Literature Cited

1. A. Elliott, E. J. Ambrose, and R. Temple, J. Opt. Soc. Am. **38**. 212 (1948)
2. J. Ames and A. M. D. Sampson, J. Sci. Instr. **26,** 132 (1949)
3. R. Duverney, J. Phys. Radium **20,** 66 (1959)

---

*Merck; need not be pure.

2.33 Ordinate Scale Expansion for the Precise Wavenumber Measurement of Broad Infrared Absorption Bands

W. F. Ulrich and H. J. Sloane

Beckman Instruments, Inc.
Fullerton, California

The current capability of high resolution, high wavenumber accuracy infrared instruments offers the potential for conveniently studying very subtle (one or two cm^{-1}) band displacements as a function of structure or solvent *(1)*. For measurements of tenths of cm^{-1} accuracy, it has formerly been necessary to calibrate the instrument carefully, using the known locations of the rotational bands of various light gases *(2)* and also to know the repeatability of the instrument to allow for errors in temperature variation, mechanical linkages, etc. The built-in accuracy of some of the newer instruments makes this procedure unnecessary.

Even so, another problem often arises in making a precise frequency measurement. This derives from the true band width of the sample band being measured. Most light gases present no obstacle, since the fine structure lines are usually sufficiently narrow to allow precise location of the band maximum. The much broader bands found in pure liquid and solution spectra are not so accommodating, however.

Jones and co-workers *(3)* have suggested a method of objectively locating the precise maximum of a broad band mathematically by computer fitting of the band maximum to a polynomial function and calculating the frequency of zero slope. We are suggesting a less elegant but more convenient approach. By a ten-fold ordinate scale expansion of the region of the peak, we have found that it is possible to reduce the uncertainty of locating the maximum from an estimated ± 0.7 cm^{-1} to about ± 0.2 cm^{-1} for a band of about 30 cm^{-1} natural half-band width.

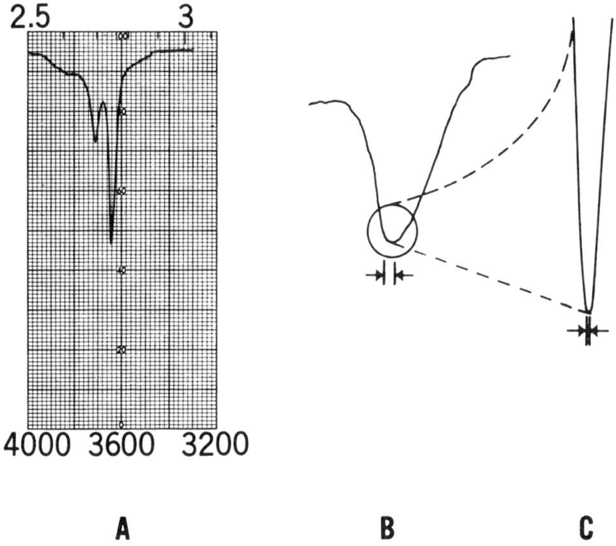

FIG. 1. TECHNIQUE FOR LOCATING THE WAVENUMBER MAXIMUM OF BROAD BANDS—n-HEPTANOL 3640.2 cm^{-1}

A—Format presentation, Beckman IR-9, 200 cm^{-1}/in., B—Same band, abscissa expanded, 20 cm^{-1}/in., C—Ten-fold ordinate scale expansion of circled portion of B. The spacing between arrows represents the uncertainty in locating the band maximum.

The technique is illustrated in Figure 1 for the "free" OH stretching band of *n*-heptanol in 0.005 *M* carbon tetrachloride solution. This band near 3640 cm^{-1} is shown in *A* for the ordinary chart format presentation, 200 cm^{-1}/in., of a Beckman IR-9 infrared spectrophotometer. The weaker band at 3710 cm^{-1} represents a trace of residual water. In *B* the 3640 cm^{-1} band is recorded at 20 cm^{-1}/in. Here the very gradual change in slope at the peak illustrates the difficulty in locating the center. The uncertainty shown by the spacing of the arrows below the band was estimated at ± 0.7 cm^{-1} from the wavenumber optical readout. The circled portion of the band in *B* is shown at a ten-fold ordinate scale expansion in *C*. Under these conditions, providing that a high signal-to-noise ratio is used in conjunction with the scale expansion, the reduced uncertainty shown by the arrow spacing in *C* was estimated at ± 0.2 cm^{-1}.

Thus, the peak wavenumber was measured as 3640.2 cm^{-1}. Allowing ± 0.2 cm^{-1} for the uncertainty in peak reading and a maximum of ± 0.5 cm^{-1} for the maximum possible absolute error of the instrument in this region with no previous calibration, the band position is 3640.2 ± 0.7 cm^{-1} assuming the worst case, *i.e.*, all errors in the same direction.

Literature Cited

(1) N. Shifrin, J. Ashley, and H. Sloane, *Frequency Calibration and the Importance of High Accuracy in the Modern Infrared Instrument,* Pittsburgh Conference on Analytical Chemistry and Applied Spectroscopy, 1963

(2) IUPAC Commission on Molecular Structure and Spectroscopy, *Tables of Wavenumbers for the Calibration of Infrared Spectrophotometers,* Butterworths, London, 1961

(3) R. N. Jones, K. S. Seshadri, and J. W. Hopkins, CAN. J. CHEM. **40,** 334 (1962)

2.34 Supplementary Optics For Perkin-Elmer Model 21, Double Beam Infrared Spectrophotometer

L. H. Little*

Department of Colloid Science, Free School Lane, Cambridge, England

While studying the infrared spectra of molecules adsorbed on solid surfaces, it was desirable to have the

*Present address: Dept. of Chemistry, University of Western Australia, Nedlands, Western Australia

sample placed at a focal point in the infrared beam and not at the normal sample position used in the Model 21. Moreover the sample space in the instrument is 12 cm and it was necessary in this work to accommodate samples with path lengths up to 25 cm, when equipment was used for low or high temperature infrared studies. The simple optical system, shown in Figure 1 (a), was constructed to meet these requirements. In Figure 2, the optical system, with a sample situated at the focus, is shown attached to the spectrometer.

A T-shaped piece of fibre board (Fig. 1 (a)), ¾ in. thick, was cut to fit into the space between the source housing and the monochromator housing. By tightening screws at G_1 and G_2, covering holes in the base of the spectrometer, the fibre board was rigidly attached to the spectrometer.

M_1, M_2, M_5 and M_6 are plane front aluminized mirrors and M_3 and M_4 are front, aluminized, concave spherical mirrors, with apertures of 10 cm and radii of curvature, 26 cm and 28 cm, respectively. The distances between the centres of the mirrors are as follows: M_1M_2 = 15 cm, M_2M_3 = 26 cm, M_3M_4 = 47 cm, M_4M_5 = 25 cm, and M_5M_6 = 13 cm. Figure 1 (b) shows the method of mount-

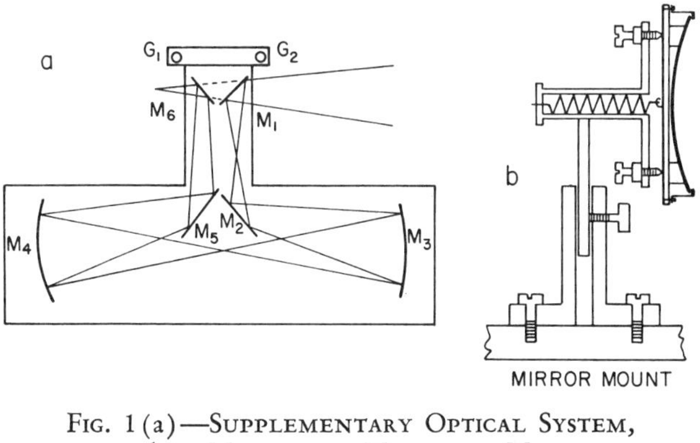

FIG. 1 (a)—SUPPLEMENTARY OPTICAL SYSTEM, (b)—METHOD OF MOUNTING MIRRORS

FIG. 2. SUPPLEMENTARY OPTICAL SYSTEM ATTACHED TO SPECTROMETER

ing the mirrors. The optical arrangement was designed to minimize the off-axis use of the spherical mirrors. The front, aluminized spherical mirrors* were inexpensive and were of the simple watch-glass type.

*Supplied by Gowllands, Croydon, Engl., for less than $3 each.

In operation the complete optical unit may be attached to the spectrometer within a few min., the only adjustment necessary is to turn mirror M_6, about its vertical axis until maximum energy is obtained. When carefully focussed 70-75% of the incident energy is transmitted by the complete system. The spectrometer is returned to normal operation, simply by removing the supplementary optics. In regions of atmospheric absorption, there is incomplete compensation owing to the increased path length in the sample beam. However this absorption is not intense (15% absorption at the most intense lines in the water vapour spectrum) and allowance may be easily made for it by first recording a background spectrum.

The author is grateful to Dr. N. Sheppard for discussion and to Mr. J. Pratt for construction of the apparatus.

The Construction of an Infrared Calibration Scale for the Perkin-Elmer Model 13-U Spectrophotometer 2.35

J. I. Peterson*, R. H. Johns†, and C. Clancy**

Research Division, Melpar, Incorporated, Falls Church, Virginia

Modern infrared spectrophotometers have the convenience of direct recording on a chart marked with a wavelength or wavenumber scale. Many laboratories, as ours does, own the older Perkin-Elmer model 13 spectrophotometer, or other instruments using the same monochromator. This instrument records on a Leeds and Northrup potentiometer recorder with no simple means of directly reading spectral positions on the curves. In order to avoid the tedious procedure for assigning wavelengths to absorption spectra by chart measurement and reference to a calibration curve and to allow observation

*Present address: Woodard Research Corporation, Herndon, Va.
†Present address: Atlantic Research Corporation, Alexandria, Va.
**Present address: American Chemical Society, Washington, D. C.

of the 2 to 15 microns recorded spectrum directly by inspection, our instrument recorder was modified and a transparent plastic overlay with wavelength, wavenumber, and "drum turn" scales was prepared. Since many of these instruments are in use and some are still being sold, it is felt that the procedure for doing this would be of interest to other users.

In order to have convenient scaling the chart drive gear was changed with a new set* so that one in. chart travel represented one "drum turn" on the monochromator,. at wavelength drum speed setting "one". This produces a convenient fifteen in. chart and allows the inch marks on the paper to be used for positioning the scale.

The recorder was modified electrically to transpose the scale, so that the resulting chart would be observed with the percent transmission scale reading up and with absorption peaks at the bottom as the wavelength scale reads increasing wavelength from left to right. This modification merely required reversing the leads to the recorder potentiometer slide wire and reversing the leads feeding the amplifier signal to the pen motor.

A more accurate "drum turn" or inch scale *vs.* wavelength relationship than furnished with the instrument was prepared by recording polystyrene and ammonia spectra and carefully plotting the wavelength values on graph paper at appropriate "drum turn" or inch points. A scale was then prepared by first finding the equation for the above curve, then drawing the scale with inch values derived from the equation. The equation is readily found so this is easier than using the curve directly. To find the equation for the curve, the slopes $S_1 = \Delta i_1/\Delta\lambda_1$ and $S_2 = \Delta i_2/\Delta\lambda_2$ are measured at two wavelength points (λ_1) and (λ_2). The rate of change in slope over this interval, a, is then calculated from $a = (S_2 - S_1)/(\lambda_2 - \lambda_1)$. The rate of change in slope with respect to the wavelength is assumed to be constant. (It is in fact constant

* Leeds & Northrup, Philadelphia, Pa.: part no. R-502X8 for this recorder without (A) in serial no., kit no. 124220 for later recorders with (A) in serial no.

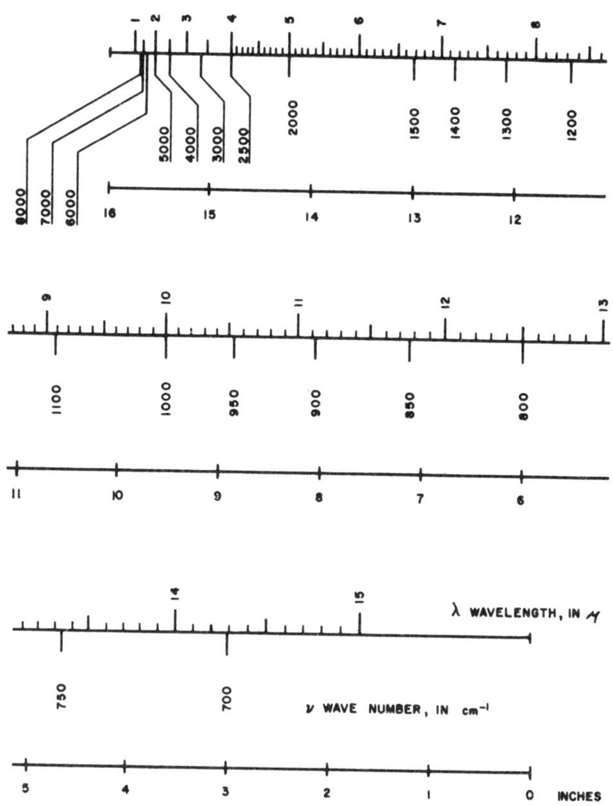

Fig. 1. Calibration Scale for Perkin-Elmer Model 13U Spectrophotometer

at $\lambda > 2.5$ microns). Integration of the constant, a, with respect to wavelength then yields the equation for the slope of the curve: $S = a\lambda + C = a\lambda$ where the constant of integration, C, is zero, since the slope of the curve is zero at $\lambda = 0$. Integration of this equation yields the equation for the curve, $i = (a\lambda^2/2) + b$.

The constant of integration, b, is evaluated from a point on the curve. It is necessary to adjust the value of a experimentally so that the equation fits the curve at both ends, as a result of the error in initial measurement of slopes. The constants for our instrument were a = 0.1254 and b = 15.8. It is not known how closely other instruments will match this. A table of appropriate wavelength and wavenumber positions, in in., was then calculated for drawing the overlay.

The overlay scale was prepared by drawing it on paper according to the plan of the accompanying picture of the scale (Figure 1) preparing an ink copy on linen and photographically reproducing this on Mylar film*.

The scale is somewhat in error below 2.5 microns because this region was extrapolated from the longer wavelength portion, whereas in fact the extrapolation is not valid. A correction to make the scale more accurate in the 1 to 2.5 micron region was not deemed necessary because of the scale compression in this region, which makes it of limited utility.

A compilation of the absorption bands useful for calibration has been published by Plyler *et al.*, *(1)*. Another procedure for calibration has been suggested by McKinney and Friedel *(2)* in which the expression has the same mathematical form, but the inclusion of an additional value for the Reststrahlen frequency of the prism leads to unnecessary complexity of calculation. They showed how the inclusion of an added factor in the expression allows extrapolation to shorter wavelengths for the NaCl prism.

Literature Cited

(1) E. K. Plyler, A. Danti, L. R. Blaine, and E. D. Tidwell, J. Res. Nat. Bur. Std. **64A**, 29 (1960); Nat. Bur. Std. Monograph **16**, 20 pp. (1960)

(2) D. S. McKinney and R. S. Friedel, J. Opt. Soc. Am. **38**, 222 (1948)

*Du Pont Cronaflex direct positive matte 0.007", Cat. DPm7, E. I. Du Pont de Nemours and Company, Wilmington, Del. If a transparency rather than a matte overlay is desired, Du Pont Cronar COS-7 may be used.

Simple Technique for Polishing Barium Fluoride Windows

2.36

D. S. Erley, B. H. Blake and A. W. Long
Spectroscopy Laboratory, The Dow Chemical Co., Midland, Michigan

This laboratory has often been faced with the problem of cleaning and polishing hard optical materials such as barium fluoride, calcium fluoride and lithium fluoride. The standard water techniques for polishing sodium chloride and potassium bromide *(1)* are not effective for the fluorides because of their low solubility in water. Other methods such as those used for polishing glass *(2)* are very time consuming. The increasing use of barium fluoride for water solution work in this laboratory made it particularly desirable to find a rapid, simple, manual method for polishing this material. It was found that by simply substituting concentrated HCl for water during the polishing process, barium fluoride could be polished to a clarity and flatness comparable to that obtained by water polishing sodium chloride.

Barium fluoride windows were hand polished for 5-10 min. on a 6 inch diameter pitch lap with a slurry of concentrated HCl and *Shamva**. This procedure was sufficient to eliminate the sulfate absorption bands from a window which had become contaminated with barium sulfate. Two windows which had become cloudy due to acid attack (50% transmission at 2.5 microns) were polished by the same technique to give 81% transmission at the same wavelength. (An unused barium fluoride plate transmitted 90% of the light at 2.5 microns).

Rough ground barium fluoride blanks may be polished to optical clarity if #600 *Aloxite*† is used instead of *Shamva* on the pitch lap. The time required is only slightly longer (~15 min. per side). After polishing the flatness of all plates has been ~5 fringes of sodium light

---

*Available from Golwynne Chemicals Corp., 420 Lexington Ave., New York, N. Y.

†Available from Carborundum Co., Niagara Falls, N. Y.

when placed on an optical flat, but this can be improved by longer polishing times.

Calcium fluoride and lithium fluoride have also been polished by this technique but with less success than barium fluoride. It is possible that more effective slurrying agents than HCl could be found for these crystals.

Concentrated HCl does not attack the pitch lap, but the usual safety precautions for working with it must be observed. Rubber surgical gloves, a rubber apron, safety glasses and a good fume hood should provide adequate protection. The use of less concentrated HCl solutions increases the polishing time considerably without materially reducing the hazard.

Literature Cited

1. R. C. Lord, R. S. McDonald and F. A. Miller, J. Opt. Soc. Am. **42**, 149 (1952)
2. J. Strong, "*Procedures in Experimental Physics*", Prentice Hall, New York, Chap. 2 (1939)

See also 8.2, 8.4, 8.5

2.37 Circular Correlation Charts for the Assignment of Bands in Infrared Spectra

H. K. Palmer*

Imperial Chemical Industries Limited, Dyestuffs Division
Hexagon House, Blackley, Manchester, England

Several correlation charts are available in the literature for the assignments of infrared bands to chemical groups. Because of the difficulty of condensing the required infor-

---

* Present address: Department of Physical Chemistry, The University, Bristol 8, England

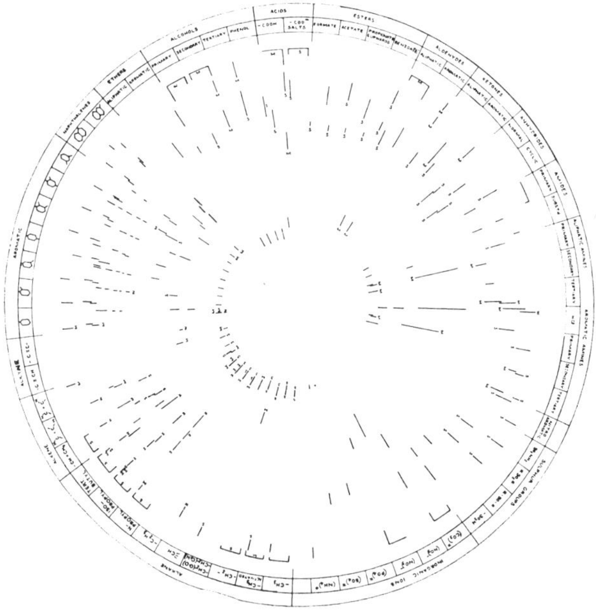

FIG. 1. SCALE FOR CHART 1

mation on to a small area, these tend to be inconveniently large or somewhat congested and difficult to read.

The two charts described in this note are an attempt to overcome these disadvantages. They are conveniently small and robust for laboratory use and present the data in such a way that the tracing of guide lines is unnecessary. In practice both charts may be combined as one unit with the scales occupying the front and back faces.

Chart 1

This chart automatically presents the wavelengths of the main absorption bands due to any of 61 classes of chemical compounds. Figure 1 shows the lower disc, which is marked in segments each carrying the name of a chemi-

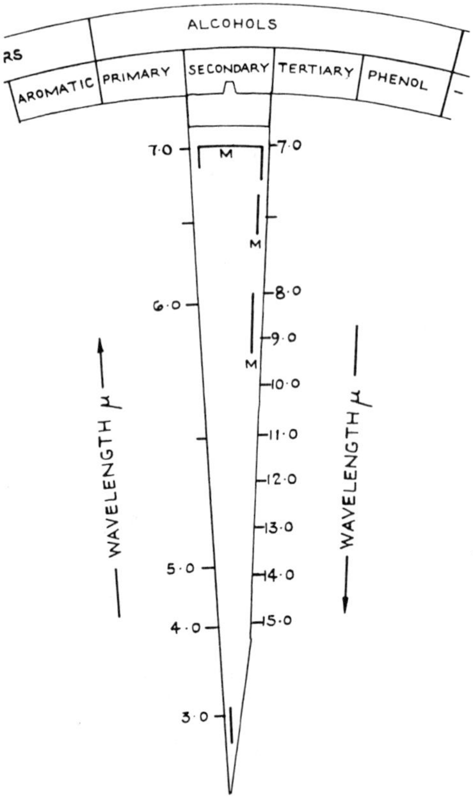

FIG. 2. PORTION OF CHART 1 SHOWING WAVELENGTH SCALE

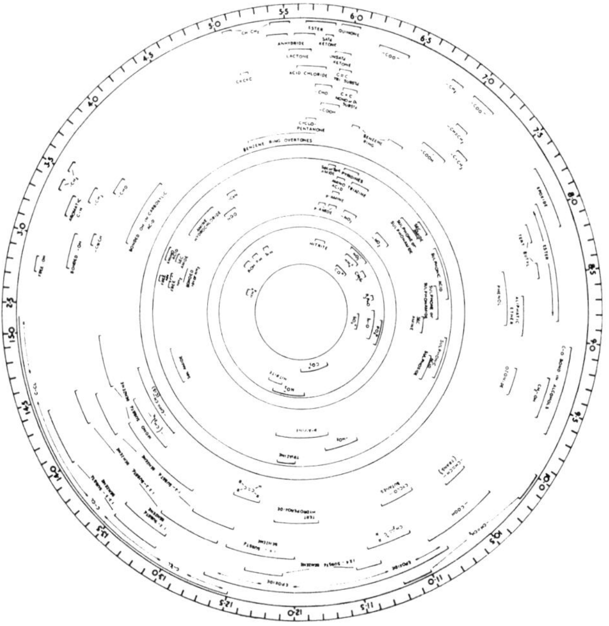

FIG. 3. SCALE FOR CHART 2.

cal class and its ranges of probable absorption. The chart is used by setting the pointer on the upper disc against the appropriate type and reading off the band positions from the cut out segment of the upper disc. Figure 2 shows a portion of the chart as it would appear in use. The arrangement of the wavelength scale along the edge of the cut-out sector can be seen.

Chart 2

The chemical groups that may be responsible for an absorption band at any particular wavelength are shown by this chart. The design of the lower disc of this chart is shown in Figure 3. The chart is operated by setting the pointer to the required wavelength and reading through the cut-out segments in the upper disc those groups which might be responsible for bands at this wavelength. The operation of this chart can be seen in Figure 4.

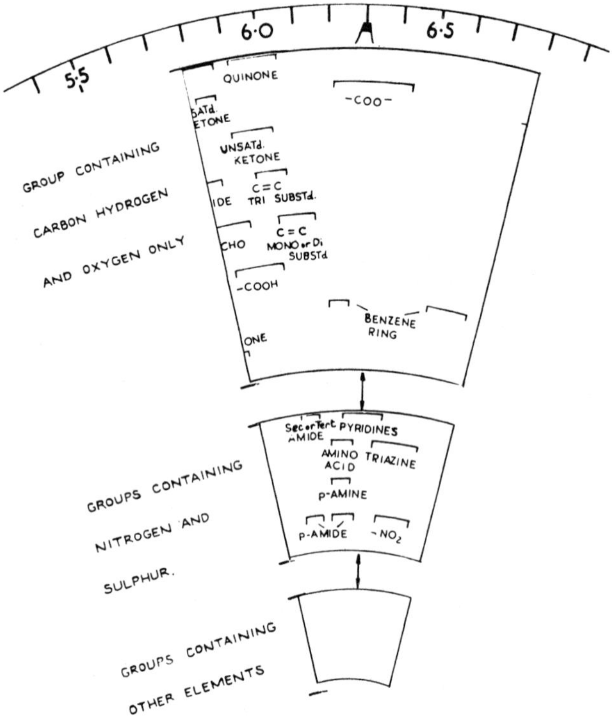

FIG. 4. PART OF CHART 2 SHOWING PRESENTATION OF THE DATA

SECTION 3
MASS SPECTROSCOPY

Sampling of Gaseous Components Contained in Glass Bulbs in Mass Spectrometry 3.1

L. D. Shubin, J. I. Peterson*, and R. W. Fitch†

Research Division, Melpar, Incorporated, Falls Church, Virginia

A common analytical problem, particularly for those involved in mass spectrometric analyses, is breaking glass bulbs *in vacuo* to release their contents. Normally, this is done by smashing them inside an evacuated glass bulb against a metal block by a magnet. The advent of smaller, heavier walled bulbs make this a difficult process. This laboratory, therefore, used a different approach to the sampling problem.

An induction generator was used to heat a wire wrapped bulb in an evacuated sample container. The bulb of interest is first scratched, then wrapped with three or four turns of platinum or tungsten wire, B and S 25 to 28 gauge, and placed in a borosilicate glass container (Figure 1) which is provided with a fitting for attachment to a mass spectrometer.

*Present address: Woodard Research Corporation, Herndon, Virginia
†Present address: Atlantic Research Corporation, Alexandria, Virginia

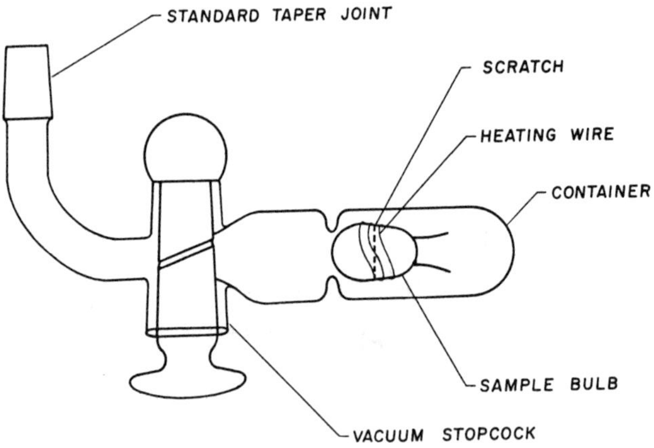

FIG. 1. SAMPLING APPARATUS

The selection of the wire is important since it must not react with, adsorb, or catalyze any reactions of the gaseous components. Scratching very thin walled bulbs is not required and may lead to premature fracture of the glass.

The procedure involves preparing a borosilicate glass container (Figure 1) of suitable dimensions, leaving one end open to receive the samples. A sample is inserted, prepared as noted previously, into the container, allowing it to rest upon the glass fingers, and the open end of the container is sealed with a torch. The container is evacuated, and the sample is placed inside a suitable induction heating coil. The bulb is fractured by rapid heating, and then the container is attached to a mass spectrometer for analysis of the gases.

This procedure is applicable to any glass bulb which is in general use, such as glow discharge tubes, electric lamps, trace gases in vacuum tubes, etc.

Use of A Getter-Ion Type Pump with A Mass Spectrometer* 3.2

A. A. Ebert, Jr.

Jackson Laboratory, Organic Chemicals Department,
E. I. du Pont de Nemours & Company, Wilmington, Delaware

A General Electric analytical mass spectrometer has been in use in this laboratory for the past eight years. During this period, most of the down-time experienced with the spectrometer has resulted from failure of the mercury diffusion pump. Such mishaps as burst water lines, broken glass boilers, and broken pump belts have caused the pump to fail often resulting in other damage to the spectrometer. The accumulative effect of pump failures together with associated mishaps have accounted for about 75% of the total down-time.

In addition to the problem of pump failure, a diffusion pump presents a serious maintenance problem. It requires a liquid nitrogen cold trap which must be filled either manually or automatically on a continual round-the-clock basis. Manual filling demands personnel on a daily 24 hr basis. Automatic filling is wasteful of liquid nitrogen and often involves an awkward physical set-up. In either case, the cost of the liquid nitrogen consumed in a year's time becomes significant. In view of these difficulties it seemed desirable to investigate another type pump.

The Varian Vac Ion pump *(1,2)* was investigated because of its many advantages with respect to maintenance. It eliminated the need for a cold trap, cooling water, and a mechanical forepump. The electronic pump had no moving parts, no hot filaments, and no periodically-replaceable components. This obviated the periodic shutdowns required by the diffusion pump for replacing mercury and changing pump oil. The lack of wearable parts assured long life and continuous, uninterrupted service which is essential for optimum mass spectrometer operation.

The life of the pump is a function of the pressure in the system and ultimately depends on the supply of

*Research Division Contribution No. 301

titanium in the pump because titanium is necessary to maintain the pumping action. The economical use of titanium, which has been reported is of interest *(1)*. It has been estimated that in pumping such gases as air, CO_2, and H_2 approximately one half to one gas molecule is pumped for each atom of titanium sputtered. Because of the nature of the pumping mechanism, only as much material is sputtered as is necessary to pump the gas present. With this self-regulating behavior, the pump can be expected to have a life of several years, if it is operated by at very low pressure.

The electronic pump has been in service with the mass spectrometer since October, 1958 and has proved to be completely satisfactory. It produced no difficulty with start-up and reached a good operating range with an overnight pump-down. A pump with a 5 l/sec capacity has been used which pumps a spectrometer volume of about 1.5 l. Between samples, a vacuum of about 1 x 10^{-7} mm Hg is produced. The pump-out time for samples is largely controlled by the speed of evacuation of the expansion chamber, which is pumped by an oil diffusion pump. It normally requires six to seven min to evacuate the expansion chamber, and at the end of this period the analyzer tube is completely clean and ready for the next sample. It would not be feasible to use the electronic pump to evacuate the expansion chamber because of the high pressure involved.

If no samples are introduced into the system for a few hr, or after an overnight pump-out, a vacuum in the 10^{-9} mm range is produced. Pressure in this region cannot be measured precisely because the meter reading is very low or often the needle does not leave its zero position. A reading of 0.1 μa, about the lowest reading possible, corresponds to a pressure of 5 x 10^{-9} mm. These higher vacuum conditions are of significance only with regard to prolonging the life of the pump. If the pump operates in the 10^{-9} mm region the greater part of the day, the pump should last indefinitely.

From an operational standpoint, the principal advantage of the electronic pump is the cleaner spectral background it provides. Mercury is, of course, eliminated, and except for nitrogen and water peaks which are negligibly small no other peaks appear in the background.

Aside from improved backgrounds, little change is noted in general spectrometer performance. Cracking patterns exhibit no anomalies and sensitivities are essentially unchanged. Our experience has shown that sensitivities are largely determined by the conditioning of the ion source, other factors being equal (alignment, focusing, etc.).

The mass spectrometer is used for assistance to general exploratory organic research, and all types of materials have been put through the instrument. Out of a wide range of chemicals examined, none has been encountered that could not be pumped readily, with the exception of inert gases. The pump has worked successfully with hydrocarbons, inorganic gases, halogenated hydrocarbons, strong acids, water vapor, oxygenated compounds, and other organic compounds. Inert gases such as argon and helium are noticeably slower pumping than other materials, and if handled in large quantities over a period of time, they would build up a background. However, if encountered only occasionally in non-excessive amounts ($<50\%$), they produce no problem. It is not recommended that pure argon or helium be admitted to the spectrometer in the usual amounts because they would overload a pump of this size. If these gases are to be analyzed often, a larger pump or several small pumps connected in parallel using the same power supply should be employed. The pump if overloaded by inert gases will overheat and cease to pump and should be shut off when this condition occurs. After about five min cooling, the discharge can be started again, and the pump will quickly produce a good vacuum.

Most of the materials encountered have sufficiently similar pumping rates so that good analytical results can be obtained using conventional sensitivity values. Even materials differing in pumping rates do not seriously affect the accuracy of an analysis as shown in Table I. Although hydrogen has a rated pumping speed about twice that of nitrogen *(3)*, there is no measurable analytical difference in relative concentrations between a blend of butane in hydrogen and butane in nitrogen. This represents an extreme case of differential pumping rates, but no analytical

TABLE I
ANALYTICAL RESULTS ON BLENDS HAVING DIFFERENT PUMPING SPEEDS

Blend	*Component*	*Blend, %*	*Mass Spectrometer Analysis, %*
1	Butane	10	9.9
	Nitrogen	90	90.1
2	Butane	10	9.9
	Hydrogen	90	90.1

problem is encountered. The results in Table I were computed using sensitivities calculated from a scan of the pure materials. If materials are found differing too widely in pumping rates, they can, of course, be calibrated for the matrix in which they occur.

From the experience gained from its use, the getter-ion type pump appears to be satisfactory for mass spectrometer application and offers many advantages from a maintenance standpoint.

Literature Cited

(1) L. D. Hall, REV. SCI. INSTR. **29**, 367 (1958)
(2) L. D. Hall, SCIENCE **128**, 279 (1958)
(3) *VacIon High Vacuum Pump*, Data Sheet V-11402, Varian Associates, Palo Alto, Calif.

3.3 Mass Spectrometric Sampling from Micro Infrared Plates and Recollection of Sample for Further Analysis

M. G. Moshonas and G. L. K. Hunter

U. S. Fruit and Vegetable Products Laboratory*
Winter Haven, Florida

A simple device has been developed to facilitate the transfer of submicroliter liquid samples directly from

*One of the laboratories of the Southern Utilization Research and Development Division, Agricultural Research Service, U. S. Department of Agriculture.

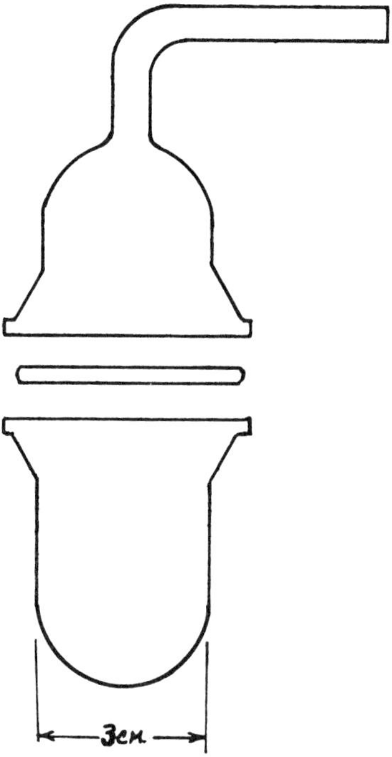

FIG. 1. MASS SPECTROMETER SAMPLE TRANSFER DEVICE

small infrared plates *(1)* or cavity cells into a mass spectrometer. It also allows for recondensation of the remaining sample following mass spectral analysis.

The all-glass device, shown in Figure 1, was constructed from a Delmar-Urey, greaseless, twenty mm i.d. ring joint.* The large open end of the joint was sealed approximately four cm below the lip. A five mm x 10 cm glass tube was fused to the hose nipple at the other end and bent at a right angle to provide for insertion into the mass spectrometer liquid inlet system.

* Delmar Scientific Company, Chicago, Illinois. Reference to this manufacturer does not imply recommendation over similar products of other manufacturers.

In practice, the device is fitted to the mass spectrometer liquid inlet system by replacing the inlet system septmum with a suitable "O" ring. The infrared plates or micro cell, containing the sample, are placed into the device which is then sealed by means of the Viton "O" ring provided as an integral part of the original joint. The device, containing the infrared plates or micro cell, is cooled by immersion in liquid nitrogen and the entire system evacuated. When the proper vacuum is attained, the sample is transferred into the mass spectrometer sample handling sphere by heating the device with a hot-air gun. Upon completion of the analysis, the device is again immersed in liquid nitrogen at which time the remaining sample recondenses on the glass walls. The salt plates or cavity cell, now free of sample, are removed and the sample is available for further analyses.

Literature Cited

(1) G. L. K. Hunter, APPLIED SPECTROSCOPY **18**, 159 (1964)

SECTION 4
NUCLEAR MAGNETIC RESONANCE

Dosimetry of Reference Tetramethylsilane in Nuclear Magnetic Resonance Spectroscopy 4.1

W. G. Gorman, R. K. Kullnig, and F. C. Nachod

Sterling-Winthrop Research Institute, Rensselaer, New York

Tetramethylsilane (TMS) is a convenient standard ($\delta = 0$ or $\tau = 10$) in nuclear magnetic resonance spectroscopy. However, owing to its high vapor pressure, its specific gravity and low surface tension, pipetting of TMS is difficult. The alternative is the use of TMS in a micro-capillary as an external standard. This again brings about the necessity for correcting for the bulk susceptibility, which differs from solution to solution *(1)*.

Workers in the field have resorted to "doping" of solvents, but again the high partial pressure of TMS results in its rapid loss from the solvent. We have, therefore, sought means of adding reasonably reproducible amounts of TMS to individual solution samples of about 0.5 ml.

Pressurized vials of TMS were prepared in the following manner. Clean, dry 10 ml plastic coated aerosol bottles (No. S-32-F1 clear, Wheaton Plasti-Cote Corp., Mays Landing, N. J.) were filled with approximately 6 ml of

TMS (Peninsular Chemresearch, Inc., Gainesville, Fla.). After allowing a few sec for the TMS vapors to replace the air above the TMS liquid, the bottles were sealed tightly with No. 5883-0.05X Magna-Meter valves (Risdon Mfg. Co., Naugatuck, Conn.). Since the vapor pressure of TMS (700 mm Hg at 25°C) was too low for adequate valve operation, the sealed bottles were pressurized through the valve with nitrogen to a pressure of approximately 80 psi. A modified actuator prepared by attaching a stainless steel tube (approximately 0.058 in. od and 1.5 in. long) to a No. 5618EF-1 actuator (Risdon Mfg. Co., Naugatuck, Conn.) was then fitted to the valve stem. The actuator tube was bent downward, about 60° below horizontal, so that it could be readily inserted into an upright sample tube. Actuation of the valve then delivered a metered quantity of TMS through the actuator tube into the sample tube. With these units, an average of 60 $\pm$ 10 mg of TMS can be discharged into the sample tube with each valve actuation.

After adding TMS to the tube, mixing by up-ending is rapid, and the sample is ready for insertion into the probe.

Literature Cited

(1) J. A. Pople, W. G. Schneider, and H. J. Bernstein, *High Resolution Nuclear Magnetic Resonance*, McGraw Hill Book Co., New York, 1959, p. 78

Nuclear Magnetic Resonance in Metal Powders at Low Temperatures* 4.2

Rex J. Snodgrass and Lawrence H. Bennett

National Bureau of Standards, Washington, D. C.

An improved method for low temperature nuclear magnetic resonance (NMR) measurements on metal powders is presented. A Varian Wide-Line NMR Spectrometer of the crossed-coil type is used to observe the resonance in metallic powder samples at liquid nitrogen and liquid helium temperatures. The spectrometer probe, dewar and sample are shown in Figure 1. Powders having particle sizes less than the skin depth are used to permit sufficient penetration of the sample by the radio-frequency magnetic field. Motion of the sample caused by the bubbling refrigerant introduces electromagnetic noise and represents the limiting factor in making accurate measurements. We find that the most satisfactory method for holding the sample stationary in the probe and thereby eliminating this noise is to glue it to the bottom of the dewar with paraffin oil.

The NMR signal voltage induced in the receiver coil of the probe by the precessing nuclei of the sample appears as a modulation of the magnetic coupling (leakage) between the transmitter and receiver coils. The leakage can be controlled by coupling devices called paddles. The paddles must be adjusted with the sample in the probe, since the metallic sample itself affects the coupling. It is important that both the phase and amplitude of the leakage remain constant during the time of passage through a resonance curve. Incorrect leakage phasing results in the detection of a mixture of absorption and dispersion modes of the signal. The mode-mixing is reflected in distortions and asymmetries of the recorded resonance line and is a

*Note added in proof: Since the submission of this trick we noticed that Dr. T. J. Rowland, in his Ph.D. thesis (Harvard, 1954, unpublished) mentions, without details, using paraffin oil to avoid the vibration accompanying the boiling of liquid air in a single coil spectrometer.

severe hindrance to accurate measurements of centers, widths, and line shapes.

When the probe is balanced, the magnetic flux lines near the coils have a definite and stable configuration. Probe unbalance is essentially a result of disturbing these lines of force. With conducting powder samples, the main unbalancing factors are the changing conductivity of the sample due to temperature changes and any change in the physical orientation of the sample in the receiver coil. The former may be largely overcome by holding the sample at a constant temperature. The latter is a general problem faced by experimentalists who have liquid nitrogen or helium in contact with the sample. The constant bubbling of the refrigerant imparts a small motion to the sample, which disturbs the flux lines and appears as a major source of noise.

The nitrogen dewar is designed so that its lower part (the finger) fits into the Varian rf probe (Figure 1). The finger is 17 mm o.d., and 13 mm i.d. The dewar is 25 cm long, and its upper reservoir is 13 cm o.d. It is silvered with the exception of the finger (since this would cause undesirable eddy-currents) and a strip for viewing the nitrogen level. The nitrogen lasts about two and one-half hr without refilling.

Observation of the resonance at 77°K was first attempted by pouring liquid nitrogen directly on the metallic powder sample which was in the finger of the dewar. A large amount of noise from the motion of the sample was detected. High pressures built up in "pockets" with the results that the sample "exploded" out of the dewar.

The metallic powder in which the resonance is to be observed is now encapsulated in glass, care being taken not to melt any part of the sample when sealing off. The glass capsule is about 38 mm long, about 11 mm o.d., and is about one-half filled with sample. The capsule is placed in the bottom of the finger of a dewar and nitrogen is poured around it. A number of unsuccessful methods were tried to hold the capsule stationary with respect to the receiver coil.

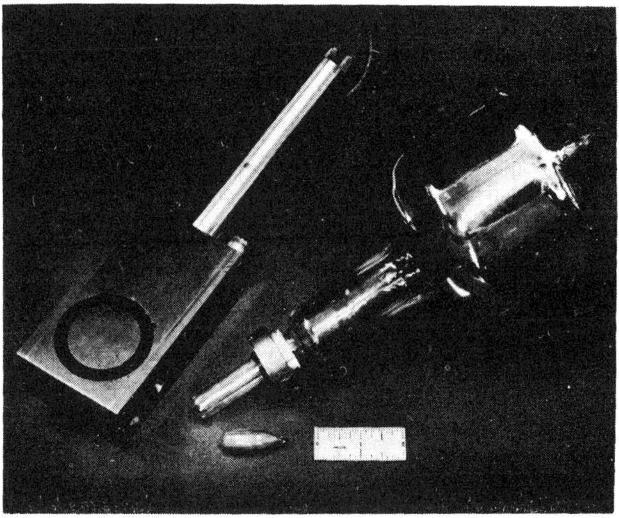

FIG. 1. SPECTROMETER RF PROBE, NITROGEN DEWAR, AND ENCAPSULATED SAMPLE

These included: 1) Glass wool or Styrofoam was wedged around the encapsulated sample. This reduced but did not eliminate the electrical noise. In addition, the nitrogen was not always able to contact the sample uniformly. 2) Duco cement was allowed to dry around the sample. The coefficient of thermal expansion of the cement is sufficiently different from that of glass to break the dewar finger when nitrogen is poured in. 3) GE low temperature cement was used to glue the sample in place. The conductivity of this cement is apparently high enough to permit eddy-currents to flow and prevent balancing of the probe. 4) A glass rod was securely fastened to the samole and clamped at the upper part of the dewar. This provided too long a "lever arm" between the sample and the point of clamping to hold the sample perfectly still. 5) Nitrogen bubbling may be suppressed by introducing a stream of a low-boiling-point gas such as helium into the liquid nitro-

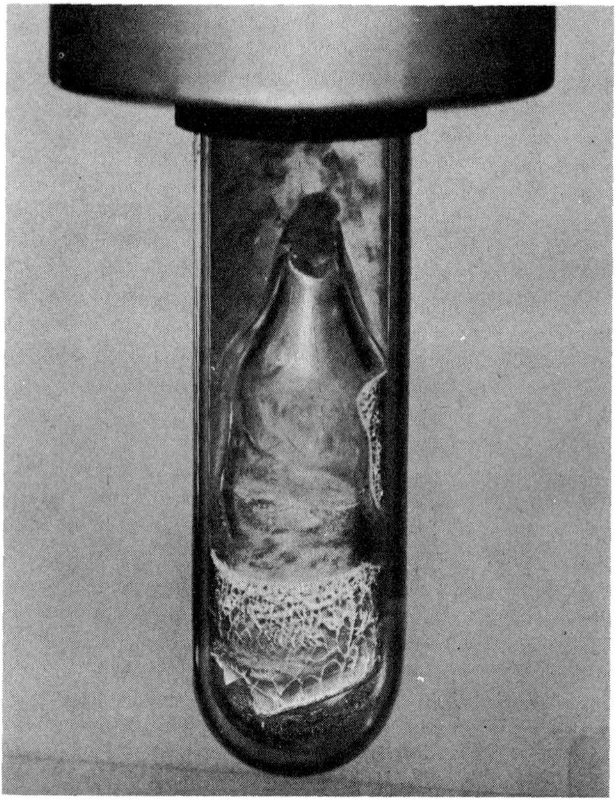

FIG. 2. FINGER OF DEWAR SHOWING GLASS CAPSULE GLUED WITH FROZEN PARAFFIN OIL NEAR THE BOTTOM

The metal powder sample fills about half the capsule. Nitrogen bubbles can be seen near the top of the capsule.

gen *(1)*. Although this method was found to be partly successful for reducing noise, it had several deficiences: a) The temperature of the sample is reduced below 77°K requiring control of the rate of flow of helium and measurement of temperature; b) It cannot be used at liquid helium temperature; and c) It is more complicated than the method described below.

We find that the best method to hold the sample stationary is to glue it by pouring in paraffin oil until the part of the capsule filled with sample is about one-half covered (See Figure 2). Paraffin oil, a liquid at room temperature, solidifies around the lower half of the sample at 77°K or lower, thus providing the low temperature "glue". The volume change of the paraffin oil upon freezing is insufficient to break the glass dewar finger. If the receiver coil is placed around that part of the sample not covered with paraffin oil, the presence of the frozen oil does not reduce the thermal contact between the sample and the refrigerant. A false bottom on the capsule would serve the same purpose and conserve the sample.

It is believed that this extremely simple and convenient way of holding small samples stationary, while in good thermal contact with the refrigerant, will be applicable to both wide-line NMR requiring the measurement of shifts small compared to the line width and to electron spin resonance at low temperatures.

Literature Cited

(1) G. J. Minkoff, F. I. Scherber, and A. K. Stober, Nature **180**, 1413 (1957). We thank Dr. E. D. Becker for calling our attention to this reference.

SECTION 5
RAMAN SPECTROSCOPY

Ignition of Low Pressure Mercury Arc Lamps with Auxiliary Condensor Battery 5.1

R. Block and F. C. Mijlhoff

Laboratory for Jnorganic Chemistry of the University of Amsterdam, Amsterdam, Netherlands

In Raman spectroscopy discontinuous radiation with low continuous background can be obtained from low pressure mercury arc lamps, preferably operated with direct current *(1)*. As the ignition voltage of the arc is well above the normal operating voltage, the excess voltage must be suppressed by means of a series resistor, which has to carry large current (approximately 20 amp). The power, dissipated by this resistor, may well be about a kilowatt. The heat generated in this way is not only wasted but is highly undesirable as it is necessary to keep the temperature constant in the spectrograph room.

In order to avoid this, we devised a simple way to ignite the arc by deriving the ignition voltage from a charged condensor (Figure 1). The condensor, *C*, is charged with direct current obtained from the line using a metal rectifier, *D;* then the line voltage is switched

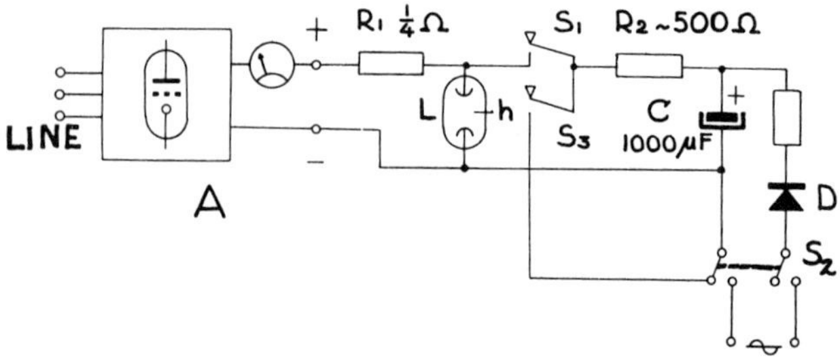

FIG. 1. IGNITION CIRCUIT DIAGRAM

off with S_2. The voltage is applied to the electrodes of the lamp, *L*, by a thyratron controlled, three-phase, half-wave rectifier, *A*. Now key S_1 is pressed, and *C* is discharged through *L* by stimulated ionization induced by a vacuum leak tester, held to the auxiliary electrode, *h*. The lamp, *L*, ignites and because of R_2 the discharge of *C* is spread over a time sufficient for the rectifier to take over. Any residual charge on the condensor may be removed by tapping key S_3. A stabilizing series resistor R_1 of ¼ ohm is sufficient.

The power rectifier is dimensioned to provide a voltage slightly above the operating voltage and the arc current may be adjusted after ignition by varying the thyratron regulation as usual.*

Literature Cited

(1) J. Brandmüller and H. Moser, Z. ANGEW. PHYS. **8,** 95 (1956)

---

* Thyratron regulation from ignition voltage back to operating voltage is undesirable because of the highly pulsating character of the arc current thus obtained.

SECTION 6
ULTRAVIOLET AND VISIBLE SPECTROSCOPY

A Microcell for Ultraviolet Absorption Studies* 6.1

W. S. Ferguson and C. W. Gullikson

The Ohio Oil Company, Denver Research Center, Littleton, Colorado

About 20% of the sample required to fill a conventional one-cm ultraviolet spectrophotometer cell is actually traversed by the instrument beam. Clearly, then, only 20% of the sample present in the cell is absorbing energy and thus producing an instrument reading. Such inefficient utilization of sample is ordinarily no disadvantage—the sample concentration is adjusted accordingly. However, with a limited amount of sample, it becomes increasingly important to achieve a high ratio of sample volume to cell volume.

Various absorption cells and positioning devices have been described in the literature (*1-7*). In all cases, either the complexity of cell construction and its positioning device, or the amount of sample necessary to fill the cell led the authors to design the present cell to overcome these disadvantages. Some cell designers may have overlooked the simple fact that the absorption of light by a sample

* Presented at the Third Annual Rocky Mountain Spectroscopy Conference, August 1960, Denver, Colorado.

is dependent solely upon the mass of sample in the light beam; whether this mass is within a volume of moderate area and small thickness, or in a volume of very small area and large thickness, has no effect if the amount of light passing through the sample is the same in both cases. However, in the latter case, the light beam must be condensed, and this leads to relatively complicated positioning fixtures. It is for these reasons that the authors decided to construct the cell described here.

This microcell for ultraviolet spectrophotometry was designed with the sample cavity cross-sectional area slightly larger all around than the cross-section of the incident light beam. Thus essentially all of the sample required to fill the cell is effective in absorbing energy from the spectrophotometer light beam and, at the same time, cell positioning is much less critical than for very small area—large thickness designs; in fact, the standard cell holders are adequate for proper positioning of this cell. Other primary objectives in the design were flexibility of cell thickness and ease of manipulations in using the cell, for example, in filling, recovering sample, and cleaning for re-use.

Figure 1 shows the microcell parts in assembly sequence. Using four screws for assembly, the cell "sandwich" is firmly compressed between the housing, *G*, and the backing-plate, *A*, which are machined from stainless steel.

The cell "sandwich" is built up as follows. A lead gasket, *F*, containing holes to match the filling ports, seals the drilled window, *E*, to the cell housing. The second window, *C*, is separated from and sealed to the first window by a lead spacer, *D*, the thickness of which can be varied from 0.1 to 1.0 mm. *B* is a neoprene rubber gasket. Both lead spacer *D* and lead gasket *F* are lightly amalgamated with mercury before assembly. The windows are constructed of quartz although other materials having transmission and mechanical properties suitable for the intended application can be used.

Ports for filling the assembled cell are illustrated on a reversed view, G_r, of the housing *G*. These ports are sealed

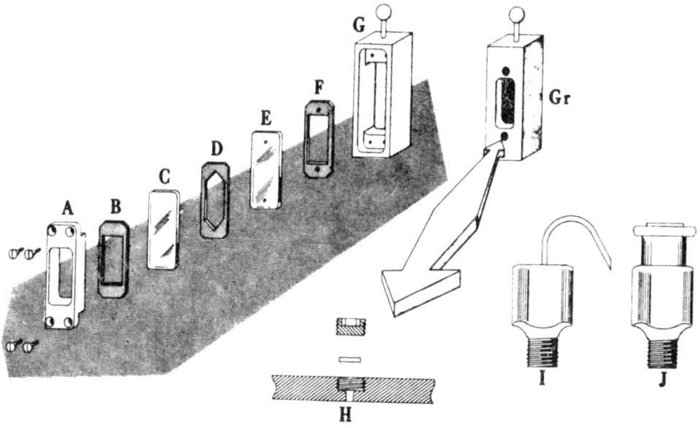

FIG. 1. EXPLODED VIEW OF MICROCELL

See text for explanation of symbols.

with Teflon gaskets retained by threaded plugs as illustrated in detail *H*. Detail *I* shows a hypodermic needle capillary fitting used in filling or emptying the cell. Detail *J* is a threaded Luer-Lok fitting used to attach a hypodermic syringe to one of the ports. The outside dimensions of the cell assembly very closely approximate the outside dimensions of conventional one-cm cells, and consequently the assembly fits directly into standard spectrophotometer cell-holders.

Filling of the cell is easily accomplished using for example a transfer micropipet controlled with a hypodermic syringe. With both ports opened the cell is positioned port side up with the top end slightly elevated to a degree best determined by trial and error. Sample solution is introduced slowly while positioning the pipet tip directly against the depression in the bottom of the lower port. The pipet tip must not exceed 0.040 in. o.d. The cell is emptied and cleaned by flushing the sample out using fresh solvent. With the cell positioned as for filling, the ports are opened and the fitting *I* of Figure 1. is installed in the top port. Fresh solvent is flushed through the cell using the same manipulations described for filling the cell.

The sample and rinsings are collected in any suitable container and the cell subsequently dried by attaching either an air or a vacuum line to the hypodermic needle fitting. An alternate method for filling the cell is to use fitting *I* alone. The end of the curved tube is "dipped" into the sample, which is then pulled into the cell by capillary action.

As has already been indicated the microcell is demountable and can be made up in sample path thicknesses from 0.1 to 1.0 mm. The minimum volume of sample solution required to fill the cell to the top of the window at various cell spacer thicknesses has been determined experimentally to be given by

$$V = 110t + 3$$

where t is the spacer thickness, mm, and V is the volume, μl. Spacer thicknesses of 0.1 and 1.0 mm yield cell volumes of about 14 and 113 μl, respectively. Factors of experimental convenience, such as the solubility of the sample in solvents having suitable spectral characteristics, have to be considered in deciding upon the best cell thickness to use for any particular application. When the amount of available sample is limited, the objective is to dissolve all of the sample in a volume of solution which will just fill the cell for the spacer thickness selected.

The microcell performance, in terms of the ratio of sample volume within the window area to the total sample volume required to fill the cell, is a characteristic of interest. This characteristic as a function of spacer thickness is given in Figure 2 where it will be seen that the proportion of sample material within the volume between the window areas varies from 0.5 with a 0.1 mm spacer to 0.8 with a 0.5 mm or larger spacer. Using a conventional one-cm cell, the proportion of sample volume within the same amount of area to the total sample volume is about 0.2.

The following experiments were performed to demonstrate some advantageous features of the microcell. Spectra were obtained on a Cary Model 14 recording spectrophotometer using a microcell with a 0.5 mm spacer and air

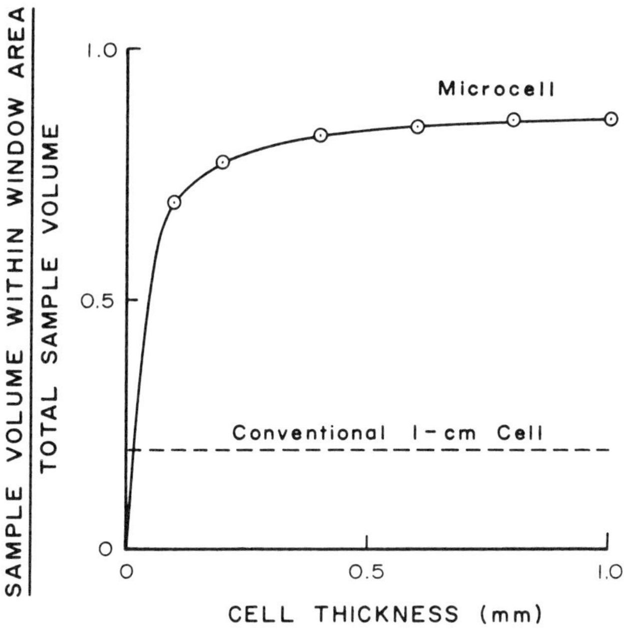

FIG. 2. THE RATIO OF SAMPLE WITHIN WINDOW AREAS TO TOTAL SAMPLE AS A FUNCTION OF THE CELL THICKNESS

as the reference. After a base line of cyclohexane was observed, the spectrum of benzene at 6.59 g/l in cyclohexane solution was obtained. The microcell was emptied by flushing with 3 cell volumes of cyclohexane with the 3rd cell volume of solvent remaining in the cell. The spectrum of the 3rd rinse remaining in the cell was essentially identical with the base line. Thus the cell can be completely cleaned (and quantitative recovery of the sample into a separate container is possible) using only two rinses. The cell design is accordingly shown to be free of dead-end spaces. Next, the benzene sample and rinsings removed from the microcell were diluted so as to fill a one-cm cell, and the spectrum was again observed. The 2490A absorbance was but 33% of that observed using the microcell. This confirms the microcell efficiency as indicated in Figure 2.

Figure 3 shows how little sample is required to obtain useful absorbances when the microcell is used. As typical examples, data are given for some aromatic hydrocarbon solutions in a microcell having a 0.5 mm spacer. For example, anthracene has an absorptivity of 46 l/g cm. Eighteen μg of anthracene, dissolved in 65 μl of solvent and loaded into a 0.5 mm cell, will furnish an absorbance of 0.7. Only 5 μg of anthracene is required to produce an absorbance of 0.2. Materials having larger absorptivities, such as naphthalene, will require correspondingly smaller sample amounts to produce equivalent absorbances. It should be noted, that because the assumption of Beer's Law is implicit in Figure 3 weights determined from that plot are approximate.

The microcell which has been described is obviously a piece of special equipment to be used when the amount of sample is too small for ordinary handling. Examples of applications which require high efficiency of sample utilization in absorption measurements are forensic investigations, air pollution studies, examination of gas chromatographic fractions, and certain clinical work. Our own requirements for a cell of this design arose from geochemical studies. The microcell is 3 to 4 times more efficient in sample utilization than ordinary cells, and when used within the qualification of applicability, it offers many experimental conveniences in use:

1. Loading the sample solution into the microcell is very easily accomplished. Once loaded, the sample chamber is completely sealed to prevent evaporation or inadvertent spillage.

2. Emptying and cleaning are effected merely by rinsing with fresh solvent. The cell need not be demounted and quantitative collection of the sample solution and rinses is easily accomplished.

3. The microcell fits into, and is adequately positioned in the instrument beam by standard one-cm cellholders.

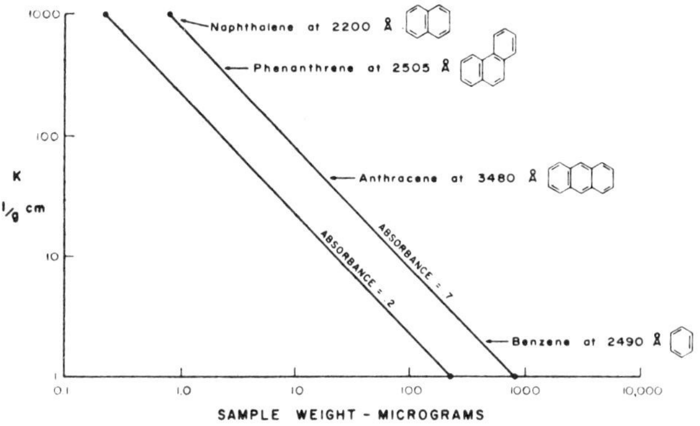

FIG. 3. USEFUL RANGE OF SAMPLE WEIGHTS FOR 0.5 MM MICROCELL

Diluted in 65 μl of solvent.

4. The sample chamber thickness may be varied to suit a particular application.

5. The assembled microcell allows contact of the sample solution only with inert materials—stainless steel, Teflon, amalgamated lead, and the cell windows.

Literature Cited

(1) R. C. Hirt and F. T. King, ANAL. CHEM. **24,** 1545 (1952)
(2) D. Glick and B. W. Grunbaum, IBID. **29,** 1243 (1957)
(3) D. C. Udy, IBID. **28,** 1360 (1956)
(4) B. L. Vallee, IBID. **25,** 985 (1953)
(5) B. G. Malmstrom and D. Glick, IBID. **23,** 1699 (1954)
(6) R. Craig, A. Bartel, and P. L. Kirk, REV. SCI. INSTR. **24,** 49 (1953)
(7) B. M. Mitzner, J. OPT. SOC. AM. **45,** 997 (1955)

6.2 A Mirrored Test Tube for Fluorescence Analysis

Milton Laikin*

Beckman Instruments, Incorporated, Fullerton, California

Various techniques have been used to increase the fluorescence energy from a cuvette by making part of the cuvette a mirror *(1)*. This is particularly important when one tries to record the fluorescent spectra of weakly fluorescing solutions. The use of most mirror materials (aluminum foil, evaporated aluminum, silver, etc.) provides a convenient but fragile mirror surface. Evaporated Nichrome V† however, provides a mirror of 50% reflectivity at 500 millimicrons which is impervious to all laboratory chemicals. It is an extremely hard film and withstands normal handling.

Nichrome V wire is evaporated from a ⅛ in. diam. tungsten rod. Since chromium evaporates more readily than nickel, the resultant film is no longer a 80-20 alloy but perhaps a 50-50 alloy. The extreme adhesion of the film is due to the chemical bond between the chromium and the glass. By means of a mask, portions of the test tube are prevented from being coated.

To use, one simply inserts the tube in the fluorescence measuring device and then rotates the tube to obtain maximum fluorescence energy output. Results with a 15 mm o.d. test tube in the new Fluorescence Accessory** on a Beckman DK-2 spectrophotometer are shown in Figure 1. For relatively strong solutions, there is little gain in using the mirror tube since the exciting light is absorbed before penetrating the tube. However, with weak solutions, there is a two-fold gain in sensitivity.

I thank Dr. Jerome Thomas of the University of California Field Station, Richmond, California for describing his use of aluminum foil on the back of a test tube to

*Present address: Pacific Optical Corp., Division of Chicago Aerial Industries, Inglewood, Calif.

†Trade Mark of Driver Harris Co. for their 80% Ni, 20% Cr alloy

**Cat. No. 73500, Beckman Instruments, Inc., Fullerton, Calif.

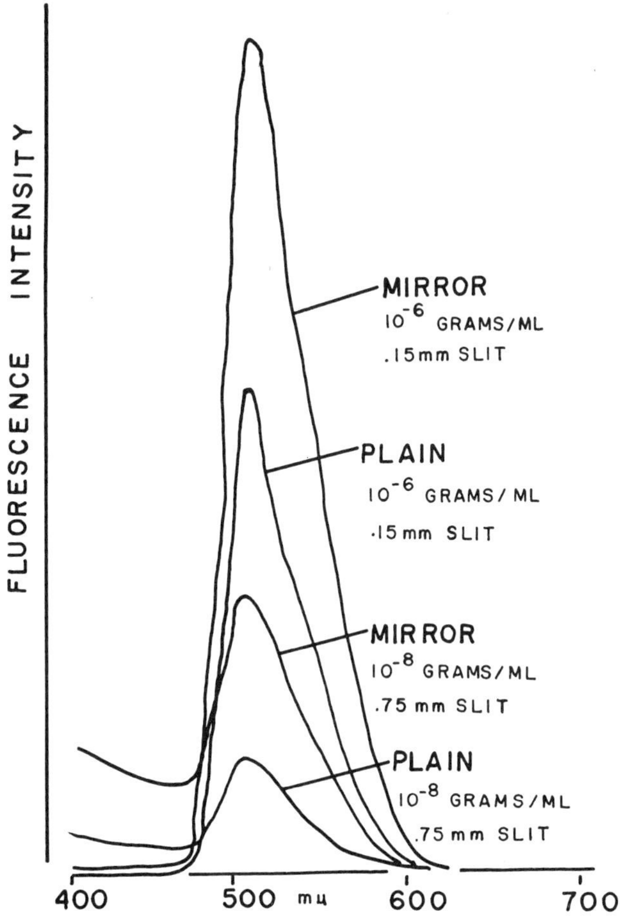

Fig. 1. Fluorescence Spectra of Fluorescein

increase fluorescence. I also thank John Pinto for performing the Nichrome evaporations.

Literature Cited

(1) C. W. Sill, Anal. Chem. **33**, 1579, (1961)

6.3 Modification of the Coleman Model 14 Universal Spectrophotometer to Simplify Wavelength Calibration Adjustment

Joseph J. Kolb

The Institute for Cancer Research, Philadelphia 11, Pennsylvania

The difficulties encountered in recalibrating the Coleman instrument, either after replacing the exciter lamp or if the wave length has shifted, are familiar to most users. These difficulties may be overcome by a few simple modifications.

1. An outside control for adjusting the wave length calibration while the instrument is in its normal position is installed as follows: The calibration screw G (as shown in the Figure 1) and retaining wire under *F*, that ordi-

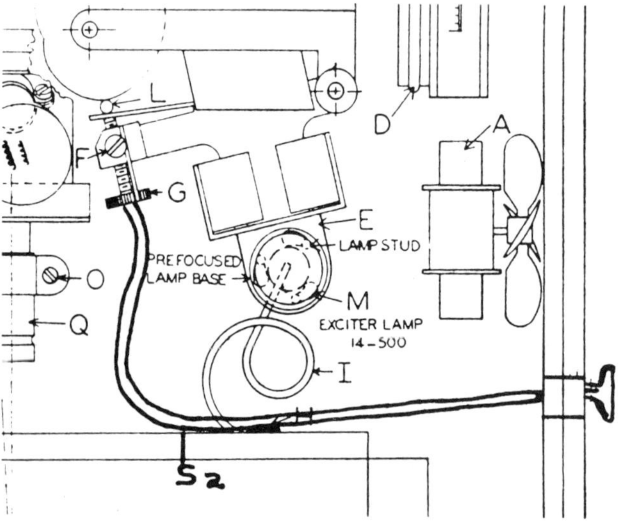

FIG. 1. PART OF INTERIOR OF MODEL 14 UNIVERSAL SPECTROPHOTOMETER

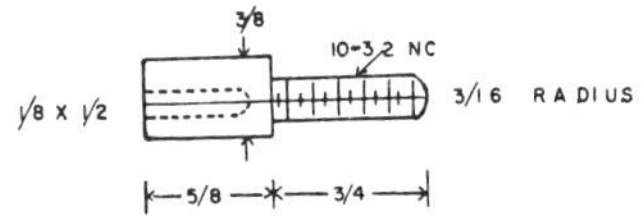

FIG. 2. FLEXIBLE CABLE ADAPTER

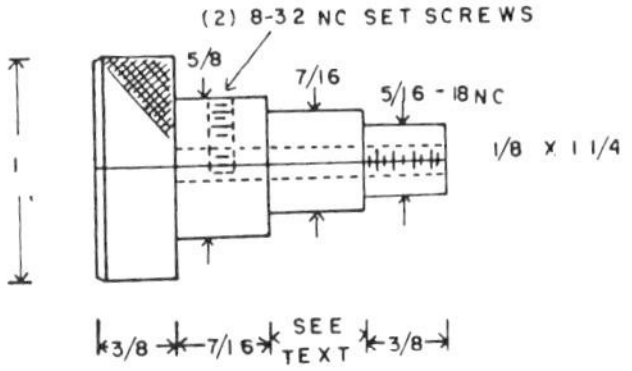

FIG. 3. ADJUSTMENT KNOB

narily meshes with the knurling on *G*, are removed. A new screw with a socket head (Figure 2, all materials are brass) is soldered to a 13-14 in. long flexible shaft, which may be a ⅛ in. speedometer cable obtainable from any auto supply store. The new calibration screw is then threaded into the place previously occupied by *G*. To prevent whip, the flexible shaft is run through a plastic clip fastened by an ⅛ in. long sheet metal screw at position *S2*. Before attaching the adjustment knob to the flexible shaft, a spring tension washer ⅝ in. diam., 7/16 in. hole, 0.012 in. thick is slipped over the shoulder, the knob is then inserted into the hole, and a collar ⅝ in. diam. 11/32 in. hole, ⅛ in. thick is put on, followed by a 5/16-18 NC nut. The outer end of the flexible shaft is fastened by means of 2 set screws to a similar but unthreaded adapter that is part of the adjustment knob. The length of the shoulder of the knob is equal to the wall thickness plus the spring tension washer plus 0.005 in. (Figure 3). This shoulder rides in a hole of the proper size in the wall of the case. The hole is drilled about 3⅝ in. from the bottom of the case and 3¼ in. from the back; in other words, half-way between the O and BLK knobs and 1¾ in. up, measured from the centers. Care must be taken that there is no interference with the movement of the cooling fans. Trial and error will soon show the degree of tension required.

2. The battery is fastened to the case by a brass strap 1 in. wide, 7¼ in. long, 0.032 in. thick, bent to form a channel cross-section whose arms are 2⅜ in. and the base is 2½ in. The ends of the strap are soldered into the slotted heads of two 6/32 NC brass screws. A pair of No. 28 holes on 2⅝ in. vertical centers are drilled through the case, the lower one is 6¾ in. in from the front of the case and 1¼ in. from the bottom.

The author wishes to express his appreciation to William F. Hafner of this Institute for his coperation and mechanical skill in making the necessary attachment and to Coleman Instruments Inc. for permission to reproduce part of Figure 1.

6.4 Modification of Water Line on Source Unit of Cary Spectrophotometer to Facilitate Replacement and Realignment of Source

D. H. Holt

Socony Mobil Oil Company, Incorporated
Field Research Laboratory, Dallas, Texas

Difficulties experienced in mounting and orienting new hydrogen source lamps on the Cary model No. 11 uv spectrophotometer have been overcome by a simple modification of the cooling water lines attached to the lamp. Short lengths of Tygon tubing originally used for connecting the envelope of the source lamp to the cooling water supply are inflexible enough to cause considerable strain on the glass tube connectors when orienting the source with the optical path.

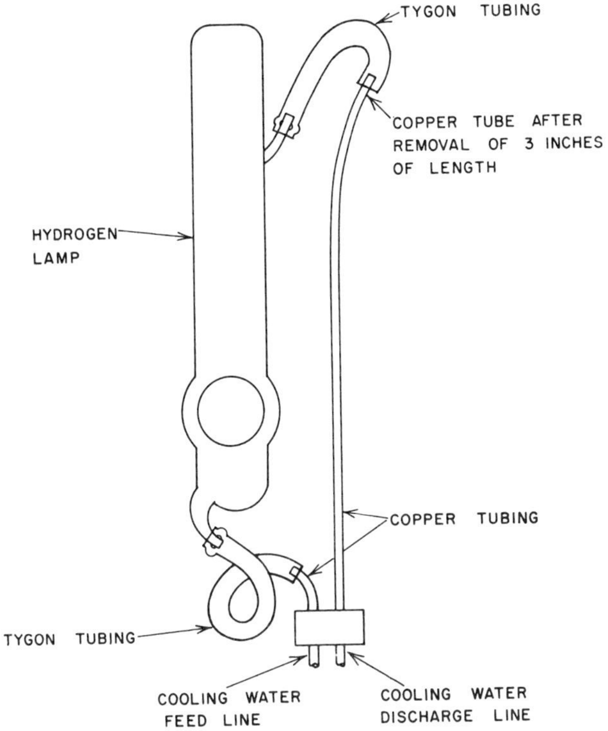

FIG. 1. DIAGRAM OF MOUNTED HYDROGEN DISCHARGE LAMP AFTER MODIFICATION

Easy orientation of the source without strain on the glass was accomplished by using a longer piece of Tygon tubing to provide a complete loop between the copper feed line and the glass entrance tube as illustrated in Figure 1.

Strain was also reduced by adding three in. to the length of the Tygon tube in the discharge line to replace an equal length cut from the end of the copper tube portion of the discharge line. This is also illustrated in Figure

1. A complete loop of Tygon could be used at this point to provide additional flexibility if needed. It is best to keep the inside diameter of the loop at no less than 1.5 in. to avoid any crimping of the Tygon tubing with age.

6.5 An Inexpensive Time-Scan Attachment for Use With The Beckman DK-2 Spectrophotometer Instrument

Ferdinand H. Zegel

Instrumental Engineering Division
U. S. Weather Bureau, Washington, D.C.

The availability of a time base scanning device is of particular importance when one desires to measure the rate of absorption change as the sample undergoes chemical degradation. Studies of chemical reactions and hydrolysis and precipitation rates depend upon the observation of the rate of change of the sample absorptivity. The accurate recording of the noise spectra of the instrument's one hundred % and zero % base lines also calls for the use of a time drive device.

This relatively simple device consists of modifying a selected pair of gears in order that the gear drive motor may operate the pen carriage drive directly, thus disconnecting the wavelength drive shaft. This arrangement allows the drive motor to operate the pen, thereby setting the operator free to select the wavelength at which it is desired to observe the absorbance change (Figure 1).

The gears* now used affect a 1 to 1 ratio and are a 48-pitch 117 teeth hubless type, with an o.d. of 2.479-in. One is limited in the choice of gear ratios to be used because the drive shafts are not movable and still be easily converted to routine operation. Therefore, the 2.4374-in.

*Cat. No. 101-117, Dynamic Gear Co., Inc., Amityville, N. Y.

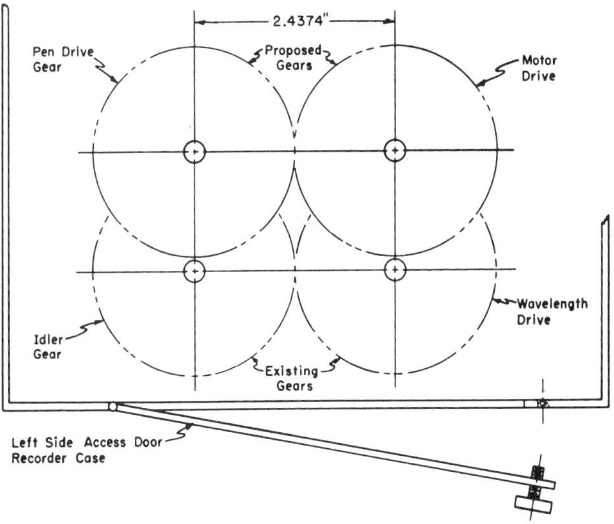

FIG. 1. TOP VIEW OF GEAR ASSEMBLY

distance between motor and pen drive shaft centers must be respected. The placement of the wavelength and idler gear shafts also restricts the maximum gear size.

The gears, however, have to be modified slightly in order that they may fit on to the unique Beckman chucks.

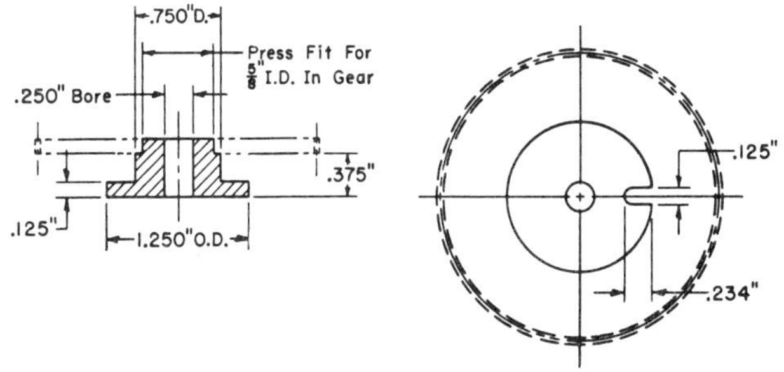

FIG. 2. DRIVE GEAR

The modification is relatively simple to accomplish (Figure 2).

The present arrangement using the 1 to 1 ratio permits a fairly wide range of pen speeds with respect to the different scanning times (1, 2, 5, 10, 20, 50, 100) as indicated in the selector knob. These speeds range from approximately 6 to 110 sec/in. No undue strain on the drive motor seems to be apparent.

The assistance of Mr. W. V. Compton is acknowledged for his help in the design.

SECTION 7
X-RAY SPECTROSCOPY

Holder and Beam Limiters for X-Ray Diffractometric Study of Rod Cross Sections 7.1

Robert L. Prickett

Advanced Metallurgical Studies Branch, Directorate of Materials and Processes (ASD), Wright-Patterson AFB, Ohio

For x-ray diffraction studies of metallurgical rod specimens and their cross sections two types of equipment are in common usage, glancing angle cameras *(1)* and diffractometers. The use of a diffractometer is generally seriously hampered in this work by the size of the specimen that can be accommodated. Philips diffractometer, for example, normally handles specimens approximately 10 mm x 20 mm, about one mm thick. This is fine for powder specimens but not entirely satisfactory for metal rods. This report outlines the use of a special holder and beam limiters built for a horizontal diffractometer made by Siemens & Halske of Germany. Siemens diffractometer normally handles thin specimens 38 mm x 38 mm *(2)*. The holder described herein accommodates rods up to 1½ in. long with cross sections down to ⅛ in. The diffracted energy is still very high—up to 70,000 cps from an irradiated area of less than ¼ in. diam.

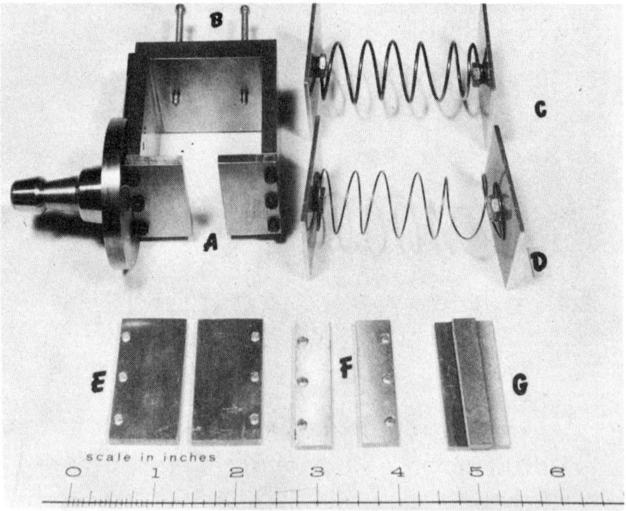

FIG. 1. PARTIALLY ASSEMBLED SAMPLE HOLDER

In Figure 1A the subject specimen holder is mounted on the regular holder base. Alignment pins are used for interchangeability with a standard holder. The two spring plate assemblies, Figures 1C and 1D, permit the firm positioning of either thin or thick specimens, respectively, with equal ease. For mounting extra long specimens, such as shown in Figure 3B, a single flat sheet of metal 1½ in. x 1½ in. (not shown) and the two screws in Figure 1B are used to bring the sample surface flush with the bottom of the end plates. Two sets of end plates, Figures 1E and 1F, exchangeable by removing six screws, permit many sample heights and diameters to be accommodated. For alignment purposes the bottoms of the end plates are coincident with the center of revolution of the goniometer. Figure 1G shows a zero alignment gauge, constructed from ⅛ in. steel, cut and ground flat, joined together with very thin strips of double sided scotch tape. Figure 2 shows the alignment gauge installed in the specimen holder; the items marked with the numeral one are small pieces of 20 mil lead sheet held in place with double sided masking tape to lower the background radiation entering the detector. The left hand piece of lead has been rotated out of place for demonstration. In Figure 3A is shown a typical beam limiter constructed to restrict the beam height and width to a circular pattern, typical holes ranging from 3/32 in. to 9/32 in. diam. These were cut from 20 mil sheet lead and bent to shape. They are attached to the end of the source collimator by double sided masking tape as shown.

As part of a study of preferred orientation in tungsten rod, using the beam limiter shown in Figure 3A, a horizontal cross section yielded the diffraction pattern 30691-29-1, Figure 4, top. The conditions used were copper radiation, nickel filter, 35 kv, 20 ma, scintillation detector, HV = 720, scale factor = 4×10^4, attentuation = 10×2, statistical error = 1.5×2, pulse analyzer at integrate, zero = 0, 0.2 receiving slit, 0.8 source slit, scan rate = 1 degree/min, chart speed = one cm/min. Tube spot focus was used for increased intensity.

For extreme reduction in beam width another limiter, a Siemens receiving slit, Figure 3B, was attached to the first, Figure 3A, by double sided masking tape. With a

FIG. 2. SAMPLE HOLDER SUPPORTING ZERO ALIGNMENT GAUGE

FIG. 3. HOLDER WITH SMALL SAMPLE ON DIFFRACTOMETER WITH BEAM LIMITERS

Inset A Showing First Beam Limiter

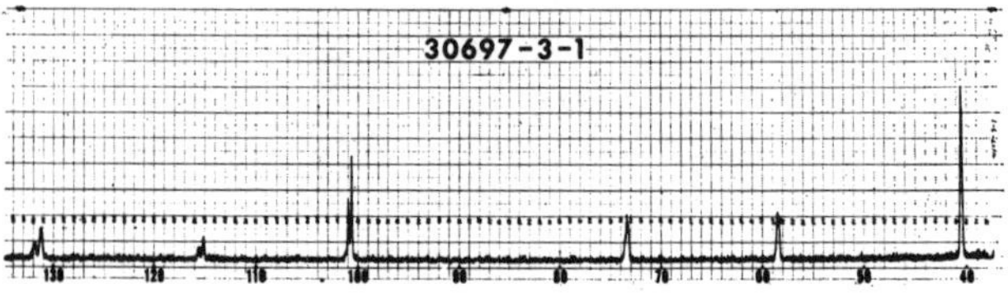

FIG. 4. X-RAY DIFFRACTOMETER CHARTS MADE FROM TUNGSTEN ROD CROSS SECTIONS

Top—Horizontal Cross Section Bottom—Vertical Cross Section

0.4 mm receiving slit, a tungsten rod vertical section 3/32 in. diam. and ¼ in. height, Figure 3C, could be studied with 13,000 cps detected from the stronger reflections. Diffraction pattern 30697-3-1, Figure 4, bottom, was thus recorded from this sample using instrumental conditions given for 30691-29-1.

The use of beam limiters produced a high peak to noise ratio, through reduction in background radiation, by restriction of the x-ray beam to the specimen surface. Both diffractometer traces were made of metal which was not free of cold work. This cold work might explain the late separation of $K\alpha_1$ and $K\alpha_2$ on the charts.

The author is indebted to Mr. Verl R. Robinson of Experimental Fabrications Shop who built and partly designed the holder.

Literature Cited

(1) G. W. Brindley and A. Hargreaves, in *X-Ray Diffraction by Polycrystalline Materials*, H. S. Peiser, H. P. Rooksby, and A. J. C. Wilson, Ed., The Institute of Physics, London, 1955, pp. 173-5 and 303-5

(2) *Counter—Tube Diffractometer—Operating Instructions Eg 404e*, Siemens & Halske Aktiengesellschaft, Karlsruhe, p. 12

An Extrusion Method For Supporting X-Ray Powder Camera Specimens 7.2

R. Bruce Scott

Research Laboratories, Parke, Davis and Co., Ann Arbor, Michigan

The advantages of mounting powder specimens free of any binder, adhesives, fibers, or tubes have led several workers to suggest methods and devices for extruding a tiny cylinder of powder. In one of the most recent of these

(1), the powder is packed into a 19-gauge stainless steel tube with a plunger made of No. 22 steel wire. A demountable assembly maintains the alignment of anvil, specimen tube, and plunger.

For some time we have been using a simpler version of the method. The powder is packed in an axially drilled brass rod which contains its own loading funnel, and when the specimen has been displaced so that it protrudes 1-2 mm out of the small orifice, the recessed end of the tube is inserted directly into the camera chuck. The mounted specimens are rugged enough, without binder, to withstand any reasonable handling. The plain end of the drill bit used to make the hole provides a suitable plunger for packing and extruding the powder. For convenience in handling, it is mounted in a small plastic handle. The loading of samples is further facilitated by use of a small plastic plate which holds the sample tube upright. A piece of *Plexiglass* (2 in. x 2 in. x ¼ in.) through which an ⅛-in. hole has been drilled, is used.

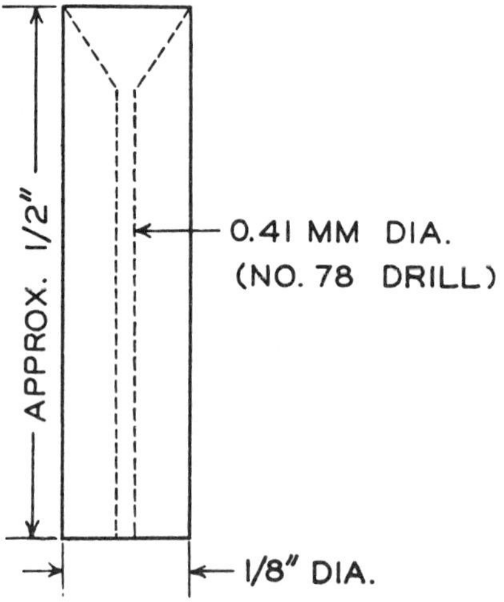

FIG. 1. EXTRUSION MOLD AND SPECIMEN HOLDER

To prepare the specimen for the camera, the drilled rod is placed in the plastic support on a flat, firm surface. The loading funnel is filled with the finely powdered specimen, and the plunger is used to work it down the hole and tamp it. With the powder packed to a depth of 3-4 mm, the tube is lifted out of the holder and the plunger is used to push out the compacted specimen the required distance.

Occasionally and especially with samples which are not easily ground to a sufficiently fine particle size, it is difficult to extrude the packed column. If the specimen should jam in the tube, it can be cleared out by using the cutting end of the drill. Usually it is sufficient merely to reduce the depth of packed material in order to extrude it, and if it is necessary to extend the column, more material may be packed in and pushed forward.

Cleaning of the holder is accomplished easily in the case of organic compounds by immersing it in a suitable solvent and working the drill through the hole several times. Those who work with inorganic and other insoluble specimens may do well to have disposable plastic mounts made up in quantity.

We wish to thank Mr. Jake Kutscher of the Research Area Engineering Shop for his competent performance of a difficult drilling job.

Literature Cited

(1) L. J. E. Hofer, W. C. Peebles, and P. G. Guest, Anal. Chem. **22,** 1218 (1950)

Simple Low Temperature Diffractometer Specimen Mount 7.3

William L. Baun

Materials Laboratory, Wright Air Development center, Wright-Patterson Air Force Base, Ohio

A number of devices for obtaining x-ray diffraction photographs at low temperatures have been described in the literature. Usually, however, these devices have been applied to single crystal cameras (*1*) or to Debye-Scherrer powder cameras (*2*). It is the purpose of this note to describe a simple x-ray diffractometer specimen mount in which the temperature may be varied from room temperature to liquid nitrogen or helium temperatures.

The low temperature mount described here is pictured in the Norelco gonimeter specimen holder in Figure 1. It consists of a small *Teflon*® block in which a shallow chamber is machined to accommodate a circular pressed sample. Underneath the sample is another cavity, smaller in diameter than the first, through which cold gas or liquified gas is carried into the specimen holder, circulated beneath the sample, brought out through a curved piece of tubing, and then sprayed over the surface of the specimen. In this way, once equilibrium has been reached, there is equal cooling from each side of the sample. Uniform sample temperature is not a serious consideration when using samples of high density, but is very important in low density materials where beam penetration becomes appreciable. An even greater advantage of this system lies in the fact that the jet of dry gas streaming over the specimen surface prohibits ice formation even in fairly humid conditions. For extensive use it is best to use the specimen holder in some sort of an enclosure so that one may take advantage of a positive pressure of dry gas within the vessel as a further deterrent to ice formation. For the specimen mount described, the standard *Norelco* can-type scatter shield, changed only slightly, served nicely as an enclosure. This scatter shield may be prepared for work at low temperatures by drilling one or two small holes in the front to accommodate incoming gas and thermocouple leads, and covering the can slit which permits beam entry and exit with a material nearly transparent to x-rays. One to two mil *Mylar*® has been found satisfactory for this purpose. Naturally, a specially constructed double wall Dewar type vessel is preferable as an enclosure but adds considerably to the expense and complexity of the apparatus.

Methods of controlling the temperature of the gas passed through the mount naturally vary considerably depending on the exact effect desired. Varying the flow of dry nitrogen through a copper coil immersed in liquid nitrogen functions well, as does cooling with nitrogen vaporized from the liquid state. In the latter case, the temperature is controlled by changing the rate of liquid nitrogen vaporization with a closely controlled immersion heater. The liquified gases themselves may be run through the specimen mount to obtain the lowest temperature for that liquified gas. The flow may be carefully adjusted to insure that the liquid vaporizes beneath the sample, resulting in a gas temperature on the sample surface approximately that of the liquified gas. The delivery tube to the specimen mount normally is a double wall tube of Teflon, or rubber, further insulated with cotton, glass wool, or foamed low density plastic. The Mylar slit covering may be kept clear of frost by passing dry air over the slit. This is usually necessary only when operating at very low temperatures and when using soft radiation such as chromium. For normal use with copper radiation frost is usually allowed to form on the slit covering since it acts as an insulator for that area and does not attenuate the beam excessively.

Although designed for low temperature work, the specimen mount may be used as it is up to 200°C and even higher with a change in construction materials. For use at higher temperatures the mount has been constructed in

FIG. 1. VARIABLE TEMPERATURE SPECIMEN MOUNT IN DIFFRACTOMETER HOLDER

two pieces using copper and fired lavite as construction materials. The mount also may be fabricated entirely of lavite using the same design as that used with Teflon. Lavite, a mixed silicate, is ideal for this use since in the unfired state it is soft and almost soap-like, while in the fired state it is stable, hard, and refractory.

Only one minor change was made on the x-ray goniometer itself. Two threaded holes were placed in the goniometer mounting head to match two holes in the rear of the Teflon block. This allows the specimen mount to be bolted rigidly to the diffractometer rather than relying on the small spring normally used to secure the sample in *Norelco* diffractometers. This change was necessary because feed tube drag at low temperatures caused some sample displacement. Attaching the specimen mount in this way minimized displacement.

The specimen mount described has proven valuable for investigating all types of materials at low temperatures and up to 200°C. Phase changes and other thermal effects have been observed in pressed solid organic and inorganic materials. Diffraction patterns have been recorded and phase changes observed from solidified organic liquids with the mount changed to accept liquid samples. Coefficient of thermal expansion is obtained easily and in much less time than with film techniques. However, it is recognized that there are inherent weaknesses in this simple mount that preclude its use with the same precision and accuracy as with film methods. The coefficient of thermal expansion for aluminum determined with this mount is 19.4×10^{-6}/-°C (-196 to 75°C) which compares favorably with early data (3) for a slightly different temperature range.

Literature Cited

1. S. C. Abrahams, R. L. Collin, W. N. Lipscomb and T. B. Reed, *Rev. Sci. Instr. 21*, 396 (1950)
2. W. Hume-Rothery and D. J. Strawbridge, *Ibid. 24*, 89 (1947)
3. *International Critical Tables*, McGraw-Hill Book Co., New York, 1927, Vol. 2, p. 459

Simple Liquid Sample Holder for X-Ray Fluorescence Analysis 7.4

J. N. van Niekerk and F. T. Wybenga

National Physical Research Laboratory, Council for Scientific and Industrial Research, Pretoria, South Africa

The conventional multi-purpose sample holder type P.W. 1527, supplied with the *Philips* X-Ray Spectrograph attachment type *P.W. 1520/10*, is not entirely leak-proof when used with aqueous solutions and cannot be used with strong acid solutions. Although the manufacturers themselves supply sample holders which are suitable for such solutions and while other liquid sample holders have been described in the literature *(1,2,3,4)*, we have found that a simple modification to the holder mentioned above has led to an extremely reliable holder for even the strongest acid solutions.

As indicated in Figure 1 the original holder consists of a metal casing *F*, a clamping plate *D* which spans a Mylar® foil *E* over the bottom of *F* and a threaded retaining ring *C* which screws onto *F*, thus clamping *D* and *E* securely into position. The casing *F* was modified by machining two mm off its lower end and increasing its internal diam. by 1.5 mm. A polyethylene sleeve *B*, two mm thick and with a rounded lip at its lower end (see

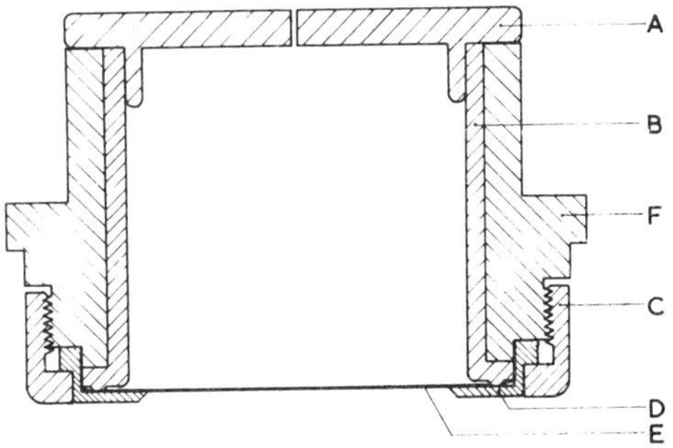

FIG. 1. LIQUID SAMPLE HOLDER FOR X-RAY FLUORESCENCE

Figure 1), was machined to slide into *F* and with its base fitting exactly into the clamping plate *D*. If a *mylar* film is now placed over the end of *B* with plate *D* pushed into position and screwed down with the retaining ring *C*, the polyethylene insert seals firmly onto the *mylar* foil. Dimensions were chosen so that the *mylar* window opening in the clamping plate was not impaired by the thickness of the polyethylene sleeve. Also by making the overall length of the modified and unmodified holders equal, the specimen plane holder was unchanged after insertion of the sample. Finally, a polyethylene lid *A* with a hole down its centre limits the escape of acid fumes.

This modified sample holder has proved to be extremely satisfactory for all types of specimens and in particular for acid solutions. It is completely leakproof, easy to clean, and the replacement of *mylar* foil is as simple as in the original holder.

The authors wish to thank Mr. J. Erasmus of the laboratory workshop who carried out the modifications.

Literature Cited

1. L. Silverman, W. Houk, and W. Taylor, NORELCO REPORTER **1**, 118 (1954)
2. G. Pish and A. A. Huffman, ANAL. CHEM. **27**, 1875 (1955)
3. H. M. Wilson and G. V. Wheeler, APPLIED SPECTROSCOPY **11**, 128 (1957)
4. D. S. Flikkema et al., A.E.C. RESEARCH REPORT *ANL* **5641**, 9 pp (1956)

7.5 Apparatus for Continuous Fluorescent X-Ray Spectrographic Analysis of Solutions

William J. Campbell

Eastern Experimental Station, Bureau of Mines
U. S. Department of the Interior, College Park, Maryland

This paper describes a continuous solution analyzer and is an extension of a previous investigation on fluores-

FIG. 1. SAMPLE CHAMBER
Left — Front view, Right — Rear view

cent x-ray spectrographic analysis of solutions *(1)*. Although this laboratory was primarily interested in studies of limited duration, the apparatus is also suitable for continuous process control.

The sample chamber shown in Figure 1 was constructed from a *Plexiglass*® block 8 cm long, 5.5 cm wide, and 1.3 cm thick. A *Mylar*® sheet, 1 mil thick, serving both as the cell window and the gasket, was placed between the polished plastic block and an aluminum sheet 1.5 mm thick. The opening in the metal sheet is slightly smaller than the size of the viewing chamber. Two holes, approximately 0.8 cm diameter, were drilled at right angles into the plastic block with a large bore drilled near each end. Tapered male plastic tubing connectors were force-fitted into these holes to serve as connectors for the plastic tubing. The viewing chamber, 3.5 cm long, 1.2 cm wide, and 0.9 cm deep, was milled out so that only the *Mylar* sheet would be between the solution and the x-ray tube window. The sample chamber is positioned on a U-shaped metal support inside a specially constructed x-ray tube protective housing. The metal support rotates in conjunction with a metal shutter over the x-ray tube window. When the shutter is open, the sample holder is 45° to the x-ray-tube window and 45° to the horizontal and as close to the window as possible. The solution flow through the plastic block is from bottom to top, thus reducing air-bubble formation. The sample chamber's dimensions will vary, depending on the particular design of the x-ray-tube

FIG. 2. APPARATUS IN USE
A — Sample chamber, B — Variable speed pump, C — Reaction vessel

protective housing. However, any of the commercially available x-ray goniometers can be used for the spectral line measurements.

The reaction apparatus, as shown in Figure 2, can be used to study various rate processes, such as displacement reactions, solubility rates, etc. Concentrational changes in the reaction vessel are rapidly and continuously measured, e.g., upon addition of Zn^{++} to distilled water (see Figure 3), the response time was on the order of several seconds. With approximately 3 ft. of ¼-in. bore tubing, containing 9 ml. solution, from the reaction vessel to viewing chamber and pumping speeds of 1200 ml. per min., the time required for the solution to reach the viewing chamber is approximately 0.5 sec. Therefore, the time constant in the ratemeter circuit is usually the limiting factor. All exposed parts (pump, stirrer, chamber, and tubing) were either plastic or plastic-lined to prevent metal ion contamination.

A previous paper *(1)* describes in detail the applications and limitations of solution analysis by fluorescent x-ray spectrography. The results of that study are directly applicable to continuous solution analysis. The system to be studied can be readily calibrated by pumping several known solutions through the viewing chamber and plotting the intensity versus concentration relationship.

For process control, each laboratory would have to determine the stability of its power supplies and electronic circuitry for long periods of time. In addition, since *Mylar* slowly embrittles upon exposure to x-rays, the maximum safe exposure time would have to be determined. Care must be taken to keep air out of the pumping system as air bubbles tend to attach to the *Mylar* window. These bubbles would affect the x-ray intensity in a manner

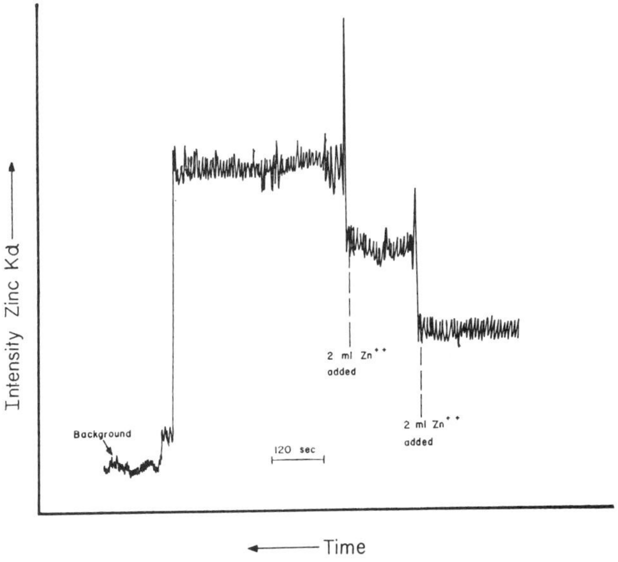

FIG. 3. VARIATION OF INTENSITY WITH CONCENTRATION CHANGES
Addition of Zn^{++} (33 g/l) to 1500 ml distilled water

similar to a rough surface on a solid or powder sample having a low mass absorption coefficient.

Acknowledgment

The author appreciates the technical assistance of John W. Thatcher, analytical chemist, of the Eastern Experiment Station.

Literature Cited

1. W. J. Campbell, M. Leon, and J. W. Thatcher, *U. S. Bureau of Mines Report of Investigations* **5497,** 24 pp (1959)

7.6 Direct Identification Of X-Ray Spectra

Edward J. Graeber
Sandia Corporation, Sandia Base, Albuquerque, New Mexico

In the qualitative x-ray fluorescence analysis of materials, this laboratory is frequently confronted with the comparison and subsequent identification of numerous samples. Each such identification, whether by calculation or tables of wavelengths, is time-consuming. The use of a transparent overlay with appropriate scale factors has provided a valuable short cut.

The transparency (Figure 1) is photographically reproduced from a drawing containing the analytical-wavelength lines of interest. Each emission line is plotted at the 2θ angle position of a crystal in Bragg reflection. This particular overlay is approximately 10 in. wide by 21 in. long, the latter dimension being governed by a chart speed of 24 in./hr. With a spectrometer scanning speed of $2°$/min and a lithium fluoride analyzer ($2d=4.0267$ A), over 1000 analytical lines are usable for superimposition over x-ray spectrograms.

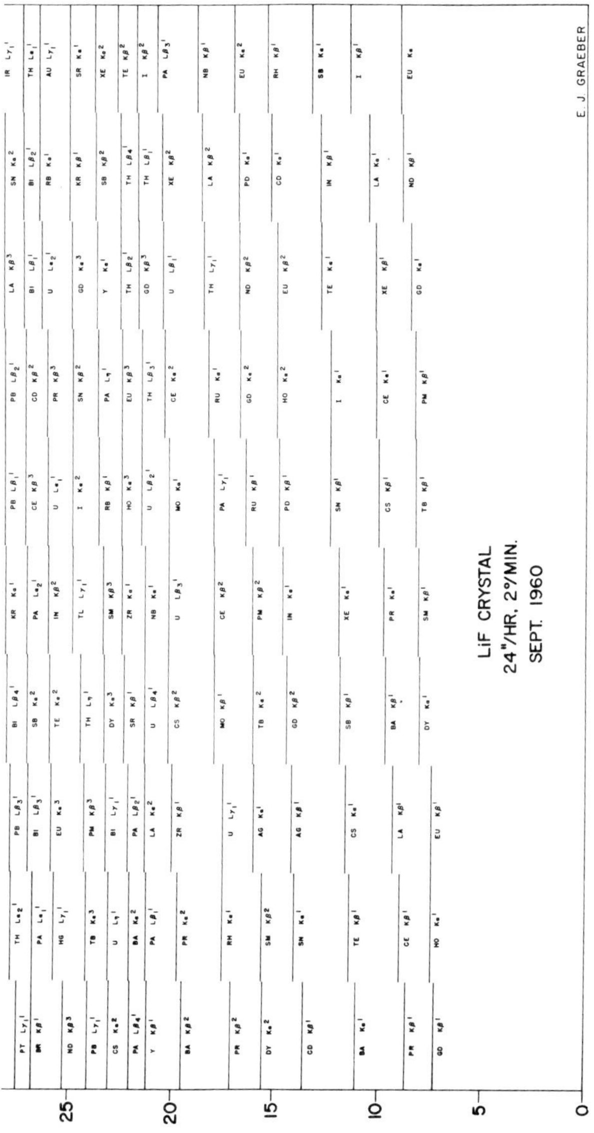

FIG. 1. TRANSPARENT X-RAY TEMPLATE FOR SPECTROGRAPHIC CHARTS

Alternate overlays for the same analyzer may be constructed easily by photographic methods if other combinations of scanning and chart speeds are desired. Only one original drawing per analyzing crystal is needed to complete a series of overlays applicable to any qualitative analysis by fluorescence.

7.7 Ball Point Pen Adaptor for the Siemens Kompensograph

John J. Renton and William L. Baun

Air Force Materials Laboratory
Air Force Systems Command
Wright-Patterson Air Force Base, Ohio

A simple device is presented to replace the standard ink-filled scribe of the Siemens Kompensograph. Repeated difficulty with the Siemens scribe pen point from clogging and smearing prompted the design of a replacement pen. The design presented here, Figure 1, is based upon the disposable Bristol Ball Point Pen cartridge, which was available for Bristol Recorders used in the laboratory.

The adaptor as designed readily replaces the ink-filled scribe of the Kompensograph and requires no modification of the instrument whatsoever; the replacement taking only a few sec. The result is a dependable, trouble free scribe producing an even, fine line recording.

The one-in. brass barrel fits snugly into the existent cradle of the Kompensograph scribe holder, the short ⅛-in. pin on the bottom centering the barrel, and the horizontal pins hold the barrel in place by slipping the two spring clips of the cradle over them. The vertical pen plate is fixed to the barrel by a set screw and allows an adjustment of pen pressure to the roller. The bottom end of the plate is angled allowing the pen to intersect the paper perpendicular to the roller. It was found that if the pressure adjustment was set so that the pen was in con-

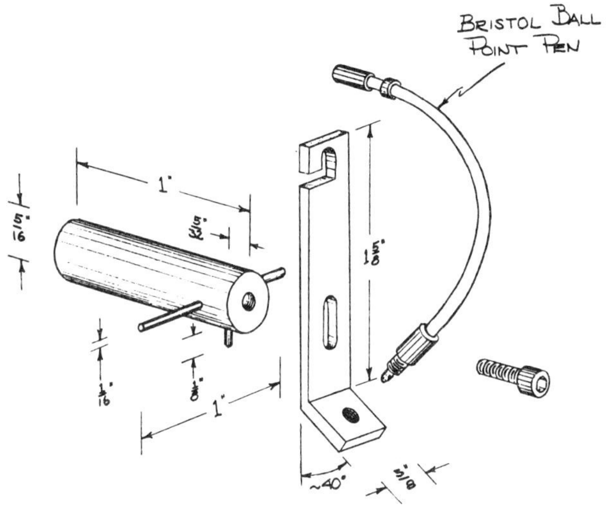

FIG. 1. BALL POINT PEN ADAPTOR FOR THE SIEMENS KOMPENSOGRAPH RECORDER

tinual contact with the paper, it significantly increased the life of the cartridge and eliminated clogging of the point due to drying of the ink of the ball.

SECTION 8
MISCELLANEOUS

Rack for Square Cuvettes 8.1

John B. Pate and James P. Lodge, Jr.
National Center for Atmospheric Research, Boulder, Colorado

For many spectrophotometric determinations, it is convenient to use a reasonably large number of cuvettes, rather than rinsing after each determination. When the color reaction used is time dependent, or when the samples are such that a dry cuvette is needed, a number of cuvettes are required. In such a case, additional spectrophotometer cuvette holders are usually obtained to hold the samples. Since these are not intended to use as cuvette racks, they tend to be expensive, corrodible, and likely to spill.

A test tube rack* has been marketed recently that is ideally suited for use as a rack for 1 cm square cuvettes. As illustrated, the cuvettes are supported in such a manner that they are accessible, but firmly supported, and the contents are completely visible. When placed in the rack so that the trade-marked or non-optical side of the cuvette faces out, the optical window is protected from

*Cat. No. 5903 Test tube rack, 10-tube, Nalge Co., Inc.

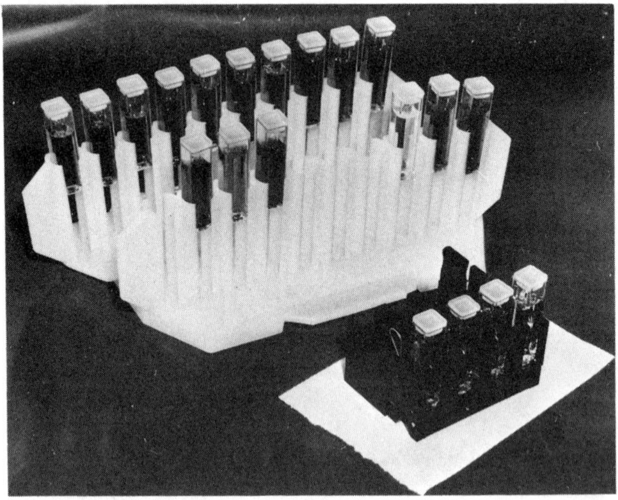

FIG. 1. RACK FOR SQUARE CUVETTES

contact with the rack by the curvature of the niche, the cuvette being supported by contact at the four corners only.

8.2 Use of Wire Screens as Variable Light Attenuators

Ford R. Bryan

Scientific Laboratory, Ford Motor Company, Dearborn, Michigan

Spectrochemical procedures occasionally call for the use of a wire screen to reduce the intensity of a light source. Sometimes the screen is specified as having a given optical transmittance; more often it is described as being of a given mesh. Such screens are presumed to be used at normal incidence and when used as an attenuator are known to be optically stable with respect to time and ideally neutral with respect to wavelength *(1)*.

It is unfortunate that the durability and neutrality properties of screens have not been more fully utilized in optical equipment. Perhaps it is because commercial screens are normally not specified in terms of optical transmittance and because screens are not often regarded as variable transmittance elements.

Most frequently employed screen materials are the U. S. Standard Sieves *(2)* which are accurately specified in terms of sieve opening and wire diameter. The Federal Specification provides the nominal dimensions, permissible variations, and limits for woven wire cloth of standard sieves. Sieve opening is specified within a few percent of a nominal value for each size or designation. Wire diameter

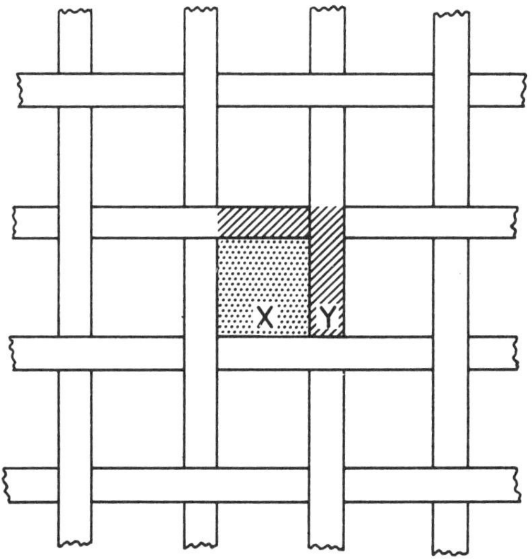

FIG. 1. DIAGRAM OF TYPICAL WOVEN WIRE CLOTH SCREEN

Sieve opening (x) and wire diameter (y) labeled to show ratio of open area (x^2) to total area of screen $(x+y)^2$

TABLE I

OPTICAL TRANSMITTANCE RANGES FOR STANDARD SIEVES AS CALCULATED FROM FEDERAL SPECIFICATIONS FOR EACH DESIGNATION NUMBER

Sieve Designation No.	*Percent Transmittance* Minimum	Maximum
10	44	55
20	36	46
30	34	45
40	32	42
50	30	39
60	28	39
80	28	37
100	29	37
120	30	37
140	29	39
170	30	38
200	30	39
230	30	38
270	29	37
325	27	35
400	27	38

is expressed as a maximum and minimum for each sieve designation. From the nominal sieve opening together with the range of wire diameters allowable for any given sieve designation, the range of optical transmittance can be calculated.

Using Figure 1 as a model, it can be seen that transmittance, or the ratio of open area to total area of screen, can be expressed as $x^2/(x + y)^2$, where x = length and width of sieve opening and y = diameter of wire.

When the Federal Specification for each sieve designation is substituted in the above expression, it is found that percent transmittance for most sieves is limited to the 25-40% range (see Table I). Although the very coarse sieves tend to have somewhat higher transmittance, designation numbers above No. 50 can be expected to transmit approximately one-third of the incident light. Since Federal Specifications permit a spread of nearly 10% in transmittance, one cannot expect to obtain a screen of an exact predicted optical transmittance by purchase of a standard sieve.

It is well known that a screen if tilted from the normal will transmit less light than at normal incidence. The amount of transmitted light is governed by the relationship:

FIG. 2. DEVICE USED FOR MEASUREMENT OF ROTATION OF A SCREEN ABOUT A VERTICAL AXIS PERPENDICULAR TO A LIGHT BEAM

$$I = k I_0 \sin \Theta$$

where Θ is the angle between the screen and the axis of the light beam. This principle has recently been used to provide adjustable combinations of tilted screen elements in an optical system *(3)*. Therefore, if one requires an optical element of prescribed transmittance, a screen can be utilized that provides more than the desired transmittance at normal incidence and, by tilting, adjust transmittance to the desired value. If a precise means of tilting a screen in an optical beam is devised, one thus has a limited range, continuously variable light attenuator.

The principle of controlled tilting of a screen is employed in the device shown in Figure 2. The device consists of an optical bench carriage equipped with a protractor indexing ring with vernier scale. A vertical shaft which supports the screen is equipped with matching protractor scale graduated in one-degree increments to measure rotation of the screen about the vertical axis.

The 2.5-in. square screens were, for this experiment, prepared from larger commercial screens by making a relatively heavy brass frame and cementing the frame to the screen by means of epoxy resin while the screen was taut in its original frame. When the cement had hardened, the screen was then cut around the exterior edge of the smaller frame.

Measurements of transmittance versus degrees of rotation from normal incidence were obtained for several screens by means of a microphotometer employing white light. Screens ranged from Nos. 20 to 200 mesh and were first measured in steps of 15°, starting at normal incidence and extending to 60° from normal. The range of transmittance variation for four representative screens is shown in Figure 3. The sine function character of the transmittance change with angle of rotation reveals that more precise control of transmittance is possible at angles near normal incidence. At near normal incidence, one-degree adjustment of rotation controls transmittance to approximately 0.1%. At 45°, a rotation of one-degree causes a change of about 1% in transmittance. At 60° the control becomes less effective, and transmittance measurements are less pre-

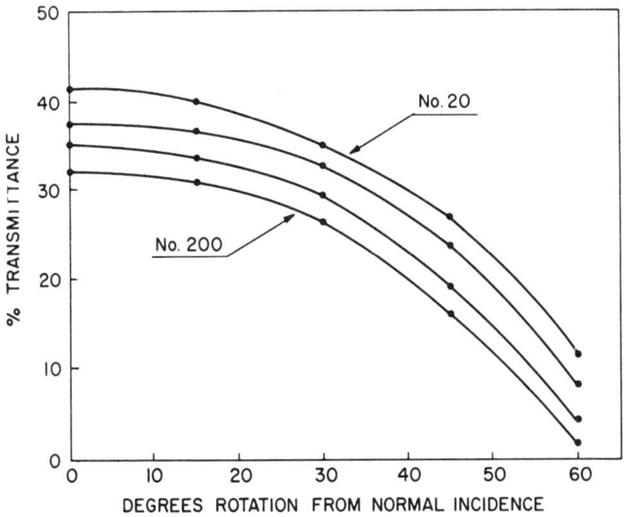

FIG. 3. TRANSMITTANCE VARIATIONS OF TYPICAL COMMERCIAL SCREENS WHEN ROTATED BY MEASURED AMOUNTS FROM NORMAL INCIDENCE

cise. Within the range of 40-10%, however, a commercial screen can be calibrated to provide a fairly exact and reproducible preselected transmittance.

The chief limitation of the standard sieve as an attenuator is its low maximum transmittance. In order to extend the same principle of attenuation over a greater range, two special screens were made. One was designed to transmit 80% and the other 66%. These were prepared with 150 μ grid wires running in one direction only. The wires were drawn taut between a series of pegs spaced to provide intervening openings of 4 times and twice the wire diameter, respectively. The transmittances of these screens were also measured as a function of degrees rotation from normal incidence. It was found advisable, especially in the case of the undirectional grids to guard against imaging the wires on the microphotometer slit. Where slits are used

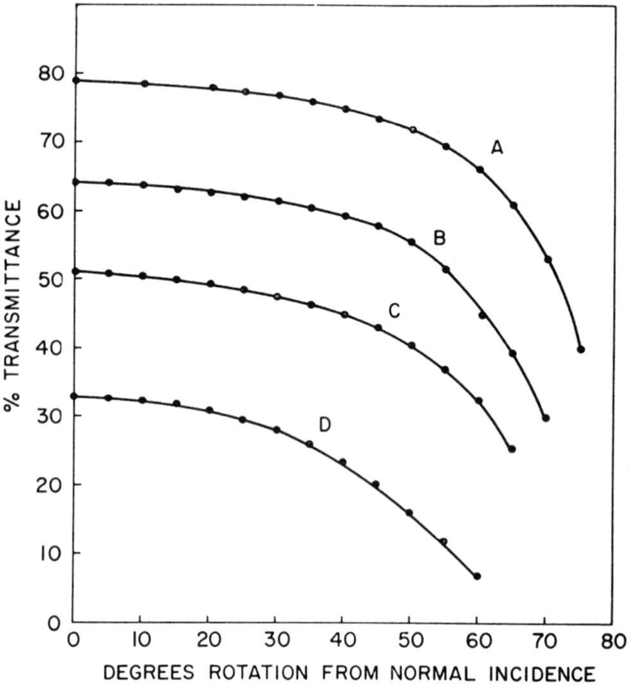

FIG. 4. TRANSMITTANCE PROPERTIES OF VARIOUS SCREENS AS A FUNCTION OF ANGLE OF ROTATION

A—Parallel-grid screen designed for 80% transmittance at normal incidence. B—Parallel grid screen designed for 66% maximum transmittance. C—Combination of screens A and B. D—Standard commercial screen.

in conjunction with screens, it is advantageous to mount the screen so that the wires do not run parallel to the slit. An angle of 45° from slit direction was adopted for these microphotometer measurements.

The experimental parallel-grid screens show transmittance characteristics similar to the standard cross-grid screens (see Figure 4). The experimental screen designed for 80% transmittance at normal incidence provides a measured maximum transmittance of 79% and can be rotated to provide reliable values to approximately 60%. The screen designed for 66% transmittance provides 64% at normal incidence and attenuation to 30%. Combining the two experimental screens so that their wires run perpendicular to one another produces a combined maximum transmittance of 51% at normal incidence and a range to 25%. Beginning with a transmittance maximum of 32%, a standard commercial screen can be rotated to provide values to below 10%.

From Figure 4 it is apparent that very accurate control can be obtained for a range of approximately 10% immediately below the maximum transmittance of a given screen. Thus with an appropriate series of calibrated screens a total range of at least 80-10% transmittance can be provided. The same range might be covered with as few as two of the screens described if approximate transmittances are adequate.

It would be especially desirable if a single grid could provide the combination of wide transmittance range together with accurate control over the complete range. Toward this end, it might be wise to investigate the optical properties of grid configurations that can now be fabricated by the various commercial electroforming techniques. The assistance of D. B. Kapustin in the design of the device and the collection of some data is gratefully acknowledged.

Literature Cited

(1) G. R. Harrison, J. Opt. Soc. Am. **18**, 492 (1929)
(2) *U. S. Federal Specification RR-S-366b*, Superintendent of Documents, U. S. Printing Office, Washington, D.C.
(3) P. A. Newman and R. Binder, Rev. Sci. Instr. **32**, 351 (1961)

8.3 Etched Wire Screens as Variable Light Attenuators

M. J. D. Low

School of Chemistry
Rutgers—The State University
New Brunswick, New Jersey

In the course of infrared studies on dense materials with double-beam instruments, it is frequently necessary to attenuate the reference beam in order to be able to record the spectrum. Also, in some studies, particularly with the interaction of gas with a solid, the sample transmission can vary with experimental conditions, so that continual adjustment of reference beam intensity must be made. Such adjustments are very inconvenient to make with wire mesh screens or slotted shutters because these produce a step-by-step attenuation. Continuous attenuation is desirable for such purposes. Some continuously-variable attenuators made of tilting vanes *(1)* or wire screens *(2)* have been described. Such devices are useful but have the disadvantages of large size and non-linearity of attenuation. The rotary motion must be controlled precisely and, because of the rotation of such a device, a substantial fraction of the reference beam space is taken up so that large compensating cells cannot be accommodated.

Continuously-variable attenuators can be made easily and cheaply by etching wire-mesh screen or wire. A rectangular frame about two by five in. is made of ⅛-in. brass rod. Three additional rods are soldered to the frame, one rod acting as handle, two being guide rods that can fit into holes cut into a holder fixed to the spectrometer. A metal wire screen of suitable transmission is soldered to the frame. The assembled device is shown in Figure 1. All of the rods, including the center frame to which the screen is soldered, are coated with wax. This can be conveniently done by "painting" the metal with a concentrated solution of wax in benzene, care being taken to

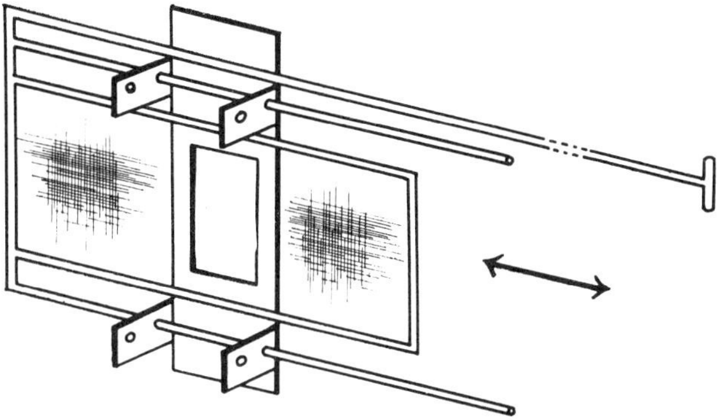

FIG. 1. VARIABLE LIGHT ATTENUATOR

avoid contaminating the screen. The device is totally immersed in concentrated nitric acid and is manually withdrawn from this etching solution at a constant velocity. Different portions of the screen are thus etched for various times, and this results in a tapering of the screen wires.

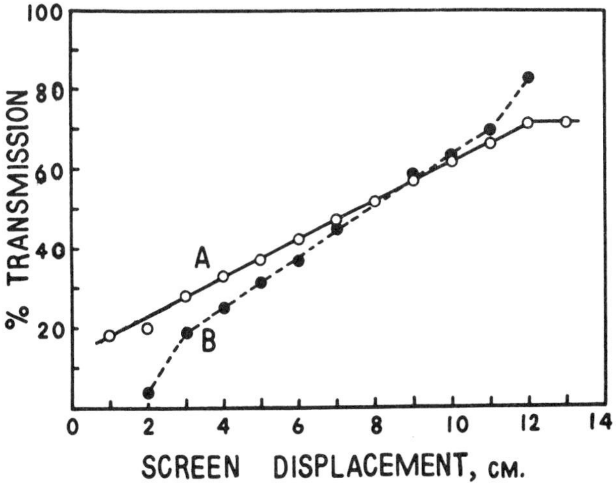

FIG. 2. ATTENUATION BY ETCHED SCREEN

The etching is repeated until the desired degree of linear tapering is obtained. The screen is then washed with water and air-dried.

Examples of the attenuation produced by such etched screens are shown in Figure 2. The percentage transmittance is seen to vary linearly with screen displacement over the major portion of the screen. Deviation at the screen ends is brought about by uneven etching because of soldering and wax masking. Such a device is about 3/16 in. thick and consequently most of the reference beam space is available for use. Two or more such screens can easily be accommodated without interference with reference cells although the use of multiple screen is hazardous and strong attenuation can have a serious "deadening" effect on the spectrometer resulting in spurious bands unless proper precautions are taken.

Support for this work by U.S.A. Signal Corps. under Contract No. DA36-039-AMC-02160(E), and N.S.F. equipment grant GP1434, is gratefully acknowledged.

Literature Cited

(1) J. P. Luongo, APPLIED SPECTROSCOPY **14,** 25 (1960)
(2) F. R. Bryan, Ibid. **17,** 19 (1963)

8.4 A Method for Grinding Silver Chloride

P. A. Romans

Bureau of Mines, Department of the Interior, Region I,
Albany, Oregon

High-purity silver chloride can be prepared by several methods, but for use as a carrier in spectrochemical analysis, it must be a fine powder. Although several procedures especially designed to produce a finely divided precipitate have been devised, extreme care is required to recover a high percentage of usable silver chloride *(1,2)*.

Silver chloride of adequate purity is readily available in the form of matted lumps, but attempts to pulverize the material by conventional techniques have been consistently unsuccessful. This problem was successfully solved, however, by cooling the silver chloride in liquid nitrogen which made it brittle enough for grinding.

The following procedure relates how the particle size of silver chloride can be reduced to almost any desired degree; approximately 15 g of coarse silver chloride is placed in a plastic vial. The vial is immersed in a vacuum flask containing liquid nitrogen and is allowed to fill partly with the liquid nitrogen. After a few min, the vial is lifted out, and its contents are poured into a Coors No. 3 porcelain evaporating dish, which serves as the mortar. An agate pestle is used to grind the silver chloride. The liquid nitrogen is replaced as it boils away, although final grinding is done with most of it gone. The best grinding conditions occur when the silver chloride and liquid nitrogen form a slurry. Approximately one lb can be hand-ground per hr with the consumption of less than one l of liquid nitrogen. All dark particles turn light in color at liquid nitrogen temperatures, and there is no darkening of the powder while it is cold. When the silver chloride becomes sufficiently fine, it is it placed in a dark bottle until ready for use.

Literature Cited

(1) D. W. Baker, CHEMIST-ANALYST **46,** 56 (1957)

(2) A. Simpson, U. S. AT. ENERGY COMM. **WAPD-CTA (GLA)-310** Rev. 1, (1957)

8.5 Minimizing the Polystyrene Contamination in Wigl-Bug Grinding

S. E. Polchlopek* and M. J. Robertson†

Stamford Research Laboratories, American Cyanamid Company, Stamford, Connecticut

In this laboratory the contamination of samples by polystyrene abraded from the plastic vials during grinding has been held well below the levels described by McDevitt and Baun *(1)* by using several small acrylic plastic balls of ⅛ in. diam. in place of the ⅜ in. diam. ball conventionally used.

Table I is based on the infrared absorption at 698 cm^{-1} which appears when 200 mg of KBr are ground in the same type of polystyrene vial on which McDevitt and Baun reported, but with ⅛ in. balls used in place of a single ⅜ in. ball. These data show about one-fourth as much contamination as when a ⅜ in. ball is used. No measurable decrease in grinding efficiency was noted when the small balls are used. It is recommended that the small balls be counted carefully as they are put in and removed from the vial since they have been known to damage dies if pressed along with the sample.

TABLE I. ABSORBANCE OF POLYSTYRENE CONTAMINATION 698 cm^{-1}

No. of Balls	*Wigl-Bug Grinding, min.*		
	1	*3*	*5*
3	0.010	0.040	0.075
5	0.020	0.065	0.110
8	0.025	0.090	0.155

*Present address: Connecticut Instrument Corporation, Wilton, Conn.
†Present address: Teleregister Corporation, Stamford, Conn.

There has been some speculation that the cracks in the bottom of the vial are the major source of contamination when the ⅜ in. ball is used. A disc of polyethylene 1/32 in. thick was pressed into the bottom of a vial and it was observed that the contamination of 200 mg charges after grinding remains at the levels already reported by McDevitt and Baun *(1)*.

In some cases three 1/16 in. diam. steel balls were used with results which approximate those for the eight ⅛ in. plastic balls. The levels of contamination are erratic and not reproducible and rise rather sharply as the number of steel balls is increased.

Literature Cited

(1) N. T. McDevitt and W. L. Baun, APPLIED SPECTROSCOPY **14,** 135 (1960)

A Multiple-Cutting Accessory for Mixing Powders in a Capsule 8.6

William L. Dutton

Research Division, American Cyanamid Company, Stamford, Conn.

When diluting or mixing powders with graphite using the Wig-L-Bug or the Flossy Amalgamator, a very complete mixing is obtained in a much shorter time with the use of a spiral coil of nichrome wire in a disposable gelatin capsule. It has the effect of 20 full-circle cutting edges with each single throw. The wire used is Nichrome Alloy V of 20 mils diam. The spiral coil, in the shape of a cocoon, has 10 complete turns in one in. of length. It is 5/16 in. o.d. at the center and tapers to an ⅛ in. o.d. at the flattened ends. This length causes it to be under slight compression when the disposable No. 000 gelatin capsule is closed, but not enough to have it trap any sample under the 2 points of contact at each end while oscillating. A convenient charge is about 200 mg. Graphite powder does not coat the wire.

Test runs have shown spectrographically no contamination by the wire of graphite or non-corrosive or non-abrasive powders.

8.7 Novel Cataloging System

Theodore H. Zink†
Vitro Chemical Company
Chattanooga, Tennessee

Stock inventory cards* are capable of filling a long-standing need for a simple and inexpensive system for the filing of references, papers and reprints in the spectrographic laboratory. The materials required consist of a number of 8½ in x 11 in stock file cards, a hole punch* and a stacking frame.* Each of these cards has a title line on its face (Figure 1). This means that a total of 7000 references can be handled by the initial system; in order to expand the system, it is merely necessary to purchase a supply of cards of a different color. In addition, a series of 3 in x 5 in file cards and two filing cases to hold the cards are needed.

The recording process is indicated by the folowing example: Assume that one wants to list the paper by Mohan and Schreiber, "Spectrochemical Analysis of a Nickel Base High Temperature Alloy" (APPLIED SPECTROSCOPY **12,** 6 (1958)). Individual cards are provided with one of the following titles: "Aluminum", "Chromium, "Iron", "Titanium", "Manganese", "Silicon", "Boron", "Nickel Base Alloy", "Atmosphere", "Spark", "Point-to-plane", "Line Pairs", and "Results". These titles represent

*Edler and Krische, Hanover, Germany
†Now at W. R. Grace & Co., Clarksville, Md.

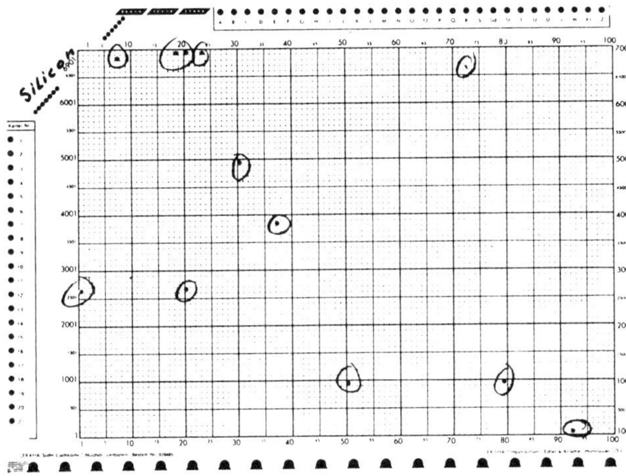

FIG. 1. THE "EKAHA" PUNCH CARD
Reference holes are circled

the points of primary interest and importance of the paper. The paper is now assigned an arbitrary number, e.g. 4371. All of the prepared cards are now placed into the stacking frame and the Square (4371) is punched. This places a hole into the 4371 square of each of the cards involved.

A small card is now marked with the number and provided with the necessary data of the reference. This may be a copy of an abstract, the title cut from the "Bibliography of Recent Papers" from APPLIED SPECTROSCOPY, or some remark as to where the reference may be found. While the abstract cards are filed numerically, the title cards are filed alphabetically for easy access. The title cards are used over and over again for other listings, the "Aluminum" card may be used to file a paper dealing with the determination of aluminum in steel, the "Nickel Alloys" card is used for each additional reference which concerns the determination of any element in Nickel Alloys. Thus each title card is used again and again and gradually accumulates a series of punched holes, which are scattered over its surface (*1*).

On the basis of these cards it becomes possible, in addition to locating references, to answer such questions as:

> To how many papers concerned with Nickel Alloys do I have access?
> (Pull the "Nickel Alloys" card and count the number of holes.)
> Which of these papers provide information on line pairs used?
> (Superimpose the "Line Pairs" card on the "Nickel Alloys" card and count the number of holes still open.)
> What methods have been used for the determination of Boron?
> (Pull the "Boron" card and count the number of holes open.)

Thus each punched hole indicates an entry and it also indicates the number of the reference card, which must be checked. Obviously, the more precise the question, the more precise will be the answer. The more cards superimposed upon one another, the fewer the open holes and the easier it is to locate a paper. Many additional questions and particularly combinations of questions may be answered rapidly and easily in this manner. The system, as installed by the author, has found a great deal of use and it has been found to be exceedingly simple to maintain on an up-to-date basis.

Literature Cited

(1) W. A. Wildhack and J. Stern, "*The Peek-a-boo System*", Chap. 6, in "*Punch Cards*", R. S. Casey et al, Ed., Reinhold Publishing Corp., New York, 2nd Edition (1958)

Optical Bench Cover 8.8

Drexel W. Baker
University of Tennessee, Knoxville, Tennessee *

The elimination of dust from optical surfaces is important in illumination systems such as the Simeon-Twyman or as used on dual grating spectrographs where several optical elements are involved. Prevention of the accumulation of dust is easier than its removal and can be achieved by placing a plastic cover over the optical bench and its components as shown in Figure 1. A cover can be adapted from commercial covers for triple beam balances or can be obtained in special sizes†. Custom units can be specified to give a sufficiently precise fit to permit the cutting of an aperture limited to the requirements of the optical rays. Slits for intermediate diaphragms or other components can also be provided. Such a shield catches considerably dust which might otherwise impair optical efficiency. The shield

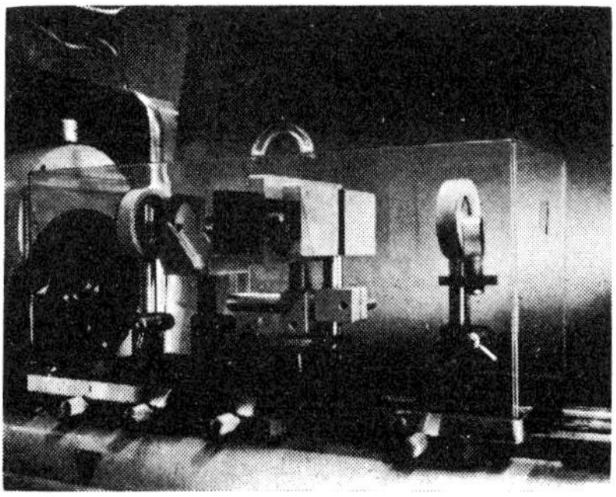

FIG. 1. OPTICAL BENCH COVER

also serves as a mechanical guard to protect the optical elements from being knocked out of alignment.

---

*Present Address: Goodyear Atomic Corporation, Portsmouth, Ohio.
†E. J. Kanter and Company, Chicago, Illinois.

8.9 Improvement of Brown Recorders Equipped with Ball Point Pens

Bernard M. Mitzner

van Amerigen Haebler, Division of International Flavors and Fragrances, Union Beach, New Jersey

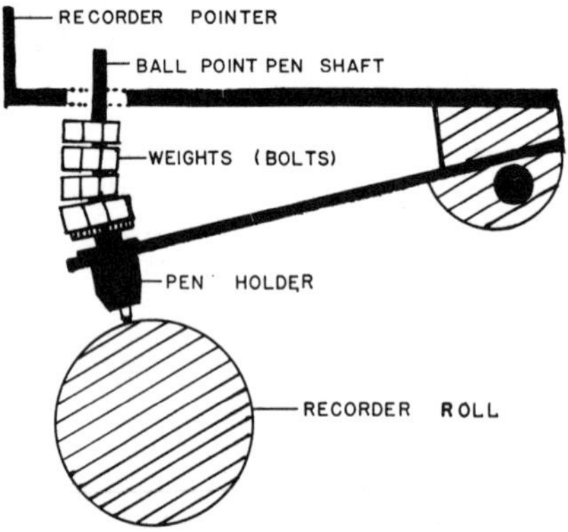

FIG. 1. SIDE VIEW OF PEN HOLDER

The Brown Recorder which has been factory equipped with a ball point pen functions very poorly as the pen skips and at times does not write at all. The holder that contained the pen was weighted with several heavy ¼ in. iron bolts, as shown in Figure 1, with the result that the pen performs very satisfactorily. This device has been successfully employed on our recorder for several months.

APPLIED SPECTROSCOPY REFERENCE INDEX

No.	Vol.	Page	Year
1.1	13	158	1959
1.2	16	195	1962
1.3	16	195	1962
1.4	15	177	1961
1.5	16	141	1962
1.6	17	125	1963
1.7	19	36	1965
1.8	19	97	1965
1.9	14	82	1960
1.10	15	179	1961
1.11	16	109	1962
1.12	18	116	1964
1.13	18	29	1964
1.14	14	80	1960
1.15	16	168	1962
1.16	18	189	1964
1.17	18	154	1964
1.18	15	150	1961
1.19	15	21	1961
1.20	17	76	1963
1.21	16	110	1962
1.22	18	64	1964
1.23	17	168	1963
1.24	19	165	1965
1.25	13	110	1959
1.26	17	54	1963
1.27	14	57	1960
1.28	13	140	1959
1.29	15	181	1961
1.30	16	113	1962
1.31	13	158	1959
1.32	14	57	1960
1.33	14	107	1960
1.34	15	153	1961
1.35	16	142	1962
1.36	19	61	1965
1.37	13	159	1959
1.38	15	82	1961
1.39	19	59	1965
1.40	15	23	1961
1.41	15	23	1961
1.42	14	24	1960
1.43	19	25	1965
2.1	14	107	1960
2.2	19	137	1965
2.3	14	139	1960

No.	Vol.	Page	Year
2.4	15	55	1961
2.5	18	94	1964
2.6	17	106	1963
2.7	13	48	1959
2.8	18	191	1964
2.9	17	166	1963
2.10	19	163	1965
2.11	16	22	1962
2.12	18	65	1964
2.13	17	74	1963
2.14	19	62	1965
2.15	17	23	1963
2.16	13	48	1959
2.17	17	125	1963
2.18	14	108	1960
2.19	15	80	1961
2.20	15	153	1961
2.21	16	25	1962
2.22	16	167	1962
2.23	13	108	1959
2.24	14	138	1960
2.25	18	113	1964
2.26	15	81	1961
2.27	16	106	1962
2.28	18	114	1964
2.29	16	112	1962
2.30	18	159	1964
2.31	14	24	1960
2.32	14	81	1960
2.33	18	64	1964
2.34	15	83	1961
2.35	17	75	1963
2.36	14	25	1960
2.37	18	191	1964
3.1	17	25	1963
3.2	15	152	1961
3.3	18	193	1964
4.1	17	77	1963
4.2	17	53	1963
5.1	17	25	1963
6.1	16	41	1962
6.2	17	26	1963
6.3	15	183	1961
6.4	17	26	1963
6.5	18	28	1964
7.1	17	169	1963
7.2	15	21	1961
7.3	13	79	1959
7.4	14	56	1960
7.5	14	26	1960
7.6	16	24	1962
7.7	18	65	1964
8.1	17	76	1963
8.2	17	19	1963
8.3	18	187	1964
8.4	16	113	1962
8.5	16	112	1962
8.6	15	24	1961
8.7	15	22	1961
8.8	13	139	1959
8.9	13	80	1959

AUTHOR INDEX

SUBJECT INDEX

T

U